# SOME OF THE TOWNS VISITED BY
# DR. HALL IN HIS MEDICAL ROUNDS

0 1 2 3 4 5 6 7 8 9 10  MILES

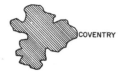

COVENTRY

KING'S NEWNHAM

RUGBY

WESTON

LEAMINGTON

WARWICK

NORTON

SOUTHAM

ITCHINGTON

R. AVON

RATFORD-UPON-
AVON

ORD-
MBERS  LOXLEY

AVON DASSET

R STOUR

PILLERTON

TON

HONINGTON

SHIPSTON-ON-STOUR

# SHAKESPEARE'S SON-IN-LAW:
# JOHN HALL, MAN AND PHYSICIAN

HALL'S CROFT

# Shakespeare's Son-in-law: John Hall, Man and Physician

By

HARRIET JOSEPH

*With a facsimile of the Second Edition of*
*Hall's "Select Observations on English Bodies"*

ARCHON BOOKS
Hamden, Connecticut
1964

Printed in The United States of America

CBS
8 00
2.12.64 mun
9-16-64ee

To Edward, for his help and support
and
To Leila, Alan and Brian, for all their love

# TABLE OF CONTENTS

## ACKNOWLEDGEMENTS

A work of this nature requires the assistance of many. From the very beginning, Frederick Kilgour, Librarian, Yale Medical Library, was helpful and encouraging, and his scholarly advice was invaluable to me. My husband, Dr. Edward Joseph, gave unstintingly of critical judgment and medical acumen. Many of the medical statements herein are based on discussions with him.

Librarians of many institutions gave willingly of their time and experience, amongst these, the staff of the Scarsdale Public Library, Scarsdale, New York; the New York Public Library; the Folger Shakespeare Library, Washington, D.C.; the Royal College of Physicians, London, and the British Museum. The latter institution enabled me to work on Hall's original Latin manuscript at home through the medium of microfilm. In particular, I wish to extend appreciation to Mrs. Elizabeth K. Berry, Assistant Archivist, Shakespeare Birthplace Trust, Stratford-upon-Avon, and to both Mrs. Alice D. Weaver and Mrs. Nancy B. Willey of the Malloch Rare Book and History Room, The New York Academy of Medicine.

Thanks are due to Mr. Levi Fox, Director, Shakespeare Birthplace Trust and to Mr. James G. McManaway, Consultant in Literature and Bibliography, Folger Shakespeare Library, for permission to use and reprint material in their libraries. The archivists at Cambridge University, University of Montpellier, France, and the

Bedford, Worcester and Gloucester County Offices, England all supplied helpful information.

My thanks are due Drs. Morton W. Bloomfield, Harvard University, and Arthur I. Bloomfield, University of Pennsylvania, for their counsel, and Mrs. Frances Ottemiller of The Shoe String Press for her ready interest.

I owe much to the many scholars who have preceded me in the Shakespearean field and upon whose findings I have drawn liberally. Finally, I wish to acknowledge again my indebtedness to Frederick Kilgour, who placed the facilities of the Historical Library, Yale Medical Library, at my disposal, and who has generously allowed its copy of the second edition of Hall's "Select Observations on English Bodies" to be reprinted herein.

# INTRODUCTION

In the seventeenth century, sometime before 1635, Lady Eliza Tyrrell wrote in a letter to her friend Lady Temple: "Noble Lady, I have lately heard of your worthy knight's mischance for which I am heartily sorry. And both Mr. Tyrrell and myself have purposely sent to inquire of his recovery. Madam, I am very glad to hear that Mr. Hall is the man of whom Sir Thomas Temple hath made choice of. In regard, I know by experience that he is most excellent in that art." Her husband, Sir Edward, added in a postscript: "Sweet Madam: I am very sorry to hear of Sir Thomas Temple's misfortune. Get Mr. Hall speedily to him. If you cannot, my wife and I will try our power with him."[1]

We do not know what Sir Thomas Temple's "mischance" was, nor whether Mr. Hall's medical service was secured. These facts have been lost in the shadows of history. We do know that the Mr. Hall referred to so highly was Master John Hall of Stratford-upon-Avon, busy practicing physician and son-in-law of William Shakespeare. He has remained a relatively obscure member of the vast body of men and women surrounding Shakespeare. This may have been due to his unique position as both medical man and Shakespeare relative, with some consequent uncertainty as to which realm of research his life belonged. Students of both medical history and of Shakespeareana could have claimed him, but neither fully did. So, in this four hundredth anniversary year of William Shakespeare's birth, the present work is devoted to a study of John Hall as man and physician, and to the publication for the first time since 1683 of "Select Observations on English Bodies," his medical casebook, unavailable for general use today.[2]

References to John Hall in the literature have been largely complimentary, attesting in general terms to his skill as diagnostician, consultant and practitioner. Though recognized in his lifetime, as his epitaph claims, as a "most celebrated" doctor, he has only been correctly identified in this century as to birthplace, background and college education.[3] His practice extended over 35 years in and around Stratford. On his death in 1635 he left as a legacy, not only a daughter, Elizabeth, but manuscripts as well. One notebook of 178 medical cases, in abbreviated Latin, was subsequently translated and published with the above-mentioned title. This notebook is extant and is today in the British Museum.[4] The whereabouts of Hall's other papers, including a second notebook, is unknown.

The book of cases was first published in 1657 under the title, "Select Observations on English Bodies of eminent Persons in desperate Diseases," translated and edited by Dr. James Cooke, one of Hall's Warwickshire colleagues.[5] The slim volume brought a measure of posthumous success to Hall, and was followed by a second edition in 1679 and a third in 1683, of which there were two printings.[6] In the second and third editions, Dr. Cooke added to the original by including cases, called Counsels, based on his own and other colleagues' medical experiences. The second edition, without the Counsels, is reprinted herein as it is most faithful to Hall's original manuscript.

Dr. Cooke, in his role as editor, divided Hall's 178 cases into two sections, the first consisting of a hundred observations, the second (called Second Century) of seventy-nine. Cooke obtained the extra case by separating into two one of Hall's observations on tumors in children. (See Observation XLV and XLVI, Second Century, concerning Lady Harrington's "first-born son" and Margaret Baker, aged nine.) To bring the total number to two hundred, to complete two "Centuries" of medical Observations, Cooke included twenty-one additional cases, from other sources, which he hoped would not "be offensive."

A case by case comparison of the original Latin manuscript with the printed editions was undertaken for purposes of this present study. It revealed that Cooke in the second edition corrected some errors and omissions that occurred in the first, thus making the second edition (and later the third) closer to the manuscript than the 1657 edition. Cooke evidently returned to the original manuscript in his preparation of the second edition because he was, no doubt, aware of certain inaccuracies in the first.

A fact not previously noted is that Hall, in the body of his manuscript, cites six medical authorities: Johannes Anglicus (John of Gaddesden), Quercitanus (Joseph DuChesne), Horst, Crato von Kraftheim, Daniel Sennert and Severinus Eugalenus. (See Notes on Observations for further details on these physicians.) A discrepancy between the original Latin manuscript and the second edition, on the one hand, and the first edition, on the other, revolves around one of these medical references. In Observation XV (First Century), Hall speaks of a syrup of Johannes Anglicus, by which "he cured many of the scab," a treatment Hall found effective as well. This reference to one of England's earliest physicians is omitted from the first edition.

The following few additional examples illustrate further original manuscript data not found in the first edition but present in the second. One complete case, that of John Smith of Newnam, Observation L (First Century), is omitted altogether in the first edition. In Observation IV (First Century) the words "By these remedies he was cured, blessed be God" appear in the Latin manuscript and second edition, but not in the first. In Observation VIII, also First Century, Mrs. Chandler's age is 34 in the manuscript and second edition, but 38 in the first. In Observation IX, same Century, Christian Bass's age is 29 in the manuscript and second edition, but omitted in the first. In Observation IV (Second Century), the manuscript and second edition end with the words, "For which God be praised that can only work wonderfully;" these are not found in the first. The second edition (1679) is thus more faithful to Hall's original Latin text, and is for this reason reprinted herein.

The present book was conceived as a tripartite unity, consisting of biographical data on John Hall, pertinent facts on persons mentioned in his Casebook, "The Select Observations on English Bodies," and, finally, the facsimile reprint of the second edition. The biographical section includes Hall's relationship to the Shakespeare family. (The footnotes to this part are found on pages 96-99.) The second section, which follows the biographical material, gives relevant facts on persons in the Casebook. These Notes to the Observations are designed to be read in conjunction with the facsimile reprint, and therefore were prepared Observation by Observation, for easy reference. They may, however, be read as an entity in themselves.

The final section consists of the facsimile reprint of the second edition. The Preface to the first edition is included, however, for its historical importance, as it describes in detail Dr. Cooke's own account of his discovery of Hall's notebooks. Also included is Linacre Lecturer Dr. John Bird's[7] Introduction to the same edition, with its appraisal of John Hall and his work.

The Casebook (often referred to as a diary and thus erroneously denoting intimate revelations and personal comments) consists of case after case of patient's name, medical diagnosis, and remedies employed, followed most often by a record of cure. It is of little medical value today, but is of importance to students of the history of medicine and to those in the Shakespearean field.

In the first instance, the Casebook sheds light on the medical practice of a well-respected, efficient Elizabethan doctor, who combined medieval procedures and herbal decoctions with an enlightened cure for scurvy. In the second instance, it discloses illuminating facts on persons close to the Bard (his daughter, Susanna, who was Hall's wife; his granddaughter, Elizabeth; the poet Michael Drayton; and members of the Green, Comb, Sturley and Quiney families, all friends of Shakespeare). The Casebook also reveals something of John Hall as man, physician and humanitarian. As the facts on his life are scant, this adds another dimension to our knowledge of him. The Casebook's value lies in these functions.

# JOHN HALL, THE MAN

That man, "most excellent in the art" of medicine, John Hall, was born in Bedfordshire, England, in the latter half of the sixteenth century. Although actual evidence of his birth is wanting, the date has been set at 1575, based on a notation in his own Casebook. He speaks of a near-brush with death from the plague on August 27, 1632, "about the fifty-seventh year of my age," thus making him eleven years Shakespeare's junior. His actual birthplace is unknown but it has been set at Carlton, Bedfordshire, as his father William was known to have resided there from 1569 to 1590. The archives in Bedford contain baptismal records of six Hall children.[8] Eleven children altogether are mentioned either in official baptisimal or marriage records and in William Hall's will.[9] There is no birth or baptisimal record however of John, nor of his older brother, Dive, who attended Cambridge with him. His parents may have lived away from Carlton for the period 1573-1578.[10]

Carlton, where presumably Hall spent his childhood, appears today an attractive rustic village, with old church and graveyard intact and a static population (about 330). John's mother, whose identity is unknown, may possibly have been a member of the Bedfordshire Dive family, thus accounting for the unusual Christian name of John's older brother. On the other hand, a "Dive" may have been the child's godfather and no blood relationship involved. A good deal is known of Hall's father through his will, located in 1931, and dated December 12, 1607.[11]

William Hall was a man of some means, owning land in Bedfordshire and in Acton, Middlesex, and possessing a coat of arms (three talbot heads erased). He seemed a Protestant by religion and a physician by profession, judging by his large library of books on "physicks" and alchemy. E. P. Scarlett[12] states he may have been trained in the tradition of Dr. Jerome Cardan,[13] Italian astrologer and physician who believed the origin of life was connected with the stars. William Hall's belief in these pseudosciences (astrology and alchemy) proved a cause of discord with his son, John. William's will states plainly that his books on "physicks" are to be given to John, but his books on astrology, astronomy and alchemy were left to his friend, Mathew Morris. If John should show interest in these subjects, the will directs Mr. Morris to "instruct" John accordingly. (Mathew Morris accompanied John to Stratford, married there, and named two of his children, John and Susanna.)

John Hall appears to have been the favorite son. He was left a house in Acton and most of his father's property. He was named executor of the will, which obligation he first declined presumably due to medical responsibilities, but later accepted. Throughout his lifetime, he showed a high dedication to his chosen profession of medicine, and would not permit any infringement on his professional duties, placing uppermost his responsibility to his patients. Late in his life (1626), when offered a Knighthood by King Charles I, he chose to pay a fine of £10 rather than accept, fearing the duties would interfere with his medical practice. Three times he was elected Burgess to the City Council, part of the Stratford Corporation. (By the Charter of 1553, Stratford acquired

a governing body of 14 Alderman and 14 Burgesses.[14])
Twice he refused to take office, pleading the exigencies
of his medical practice. When finally in 1632 he was
prevailed upon to accept office, he was shortly afterwards fined for non-attendance. A letter from patient
Sid Davenport at that time indicates that Hall's absence
from the City Council was due to the demands of his
medical practice. It would seem that Dr. Hall was not
going to be talked into anything to which he could not
devote his time and energies.

Dive, the older brother, was cut out of his father's
will except for a small bequest. The will states that Dive
had received more than his share of the estate during
his father's lifetime, and had "shown many unkindnesses,
especially since his mother's death." Aside from this suggested evidence of constant demands for financial aid
from his father, little is known of Dive. He matriculated
at Cambridge in 1589, at the same time as John, but his
education seems to have ceased there. John gave him
the house in Acton in which to live, and he died there
in 1626.

At the age of 14, John Hall, accompanied by his
brother Dive, left for Cambridge, 30 miles from their
home in Carlton. They matriculated together as Pen-
sioners at Queens' College in 1589.[15] John received a
Bachelor of Arts degree in 1593 and a Masters degree in
1597. (The BA is signed by William Connell, and the
MA by Walter House.[16]) It was not known whether
he was in residence at any time during the years 1593
to 1597 when his Masters degree was conferred. William
Harvey, discoverer of the circulation of the blood, entered Caius College, Cambridge in 1593 and received his

Bachelor of Arts degree in 1597. If Hall were in residence during this period, he may have encountered Harvey. There is, however, no evidence of any relationship between these two men, even though one of Hall's patients saw Dr. Harvey in London and Hall records Harvey's prescription (Observation XLIII, Second Century). We do not even know whether Hall sent his patient to Harvey, or whether the patient, while in London on personal matters, saw Harvey on his own. Hall does refer to Harvey though in his manuscript as "most learned."

The question of whether or not Hall was in residence after receiving his Bachelor of Arts degree has additional pertinency since it has been estimated that Hall came to Stratford about 1600.[17] If he were in residence in Cambridge until 1597, there are three years of his life to account for. If, however, he left Cambridge sometime after his BA in 1593, there is a period up to seven years during which time his whereabouts is unknown.

These three (or seven) years were probably spent by Hall in obtaining his medical education. Various sources state that Hall received some medical training at the University of Montpellier, but there is no evidence, according to the present Archivist there, to prove this. Hall is not listed in the register of the Montpellier faculty of medicine during the period from 1562 to 1669, but he may of course have attended lectures without having registered formally. Not only is there no evidence of his having attended Montpellier, there is none regarding any other university, nor of his having obtained a medical degree at all. During Hall's lifetime he was referred to either as doctor or master, but no record is

available of a degree in medicine, a license from the
Royal College of Physicians, nor of a Bishop's license to
practice medicine.[18] John Hall apparently appeared in
Stratford around 1600, set himself up as a doctor of
medicine, and from that time on his life was bound with
that of the community, as physician, citizen and son-in-
law of William Shakespeare.

E. K. Chambers has written of the Stratford of that
time: "All around Stratford was fair, with open lands,
parks, dingles [glens] and a shining river."[19] Stratford
was then a community of 2000 inhabitants, a thriving
market town, with a good grammar school, guild and
church. These may have been some of the inducements
which attracted the young physician to this busy, grow-
ing center. As apprenticeship was the established method
of beginning a medical career, this may have been the
case with Dr. Hall. Research, however, has not uncov-
ered any medical personage with whom Hall may have
worked.

The earliest record of John Hall in Stratford is that
of his marriage at the age of thirty-two to Susanna Shakespeare, aged twenty-four, on June 5, 1607. Sometime
before that date, Hall had become acquainted with the
older Shakespeare girl and courted her. Nothing is known
of their early meeting, romance or engagement. William
Shakespeare, a family man, most likely attended the
wedding, the first of his two daughters. The next known
date pertaining to the Halls is the birth of their daughter,
Elizabeth, in February 1608. There were no other children to this marriage. The Halls presumably set up
housekeeping on Old Town Street. The property now
called Hall's Croft is owned by the Shakespeare Birth-

place Trust, and is accepted as Hall's residence prior to 1616. At that time, on Shakespeare's death, they moved to New Place, Shakespeare's home, and lived there with the Bard's widow, remaining until John's death in 1635 and Susanna's in 1649. (Anne Hathaway Shakespeare, Susanna's mother, died August 6, 1623, three months prior to the publication of the First Folio.)

Hall's Croft, stately and elegant, is characteristic of the half-timbered dwellings in Stratford of that period. Although additions and alterations took place over the centuries, the house was restored, when purchased by the Shakespeare Birthplace Trust in 1949, as much as possible to its original state. The house has oak timbered framing with many gables and chimneys. It is spacious, airy and attractive, with the suggestion of comfort and ease of living. In its walled-in garden, Hall may have grown some of the herbs and plants used so widely in his prescriptions. The gardens at both Hall's Croft and New Place were well-known for their diversity of plants. Sir Thomas Temple, in a letter dated 1631, requests his man, Harry Rose, to ride to Stratford "to desire Mr. Hall" to give him some "shutes" of his vine.[20]

Susanna, born May 26, 1583, was the eldest of Shakespeare's three children, the twins, Judith and Hamnet, being born the end of January 1585. Susanna has been portrayed as a warm, sympathetic and intelligent woman. Her epitaph is a source of information for it describes her as

> Witty beyond her sex, but that's not all
> Wise to salvation was good Mistress Hall.

["Witty" here refers to wisdom, intellectuality.] The

epitaph adds that she gave "comforts cordial" to those in need, and exhorts the passer-by to "weep with her that wept with all." It describes her as having "something of Shakespeare" in her, which may refer to qualities of gentleness, charm, and perhaps good business sense. Susanna managed capably her father's and later her husband's estates. She is mentioned a couple of times in her husband's Casebook, though she appears in general to have been a woman of good health, along with fine ideals and religious beliefs. Her one definite illness reported (Observation XIX, First Century) refers to a severe "cholick," which Hall treated by a clyster, an enema, of "sack" and a plaster. He apparently gave Susanna the best of treatment, for he records using the same clyster for the Earl of Northampton, one of his most prominent patients.

Susanna's ability to read and write has been often questioned due to a comment by Cooke in his preface to the first edition of "Select Observations." He states Susanna Hall did not recognize her husband's handwriting in the notebooks he was attempting to purchase from her. This has been taken as an indication of her lack of education, and it is not actually known how much formal learning she had. She could sign her own name though and certainly handle business affairs.

A blot upon her reputation was an accusation brought against her by one John Lane. In 1613 he accused Susanna of "running the reins of Dr. Hall's household" and of having an affair with a Rafe Smith. Hall filed a slander suit against Lane in the Consistory Court at Worcester Cathedral, July 15, 1613.[21] As a result of this legal action Lane was excommunicated. Lane is known to have made irresponsible charges in other instances and was involved in a later slanderous accusation. He was sued in 1619 for riot and libels against the vicar and aldermen and was presented at that time as a drunkard. His brother Nicholas also had charges of assault and battery brought against him. Interestingly enough, though, John Hall was made a trustee for the children of Richard Lane, their uncle, which post he apparently filled.

In regard to the marital relationship of Susanna and her husband John, the implication is one of harmony and mutual understanding. The last lines on Hall's epitaph, added on Susanna's death, read:

> Lest anything be wanting to his tomb,
> His most faithful wife is with him,
> And the companion of his life he has also in death.

The Halls held a position of prominence in both the religious and social life of the community. In July 1643, eight years after Hall's death, Susanna, living at New Place, was called upon to act as hostess to the Catholic Queen, Henrietta Maria, wife of King Charles I. (Henrietta Maria was sister of Louis XIII of France.) The Queen was on her way to join her husband at Oxford, and she and her court spent a few days at New Place. Thomas Nash, Susanna's son-in-law, was a known supporter of Charles I, and New Place may have been singled out for the royal entourage for that reason.[22]

Within a few months of this event, Stratford was occupied by Parliamentary forces during that bitter struggle between King and Parliament, the Civil War, which resulted in the beheading of Charles in 1649. It was during this period that Dr. James Cooke, in attend-

ance upon the Parliamentary troops at Stratford, bought
Dr. Hall's manuscripts consisting of two notebooks from
Susanna and arranged for the publication of one.

After his marriage into the Shakespeare family in
1607, John Hall became more engrossed in community
affairs. As both professional man and resident of Stratford, he was called upon to serve his fellow citizens, by
performing medical, religious and civic duties. The former he fulfilled with devotion and skill, but many of the
civic obligations he found irksome, and did not hesitate
to show this, as witness his refusal to accept election to
the City Council.[23] As early as 1611 his name appears on
a list of supporters of a highway bill. A year later he
bought a "close" near Evesham from Abraham Sturley
(Shakespeare's friend), though he may never have occupied this land.

In 1617, Dr. Hall was elected Burgess to the City
Council for the first time, probably, as Fripp suggests,
as the new owner of New Place, one of the largest and
most important homes in Stratford. Hall refused to take
office, but was elected again in 1623. Again he refused,
as he did not want to burden himself with civic responsibilities that might interfere with his medical duties.
His third election to the City Council took place in 1632,
at which time he accepted the position. On July 6th of
that year he was fined for non-attendance.

In the letter mentioned earlier,[24] dated July 5, 1632
from Bushwood, patient Sid Davenport wrote pleadingly
to Hall not to fail to visit him as his disease was "peril-
ous", adding he thought it "strange and unheard of" that
any town business should be considered by the Corporation more important than saving the "liefe" of a patient.

Davenport urged Hall to set aside his duties as Burgess, and attend him even though Hall had been warned he would be fined. Davenport intended not "to eat or drink" till Hall appeared. Hall evidently attended him and missed the Council meeting, which led to the fine for non-attendance. In regard to the demands of the City Council, Fripp says, "For 15 months he made unwilling compliance, aggravated by over-work and illness and championship of the vicar, Thomas Wilson, and on October 9th, 1633, he was finally allowed to retire from office."[25] He had earlier been fined for continued absences from the Council, breach of orders and other misdemeanors. The life of a Burgess was not for a man of Hall's temperament!

Dr. Hall, a conscientious Puritan, showed greater interest, however, in the church and its activities. During the latter years of his life, he accepted three church appointments. In 1627 he became borough churchman, 1629 church sideman (collector of offerings), and 1633 churchwarden for Vicar Thomas Wilson whom he greatly admired. Hall gave a carved pulpit to the Church and apparently was interested in parish activities. As churchwarden he took his duties toward delinquent parishioners seriously. Fripp states Hall reported "one 'for loitering forth of church in sermontime,' another for 'sleeping in the belfry, with his hat on, upon the Sabbath,' a third for 'keeping drinking in his house after evening prayer,' a fourth for 'wearing his hat in church' and being a 'common romler,' a fifth for 'late coming to church' and being 'abroad sermontime,' a sixth for 'late coming to church,' sitting 'very unreverently there, sometimes laughing and romling,' others for 'beastly behavior,' putting hands under plackets [openings in petticoats], being a common 'swearer and blasphemer of God.' He also accused a fellow church-warden of 'keeping back the poor's money from those in need of relief'."[26]

In those days of religious strife between Puritan, Presbyterian and Anglican, there was much unrest and turmoil in England. Early in Queen Elizabeth's reign, Puritanism had originated as a reform movement against the established church, aiming to eliminate ritual, vest-ments and hierarchical organization. At first there was no quarrel over doctrine with the High Church nor plans for secession. But by 1567 separation from the Church of England had begun. Many groups joined in this move-ment, and feelings ran high on all sides.

Stratford-upon-Avon, like other English communi-ties, shared in the religious divisions of the day, and very little pretext was needed to ignite fierce partisanship and strife. The Corporation of Stratford disliked their Vicar Rogers and made use of a petty quarrel in 1619 to dis-miss him. Sir Francis Bacon, Lord Chancellor of England at that time, granted permission to Stratford to replace him, and the new vicar was the "brilliant" Thomas Wil-son of Evesham. He was a fine speaker with definite Puritan opinions which brought him into conflict eventu-ally with the Stratford Corporation and others in the town.

John Hall early championed Wilson and sup-ported him through a number of stormy experiences. At one time Hall sold to the Corporation his lease tithes for £100 less than their value in order to keep the Vicar's salary at £60, and the schoolmaster's at £20. There was constant trouble between the Corporation and the Vicar on many matters, amongst them a fight over the timber in the churchyard. Hall took Wilson's side openly in all respects, incurring the Corporation's wrath. Hall joined the Vicar in a suit against the Corporation, and quarrelled further with them over his request to change his own church pew to one used by the Aldermen and their families. (He was successful in this.) Hall denounced the Corporation and accused them, among other things, of neglecting to increase the Vicar's salary as promised, stating that they used the revenue for "feasting and private means." The last two years of Hall's life, 1633-1635, were particularly marked by these quarrels between himself and the Vicar on one side, and the Corporation on the other.[27]

A note in Hall's Casebook, (Observation LX Second Century) dated August 27, 1632 to September 29th, "about the 57th year of my age" describes his own illness. He wrote that he was much debilitated by an "immoderate flux of the hemorrhoids, yet daily was constrained to go to several places to patients. By riding, a hardness being contracted, the flux was stayed for fourteen days. After I fell into a most cruel torture of my teeth and then into a deadly burning fever, which then raged very much, killing almost all that it did infect." He treated himself by first purging with rhubarb which had little effect. Then, as convulsions of the mouth and eyes developed, he had a pigeon cut open alive and applied it to his feet to "draw down the vapors." He was then "afflicted with a light delirium." His wife called in two fellow physicians at this point (one may have been Master Boles, mentioned in Hall's will). They prescribed an electuary (a medicine compounded with honey or syrup to form a pasty mass) and along with blood-letting, the application of leeches to the hemorrhoids and other decoctions, he became "perfectly well, praised be God." On his recovery he praised God for this great gift of life. "Oh, most merciful God and Father of our Lord, Jesus Christ, praying thee to give me a most thankful heart for this great favour for which I have cause to admire thee." Throughout the Casebook, Hall evokes the Lord's blessings for the cures he reports and uses the motto "Health is from the Lord" at the beginning.

Three years later, November 25th, 1635, Hall passed away at the age of 60 while fighting an epidemic among fellow townsmen. According to Elton,[28] the year in which Hall died the plague was widespread in England. It carried off almost 3000 people at Hull. There were constant outbreaks in Kent and other areas. Hall's death is recorded thus in the Stratford-upon-Avon Parish Register: 1635, November 26th. B. Johannes Hall, medicus peritissimus (most skilled doctor). (The "B" refers to "Burial".) His tombstone bears his coat of arms (three talbot heads erased) and an inscription, "medica celeberrimus arte" (most celebrated in the medical art). He lies close to the tomb of William Shakespeare. His will, a short one, is worth noting in its entirety:

The Last Will and Testament nuncupative of John Hall of Stratford-upon-Avon in the County of Warwick, Gentleman, made and declared the fifth and twentieth of November 1635:

I give unto my wife my house in London.

I give unto my daughter Nash my house in Acton.

I give unto my daughter Nash my meadow.

I give my goods and money unto my wife and my daughter Nash to be equally divided between them.

Concerning my study of books, I leave them to you my son, Nash, to dispose of them as you see good. As for my manuscripts, I would have given them to Mr. Boles if he had been here, but for as much as he is not here present, you may, son Nash, burn them or do with them what you please.

Witnesses: Thomas Nash, Simon Trapp.[29]

A year later, Susanna and her son-in-law declared that Hall's goods were worth at least a thousand pounds and that books and other valuables had been seized to satisfy an outstanding debt. There has been much speculation that the manuscripts referred to in the will may have consisted, among others, of Shakespeare's works, yet there does not seem to be any reason to make this assumption. The manuscripts of Shakespeare's plays were more likely in London, in the hands of the publishers of the First Folio, or of the Heminge or Condel families. Also, the fact that Hall stated that he would have left the manuscripts to Mister Boles suggests that they were medical material, as Boles has been identified as a colleague of Hall who practiced in Stratford.[30]

Elizabeth, who was born in 1608, was Hall's only child. He refers to her as "filia mea unica," and in Observation XXXVI (First Century) describes a period of illness during her seventeenth year. In the course of his detailed account of her symptoms (wry neck, fever, etc.), he mentions a trip of hers to London in 1624. Hall's will indicates that he owned a house in London, and it was most likely used by the family on a number of occasions.

Hall's account of Elizabeth contains a curious additional personal fact ("she eats nutmegs often"), and reveals deep parental concern for her health. Her recovery led him to write, "Thus she was delivered from death and deadly diseases, and was well for many years." And the next known fact about Elizabeth is that two years later, in 1626, at the age of eighteen, she married Thomas Nash, thirty-three, a barrister of Lincoln's Inn. Thomas was the son of Anthony Nash of Welcombe, a well-to-do landowner and friend of William Shakespeare. (Shakespeare, in fact, left money in his will for memorial rings for Anthony and his brother, John.) Elizabeth and Thomas apparently had a happy life together though no children were born to them. Nash died suddenly, possibly of the plague, on April 4, 1647, at the age of 53, and was buried beside his father-in-law in the Church of the Holy Trinity. He left his mother-in-law, Susanna, perhaps as a token of respect, the sum of £50 in his will.

At the time of Thomas Nash's death, he and Elizabeth were residing next door to New Place, then occupied by the widowed Susanna Hall. Today in Nash's house, a property owned by the Shakespeare Birthplace Trust, a picture of an older man and young woman, in modish dress, hangs on the wall. It has only recently been identified as a portrait of Thomas and his young wife, Elizabeth. It looks out, with solemn serenity, on the house once occupied by them.

In June 1649, a month prior to the death of Susanna Hall,[31] Elizabeth married again, this time also to a much older man, John Barnard, Lord of the Manor at Abington, Northamptonshire. Barnard, a widower with grown children, was a scholarly man, with a fine library. The Barnards apparently spent part of their married life at New Place in Stratford and part at Abington, described by Elton as "drearily situated on the road from Northampton to Cambridge." Great tracts of common field lay on either side of it. Life in Stratford must have been gay for the Barnards in contrast to Northamptonshire said to be "wanting in fish, fowl and fuel." On November 25, 1661, Charles II created John Barnard a baronet, giving Elizabeth the title Lady Barnard of Abington for the last nine years of her life.

Elizabeth died childless in 1670 at Abington and with her death, Shakespeare's direct line ceased.[32] Her husband died four years later. There is no indication of Elizabeth's relationship to her step-children (four boys and four girls) other than they are not mentioned in her will, an omission which may be of no significance.

# JOHN HALL AND SHAKESPEARE

The question of John Hall's relationship to his celebrated father-in-law has been a matter of conjecture over
the centuries. Essentially little exists to suggest that the
two men were even acquainted, but the few known
facts are important. First of all is the obvious fact of Hall
having married Shakespeare's daughter. It is known that
Shakespeare lived in Stratford from about 1611 to the
time of his death in 1616. New Place, Shakespeare's
home, and Hall's Croft, are relatively close together. It
would not be too great a stretch of the imagination to
presume that the two men would have been in each
other's company from time to time. Hall's learning and
experience as well as his devotion to his practice, and
perhaps a scientific enthusiasm, probably would have
appealed to a man of Shakespeare's broad interests.

It is known that Hall and Shakespeare were together
in London in 1614, at which time Shakespeare was see-
ing about land enclosures, a matter which occupied his
attention in the last years of his life. Thomas Greene,[33]
Shakespeare's close friend who addressed him as "Coz,"
joined them on this occasion and after the meeting recorded in his diary "Hall and Shakespeare did not think
anything would come of the enclosure matter." Regret-
tably Greene did not record any personal details about
the two men. From the fact however that the younger
man accompanied his father-in-law to London, an in-
ference may be drawn both of an established relationship
between them and perhaps of a suggestion that Shakes-

peare placed confidence in the business acumen of his
son-in-law. To lend credence to this last conjecture is
the third fact, that both John Hall and Susanna were
named executors of Shakespeare's will. This again re-
inforces the impression of Shakespeare's trust and
confidence in his son-in-law. (Hall in 1617 filed
Shakespeare's will for probate in the Archbishop of
Canterbury's Register, an office then situated near
St. Paul's Cathedral in London.) There is one additional bit of indirect evidence indicating the possible relationship between the two men. Lee[34] states that in 1614
a minister of Puritan leanings was entertained at New
Place by Shakespeare, after having delivered a sermon
in Stratford. He conjectures that Hall was probably the
instigator of this act of hospitality and cites it as possible
evidence of a close relationship between the Hall and
Shakespeare families.

Scholars have frequently raised the question as to
why Hall did not mention Shakespeare in his Casebook.
According to Cooke's preface to the "Select Observations
on English Bodies," he bought two notebooks, "this and
another," from Susanna after Hall's death. From all that
is known, only one notebook was published, with the
above-named title, and is today in the British Museum.
The second notebook appears to have been lost and its
whereabouts is still a mystery. The nature of this notebook also remains in doubt, but it most probably was
another record of medical cases, similar to the one published, since Cooke states both "were intended for the
Presse." It *is* possible that Hall may have mentioned his
father-in-law, and that this entry is recorded in the lost
book. It does seem likely though that Shakespeare was

mentioned only if he presented a therapeutic problem Hall found sufficiently interesting. This was Hall's chief guide — to record only the medical cases most interesting and "most fittest for public view." For example, the letter from patient Sid Davenport certainly suggests that he was a patient of Hall, but his case is not reported in the known manuscript of the "Select Observations." It is also more than likely from the tone of Lady Tyrrell's letter that she and her husband were also patients of Dr. Hall, but their cases likewise are not recorded. These examples bear out the supposition that Hall's criteria for the selection of the cases that appear in his manuscript and hence in the published versions were solely their medical and therapeutic value.

As for Shakespeare's last illness in 1616, Hall may well have treated him and may possibly have recorded it in the missing notebook, or possibly in another source in the manuscripts mentioned in his will. Or it may not have been recorded at all if it did not fit Hall's criteria. The notebook that has come down to us as the "Select Observations" is not in any sense a diary, though as mentioned above, it has been erroneously referred to in this manner. If Hall had been more interested in keeping a diary with the usual comments on persons, events and scenes, it is highly probable that Shakespeare would have been mentioned. This however was not Hall's intent as revealed in the notebook available to us at present. He was rather a dedicated medical man who wanted to record for posterity some of his most interesting medical cases.

There is no reason to believe that Hall had greater prescience than many of his contemporaries and hence was more aware of Shakespeare's genius. Hall most probably thought the work he was doing to be of at least equal importance to that of his father-in-law and possibly of greater value. After all, he was ministering to the sick and healing the infirm. Medical personages stood high in the social scale of that day. They were often the scholars and men of learning of their time, and Hall's place as a successful practitioner would have given him much esteem and respect in the community.

Scholars have also speculated as to Hall's influence on Shakespeare's astute medical knowledge as revealed in his plays. Simpson, in a thorough study, points out that the majority of medical references in Shakespeare's plays occur in those written before Hall even arrived in Stratford.[35] On the other hand, doctors as characters in his plays do not appear until after the date when Hall is presumed to have come to Stratford (1600). Simpson lists seven of these medical characters, which in chronological order are: Dr. Caius in Merry Wives of Windsor, 1600-01; the physician in King Lear, 1605-06; the two doctors in Macbeth, 1605-06; Cerimon in Pericles, 1607-08; Cornelius in Cymbeline, 1609-10; and Dr. Butts in Henry the VIIIth, 1612-13. Shakespeare depicts physicians for the most part in a sympathetic manner and presents them with dignity and respect. In this depiction of doctors as human beings, Hall may have been an influence on his father-in-law. But, with Shakespeare's great unerring ability to endow all characters he touched with humanity, this assumption is difficult to substantiate.

The play that most suggests a possible connection with Hall is "Pericles," through the character of Lord

Cerimon. This play is ascribed to the year 1607 (when Hall entered the Shakespeare family) or possibly early 1608. It was not included in the First Folio and its exact authorship remains in doubt even today. It is generally held that the last three acts were written by Shakespeare with the first two acts the work of an unknown playwright.[36] The character of Lord Cerimon, the kindly humane doctor, enters the play only in the third act. This fact lends to the possibility that Shakespeare may have been influenced in this characterization by his new son-in-law.

"Pericles", written in Shakespeare's final creative phase, depicts the mood of the Bard's last great works, "Cymbeline," "Winter's Tale," and "The Tempest," in which human goodness, forgiveness and a reconciliation to life are the themes. Lord Cerimon, in stating his creed of life, says:

> I hold it ever
> Virtue and cunning were endowments greater
> Than nobleness and riches. Careless heirs
> May the two latter darken and expend,
> But immortality attends the former,
> Making a man a god. 'Tis known I ever
> Have studied physic, through which secret art,
> By turning o'er authorities, I have
> Together with my practice, made familiar
> To me and to my aid the blest infusions
> That dwells in vegetives, in metals, stones;
> And I can speak of the disturbances
> That Nature works, and of her cures;
>       which doth give me

A more content in course of true delight
Than to be thirsty after tottering honour . . .

When Thaisa, Pericles' wife, is cast ashore, half-
dead, ill and cold, Cerimon efficiently administers to her
needs, restoring her to life and to eventual reunion with
Pericles. Gower, the Chorus, refers to Cerimon as
"In reverend Cerimon there well appears
The worth that learned charity aye wears."
This characterization, if indeed based on Hall, speaks
well of the regard in which the younger man was held
by his father-in-law. There can, however, be nothing
conclusive about this.

# JOHN HALL, THE PHYSICIAN

The possible parallel drawn between Lord Cerimon, the kindly, efficient physician of Epheseus and John Hall leads to a consideration of Hall as an Elizabethan medical practitioner. The Casebook reveals a great deal about Hall as a man and physician, and about his place in the medical world of his day. Bird's Introduction to the first edition states that Hall's practice was large and widespread, stretching from "Persons Noble, Rich and Learned" to the most humble servant and barber. His practice, as can be inferred from the Observations in the Casebook, would correspond to that of a present-day internist. Medical practice during the Renaissance period was bound up with superstition, herb-doctoring and quackery.[37] Given the body of knowledge of his day, Hall's care and therapeutic approach indicate a high measure of skill and consideration.

For the most part, Hall's case reports were limited to the recognition of symptoms, the details of prescriptions and a statement of results. Even then, symptoms were not described in detail, nor is there any attention to pathology as it is known today. Hall's therapeutic interventions consisted mainly of elaborate pharmaceutical prescriptions in which over one hundred separate botanical herbs were used. He apparently believed, as did Friar Lawrence, in "the powerful grace that lies in plants, herbs, stones and their true qualities." The extensive use of botanical herbs was a reflection of the then-current medical thinking. Hall's therapeutic armamentarium was characteristic of normal medieval and Renaissance medical practice with its leeches, blood-letting, elaborate herbs, minerals, purges, laxatives, and a physiology based upon the Hippocratic humoral concept. On the other hand, Hall seems to have shown a degree of independent thinking and judgment that lifted him above the average practitioner of that day. He used venesection moderately although it was in great general use. Because of this, Elton states Hall must have been a follower of Dr. Jacques Pons (1538-1612) of Lyons, who wrote a major tract, dedicated to Henry IV, on the abuse of the practice of blood-letting.[38]

Hall does not mention Pons in his manuscript, nor Pons' contemporary, Jean Liébault, as has been claimed. On the other hand, he specifically refers to six medical authorities, mentioned earlier, and references to them are scattered throughout his manuscript. He uses Sennert and Eugalenus for diagnostic criteria, and the others, Johannes Anglicus, Quercitanus, Horst and Crato, for prescriptions. It is of interest that both Sennert and Eugalenus wrote on scurvy, a condition Hall frequently treated.

Hall's case reports indicate, for that day, some psychological understanding of the needs of his patients, though evidence is not abundant. An example is the case of Dr. Thornberry, Bishop of Worcester, aged 86, who had long "been tormented with a scorbutic wandering gout" and had fallen into a deep melancholy. Hall knew, both from his advanced age and from a tragic family event (a murder) that Thornberry "might be eased but never perfectly cured." While this prognosis might not have required great acumen. Hall's mention of it does indicate a humanitarian feeling. Hall's advice to the parents of Editha Staughton, aged 17, who was afflicted with melancholy and the "mother" [archaic term for hysteria] was that "few should trouble her," again a sympathetic attitude toward a patient's distress.

In most medical conditions described in the Casebook, Dr. Hall's cures reflect the complicated pharmacy of the Elizabethan day. His cases abound in the use of offensive animal matter, webs of spiders, powder of nut shells, excreta, dried windpipes of cocks, etc. Yet, in regard to his treatment of scurvy, Hall employed a simple, and as can now be realized, enlightened cure. Scurvy was one of the great Elizabethan scourges, protean in its manifestations. It was brought on by the prevalent diet of salt meat, salt fish, few vegetables, and limited seasonal fruits. It is in this field that his contribution to medical practice may be considered above average.

Hall's clinical description of scurvy was "general lassitude, filthy yellow jaundice, pains in the loins, weakness of legs, frequent changes of urine, tumors of the gums, swelling of the fingers, sweating and wandering pains." His scorbutic patients were treated with a mixture of plant and vegetable juices made from water cress, brooklime (veronica beccabunga) and scurvy grass (barbari vulgaris or yellow rocket), all herbs now known to be rich in ascorbic acid.[39] These he sometimes made into a beer, flavored with sugar, cinnamon or juniper berries, or into an apozeme (an infusion), not unlike Cerimon's "blest infusions." (See Observation I, the Countess of Northampton for full scurvy prescription.)

Hall does not state in his notes how he arrived at his scurvy prescription. It is known that some doctors more than a hundred years before James Lind's use of lime juice for scurvy had utilized a cure similar to Hall's.[40] When Hall employed his remedy he was in advance of his time, but not alone in his method. Cooke states Hall had the "happiness" to lead the way to "that practice almost generally used by the most knowing of mixing scorbutics in most remedies." The "most knowing" apparently did not coincide fully with the "most famous," for Cooke also adds Hall's treatment of scurvy brought "reproach upon himself by those most famous in the profession." This censure by medical colleagues did not seem to change Hall's course of treatment. In whatever manner he came upon this remedy, he found it effective and continued to employ it. His inclusion of a number of successfully-treated scurvy cases in his Casebook may have been both his empiric answer to the criticisms directed against him, and a recommendation for the use of his anti-scorbutic method. In this instance, as in his stand against the Stratford Corporation, Hall seems to have shown an independence of thinking and a steadfastness in the face of opposition.

Hall was evidently highly regarded by his patients both as a person and as a physician. Dr. John Bird wrote in his preface to the first edition of the "Select Observations": "and this I take to be a great sign of his ability. Such who spare not for cost, and they who have more than common understanding, nay, such as hated him for his religion, often made use of him." Hall treated alike Protestant and Catholic at a time when religious affiliation played an important role, or as Halliwell-Phillipps expressed it, "at a time of fierce religious animosities." The confidence and belief shown in him by his

38691

patients surmounted any prejudice they might have felt toward him as a Puritan.

Further evidence of Hall's popularity is indicated by the fact that he visited patients as far as forty miles from Stratford, e. g. the Earl and Countess of Northampton at Ludlow Castle. As horseback riding would have been the method of transportation used, this was no mean feat. His advice was sought by a variety of persons, "aristocracy, Catholics, Protestants, barbers, children, servants and priests." The nature of his practice as revealed in his Casebook led Dr. Harvey Graham to write: "His patients were in fact very much the kind of patients who in London would have consulted Dr. William Harvey."[41] The letter from Lady Tyrrell and the following from Sid Davenport (quoted in its entirety)[24] substantiate this impression:

Good Mr. Hall,

I sent my boy to you this morning to carrie my water & acquaint you with what daunger & extremitie I am faullen into in respect my shortness of breath & obstructions of my liver, that I cannot sleep nor take anie rest, and although I have more need of yr presence this daie than to stay untill to morrow yet in regard of the multitude of yr affairs being ye Markett daie yet I well hoped you would not have failed me to morrow morning being fridaie at 7 of the clock in the morning, for I will not eat or drink untill I see you. My owne Servante is not yet returned from [Davenport has here crossed out a second "from"] Stratford, but about dynner time this daie I re-

ceived a note from you howe that you cannot be
here at Bushwood with me to morrow in respect
of some private meeting at yr hall concerning the
affairs of yr Towne you saie you are warned to be
there & if you be absent you are threated to be
fined, I did not expect to receive such a kinde of
excuse from you, considering the daungerous
estate I am in, as maie appear bie my water, &
the relation of my servant whome I sent to you
this morning of purpose, & therefore I think it is
not anie Towne business, that can hinder you but
rather that you have promised some other patient
& would put me off with this excuse: And if it
were so indeed that you are sommoned & warned
to appear as you wright & for not appearance to
be fined, it is verie strange to me, [the word "that"
is here crossed out] & unheard off that a Phisitian
should be incorporated of anie Towne or made a
Member of anie corporation, not onlie to interupt
his Studies, hinder his practice but also to in-
daunger the liefe of his patient for want of his
presence, because in a tedious and [Davenport
here used "and" as well as the "&" sign] daungerous disease his presence is to be preferred before
his private occasions, for what cannot a daie bring
fourth & a little error causeth a relapse wch is
worse than the disease, I know my disease is pilous
& procrastination is daungerous. I have relied on
you I trust you will not faile me now, I know you
cannot be fined for visiting yr patients. Neither the
Towne so barren of able men, nor the Magistrates
so [looks like the word "different" has been crossed

out] indiscreet to lay this burthen uppon you
whose profession is to be most abroad & cannot
be effected by an apprentice as theirs maie, & for
you to be vexed with Towne buissenes whose calling is out of Towne it would seem a great folly
in you & more mallice in them to requier. Therefore I councell you as a friend never be bounde as
long as you may be free you shall but derogat from
yr selfe, heap a great deale of troubles uppon you
distract you from yr Studie wch deserveth the
whole employment of anie Man, had he a 100
yeres to lyve longer: Therefore I pray you all ex-
cuses set a part that you wilbe here to morrow
morning by 7 of ye clock for I will fast untill ye
come, and I know you cannot incurr anie daunger
having so lawfull a calling. Thus with my best
wishes & hartie love remembered to yr . self & ye
rest of my good friendes with you I commit you
to Gods holie protection & ever remain
                    Yor trewly loving friend
                         & Servant
                       Sid Davenport.
My brother Colmores Phisick is ended & all is
taken he staieth at home purposely to speak with
you tomorrow morning for further directions.
Bushwood. thursdaie 5 July 1632[42]

While this letter reveals more of Davenport, the
patient, than of Hall, the physician, it does show the ail-
ing person's need of his doctor to take care of and cure
him. As can be seen by the letter, Davenport is alter-
nately pleading, suspicious, insolent, demanding and

finally convinced that his physician will not fail him. That Davenport was right in the latter supposition is certainly suggested by the fact, noted earlier, that Hall missed the Stratford Council meeting on the following day. Basically the relationship between patient and doctor has not differed too much over the years.

The medical conditions reported in the Casebook cover a wide diagnostic range—abortion, asthma, dropsy, sterility, cancer, dysmenorrhea, melancholy, empyema, worms, and jaundice are but a few of the conditions Hall treated. Scholars have commented that Hall reports very few failures in his Casebook. There is no doubt after reading the Casebook that Hall intended this as a guide to treatment for other medical men, and as a contribution to the medical literature. He therefore reported the methods, prescriptions, and formulae of therapy which in his hands had proven useful. This may account for the predominance of cures recorded. His approach is that of the medical teacher who wishes to impart his therapeutic successes to his peers. He was more interested in reporting the therapeutic management of the various conditions than in describing the diseases in their minute form and variations, and he does not go into what in modern times would be considered the physiology and pathology.

# JOHN HALL AND THE CASEBOOK

A statement in Hall's will directed his son-in-law, Thomas Nash, to burn his manuscripts or dispose of them as he pleased. Apparently Nash and Susanna did not wish to do so, for Dr. Cooke reports in the preface to the first edition of the "Select Observations" that in 1644 he was able to obtain two notebooks from Hall's widow. During the Civil War, while attending some parliamentary troops guarding the bridge at Stratford, Cooke visited Susanna to "see the books left by Mr. Hall. She brought forth this [book] with another of the author's both intended for the Presse." Cooke recognized the handwriting as Hall's and offered to buy them from Susanna. She appeared not to know they were in her husband's handwriting. After a certain amount of deliberation, Cooke succeeded in purchasing them.

As the notes were in abbreviated Latin, Cooke sent them to London to "an able doctor" to obtain an opinion about publishing them. The opinion offered was that the abbreviated Latin would cause the translator difficulty. Cooke, however, had some "spare hours" and a conviction of their worth for he set about translating Hall's condensed Latin. This he accomplished with the help of Hall's apothecary, Richard Court, and in 1657 one of the notebooks appeared as "The Select Observations on English Bodies." Whatever difficulties Cooke may have encountered in preparing the translation, his judgment was vindicated by the evaluation of Dr. John Bird. Dr. Bird's comment was that the cases "were equal to the best published."

A remark by Dr. Cooke in the postscript to his preface has given rise to a most puzzling problem in Hall studies. He states "I had almost forgot to tell you that these observations were chosen by him [Hall] from the rest of his own, which I conjectured could be no less than a thousand, as fittest for public view." This statement has given rise to a misconception perpetuated over the centuries, namely, that Hall left a thousand cases from which Cooke selected the 178 (179) that appeared in the first edition. Various scholars in this field have stated that the cases are today lodged in the British Museum as part of Egerton Manuscript 2065. A close perusal of this Manuscript shows that this is not the case. It consists solely of one bound notebook containing 178 cases in a distinctive handwriting, presumably Hall's, in closely-written abbreviated Latin, together with some pages of notes in English, Latin and Hebrew at the back, in a different handwriting than the body of the manuscript, possibly Cooke's. Egerton Manuscript 2065 ends with several pages of a table of contents (in Latin), again in Hall's writing. Cooke must have made use of the empty intervening pages for notes of his own.

According to a personal communication, the above-mentioned manuscript is Hall's only manuscript in the British Museum. Where then are the thousand "cases"? If one notebook contained 178 cases, it does not seem likely that the second (and today, lost) notebook contained 800. What is the more reasonable assumption is that Hall did not at any time write down the thousand cases. (Cooke does not actually state that he himself had the thousand cases in his possession.) Before his death in 1635, Hall was most probably selecting and distilling into two notebooks, his most interesting medical cases out of a thousand or more observations, representing his years of medical experience. His plan was, as Dr. Bird suggests, for a publication of them after his death "when men more willingly part with what they have."

The records of the British Museum indicate that Egerton Manuscript 2065 was obtained in 1848 from a Mr. William Paterson, but they do not reveal how Mr. Paterson obtained it. One clue to the fate of the manuscript is found in the copy of the third edition, now in the Folger Shakespeare Library, Washington, D.C. This copy had once been in the possession of Edmond Malone (1741-1812), Shakespearean scholar and friend of Samuel Johnson. Opposite the title page, in handwriting identified as Malone's, is a notation suggesting that Hall's original manuscript — in notebook form — passed from Cooke to a Thomas Davis, bookseller, to David Garrick, eighteenth century Shakespearean actor, and eventually to Malone. This information sheds some light on various owners of the original manuscript. The fate of the second notebook is still unknown. The only knowledge of its existence is Cooke's reference to it in his Preface.

Cooke also stated that Hall "had been a traveller, acquainted with the French tongue, as appeared by some part of some observations." There is nothing in Hall's known Latin manuscript in the French language. However, Cooke's statement might have been based upon the contents of the missing notebook or even upon his personal knowledge of Hall. The one "French" reference found pertains to Quercitanus, as seen, for example, in Observation XXXI (First Century) in regard to a "restorative of Quercitanus" used to ease patient Kempson. Quercitanus, the Latinized name of French physician, Joseph DuChesne (1544-1609), championed chemistry and alchemy in medicine. Some of his works were translated from Latin into French around 1576 and into English around 1596 and 1605. (See Note on Observation XXXI.)

There is no information on the source of Hall's knowledge of Quercitanus. He may have read any one of the three versions of this doctor's medical writings, or if he travelled, may have met him personally. Since Quercitanus favored alchemy as did Hall's father, Hall might even have read him in his father's library. The reference to Quercitanus neither proves nor disproves Cooke's statement, regarding Hall's knowledge of French. At most it indicates Hall was in touch with French medical thinking, as he seemed to be in regard to European medicine in general from the authorities cited.

"The Select Observations" was evidently a compilation of earlier notes taken by Hall, and the most telling evidence of this lies in the irregularity in dating in the Casebook. The Observations begin with a visit to the Countess of Northampton, March 6, 1622, and then record a visit a month later to her husband, the Earl of Northampton. Many pages later, Observation XCIX records a visit to the same Countess dated two years previously (1620). There are several cases with no dates at all, and some with nonconsecutive dating; for example, 1622 in the first Observation and 1617 in a later one. Another revealing statement is found in Observation XXIX (First Century), concerning Mr. Fortescue. Hall states he first saw him June 5, 1623, and ends "and now, ten years from the time afflicted he has been very well." This certainly indicates the actual report was written at least in 1633.

In the manuscript the earliest date, 1617, appears in the margin next to Observation LXVI (First Century) pertaining to Mrs. Barnes "being great with child and near delivery, fell into a Tertian fever." This date has been omitted from all printed editions. The earliest dating in the printed editions is found three cases later in regard to Baron Compton "aged 55 in 1617." This has generally been regarded as Hall's earliest dated case. There is no way of knowing if undated cases come from an earlier or later time than that. It would be reasonable to assume that a doctor, who started practicing medicine around 1600, might have selected cases from clinical data of the first seventeen years of his practice. Therefore, some of the undated cases may well go back to this early period. In view of this, there is no reason to assign any special significance to the actual date, 1617, one year after Shakespeare's death. If we could prove that Hall only began to write, for the first time, the year following his father-in-law's death, we might assume perhaps an identification on Hall's part with Shakespeare. As it stands, any connection between the date, 1617, and Hall's relationship to the Bard and his writing must remain a speculation.

Hall's manuscript ends at Observation LXXXII (Second Century), concerning the Earl of Northampton (the second of this line) who caught cold "while following his hounds in a cold and rainy day." As mentioned earlier, Cooke added cases at this point to bring the number of Observations to two hundred. Throughout the text,

Cooke included cases from continental medical sources to enhance and lend authority to Hall's writings. Even though Hall cited medical references, he mainly did so in regard to prescriptions and diagnoses, and not to the inclusion of case material.

In particular, Cooke leaned heavily upon the medical writings of two physicians, Lazarus Riverius[43] and Augustin Thoner.[44] For example, after Hall's Observation LIII (First Century), on Mr. Parker, aged 24, "greivously vexed with a long cough," Cooke added three cases from Thoner, which he stated he "could not pass, because much approved" on the treatment of coughs in general. In Observation LIII (Second Century), Cooke added a quotation on worms from Riverius to Hall's discussion of Frances Finch of Stratford, so afflicted. Another instance occurs also in the Second Century, in Observation LXVI, Mrs. Boves of Kings-cotton, suffering from an "itch in the fundament" and from worms. Here Cooke quoted Thoner and his cure of worms in a six-year old girl as being revelant to the case. Another example of Cooke's use of medical reference is in Observation XC (First Century), dealing with Wilson of Stratford, troubled with a "pain of the stomach." Cooke referred to both Riverius and Thoner on their method of curing stomach pains, which was mainly by blood-letting.

When Cooke added medical observations of his own, he made a point of stating this, for the most part. On the other hand, he omitted in all editions some of the original text, pertaining to descriptions of Hall's patients. Hall, in his notes, referred to Mrs. Smith as "pious and honest," Lady Rouse as "religious," Anne Ward as "honest and religious," Mrs. Vernon as "pretty," amongst others.

All these adjectives, and more, have been omitted from the printed editions. In regard to Lady Rainsford (Anne Goodere), Hall described her in detail as 62, modest, pious, friendly, dedicated to sacred literature and conversant in the French language. None of this is included in Cooke's editions. Also omitted is Hall's full comment on Mr. Quiney's death: "many things were tried in vain. He now sleeps with the Lord in peace. He was of good wit, expert in tongues and very learned." Cooke has only retained the last descriptive sentence.

Occasionally too the printed editions interchange Hall's Observations, e.g., in the original manuscript Anne Gibs, Observation XIII (First Century), appears before that of John Emes, Observation XII. Also Observation LXIX (First Century), eldest son of Mr. Underhill, is the third to last case in the original manuscript. In the printed editions there is also some confusion in the translation of Hall's Latin, in regard to such terms as "generosus,"[45] "ga" and "da". "Generosa" is translated for the most part as "Mrs." with the connotation of being wellbred. "Generosus" is translated as "Mr." and "ga" as a single girl (generally called "Mrs." after the custom of the time). In one instance, Observation XV (First Century), "Generosa" Hunt (clearly the feminine gender in Hall's original Latin) has been translated as "Mr. Hunt" in all editions, which led earlier scholars to speculate that it referred to Simon Hunt, school teacher in Stratford. It may perhaps have referred to his wife, but nothing definite is known except the fact that a female patient is the one described.* "Da" (domina) is usually translated as "Lady", but in Observation XXXVII (First Century), it is "Mrs." Sands. Consistency has been shown, though,

*See Addendum, p. 100

in the translation of the Latin word "oppidanus" (spelt "opidanus" by Hall). The masculine or feminine gender is used for distinguishing residents of Hall's own town, Stratford.

The variations, errors, omissions and interpositions, described above, may all be attributed to carelessness of the printers. They may, however, have been Cooke's changes, made either in haste, translation error or for some deliberate reason. Cooke had the assistance of Hall's apothecary, Court, for his translation, and the latter, living in Stratford, probably knew many of the individual patients, and guided Cooke accordingly.

It is difficult to select any one case over the others, for general interest and specific comment. A reading of the 178 (179) cases, in their entirety, reveals much that is fascinating, ingenuous and pertinent to the medical picture of that day. By and large, the cases most often chosen for detailed study by others in this field have pertained to Hall's treatment of his wife, Susanna, called "uxor mea" by him (Observation XIX, First Century); his daughter, Elizabeth (Observation XXXVI, First Century); the poet, Michael Drayton; the Earl and Countess of Northampton (known as the Baron and Baroness Compton prior to receiving the Earldom in 1613); Mr. Quiney (related to Judith Shakespeare by marriage); Esquire Rainsford (a good friend of Drayton) and Lady Rainsford (Anne Goodere, who was Drayton's "Idea" in his poem "Idea's Mirror", 1594, 64 sonnets celebrating his love for her); Baronet Puckering; Bishop Thornberry of Worcester and Minister John Trap.

But less known cases could equally be selected out for a variety of reasons: 1) Observation LII (First

Century) — this case, that of Mrs. Sheldon, is one of the few obstetrical cases reported in these Observations. Hall writes, she, "being corpulent, well colored, was wont to miscarry often, the second month after conception, yet suffered no other accident with it, required my counsel." He treated her and concluded his Observation, she used the medication "all her time and after brought forth a lusty, hearty son, and after that more."

2) Observation XLIII (Second Century) — In the printed editions there is no name given to this patient although in the manuscript he is identified by the name of Harvey. This patient, aged 65, was treated by Hall for urinary difficulties and later for a virulent gonorrhea. Hall's Observation continues, "but after riding to London (by what occasion I know not), it broke forth again, where he had the advice of the 'erudissimi' Dr. Harvey, who prescribed what follow." Hall then gives Harvey's remedy and treatment, as being worthy of note.

3) Observation XII (First Century) — John Emes, age 15, suffered from eneuresis. Hall's comment reads, "John Emes of Alcester, age 15, was cured of pissing in bed thus, Rx the windpipe of a cock dried and made into a powder and with Crocus Martis given in a raw egg every morning."

4) Observation XXI (First Century) — Mary Wilson, age 22 (perhaps Minister Wilson's daughter) had "a hectick feaver, with a cough, obstructions of her courses, and weakness" and was treated with multitudinous medications. His final note added, "she sucked women's milk, nourished with cooling and moistening diet, as lettuce. A year after this she died."

5) Observation LXXVII (First Century) — "The

Lady Beaufou, godly, honest, being of noble extract, continuing healthful until the age of 28, which was 1617, July 1, fell into a burning malign continual feaver, with great Pain of the Head, most vehement Heat, Pain in the Stomach; the Body all over, especially the Arms, was full of spots; the Urine was red and little. It was then called the New Feaver, it invaded many, I was called the third day of its Invasion. The Stomach being stuffed and burdened with ill humours, as I perceived, I advised the following vomit: Rx Emetick infusion drams 9. This gave twelve Vomits without any great trouble. The day before she had (unknown to me) drunk much Milk to quench her thirst, by reason whereof the Vomit at first draw forth a wonderful quantity of curdled Milk, so that she was almost Choaked, after came Choler mixed with Phlegm, afterward burn Melancholy. She had also six Stools Phlegmy, mixed with green Choler and much Serosities. Her Vomiting ending in three hours, I gave a Pill of Laudaunum Gr. 7 ["sure he mistook her, for four is a good Dose," Cooke added] after which she slept four hours, the Pain of her Head ceasing. Then to me unknown her Servant gave her a draught of Whey, which being drunk, she presently had three Vomits of black Stuff without any trouble and two such like Stools, and was cruelly afflicted with the Hiccough, to allay which I gave Claret wine burn with Aromatick which succeeded; she was quieter the rest of the Night but did not sleep well. In the morning I gave Chicken-Broth made with appropriate Herbs, and so for four hours she rested. At the end of that time I gave a draught of the Decoction of Hartshorn hot. On Monday morning, having some evacuation, I appointed the same Decoct.

should be given cold. She was miserably afflected with Pustles with great heat of the tongue and Throat, that she could not drink without great difficulty, for which she used the following Gargarism: [here follows a mixture of honey of roses, rose water and oil of sulphur.] After the use of the Hartshorn Decoction, the 7th day, the Pox appeared, yet the aforesaid Gargasim was used for the Throat and she drank of the Decoction of Hartshorn cold four times a day, and so she was cured. I ordered that the Pox after the eight day be annointed with this: Rx common oil and Carduus water, well shaked together, and so there was left no Scars."

This case is given in detail to show the continued care and changing prescriptions used by Hall in his treatment of various conditions. It is evident that Lady Beaufou's illness was not too severe to prevent her recovery, aided perhaps by Hall's assorted therapies.

6) Observation LXXXI (First Century) — "Richard Wilmore of Norton, age 14, vomited black Worms, about an inch and a half long, with six feet and little red heads; when he was to vomit he was almost dead, but in a little time after he revived, I gave him Merc. Vitae. The next day after, his Father brought some wrapped up in Paper. They crept like Earwigs, and were very light, save in color. He earnestly desired my best advice. I considering the state of the Disease, the strength of the Party and that for the most part he was most cruelly afflicted every New Moon, unless he devoured abundance of Meat, in so much that he was ready to tear himself to pieces, I gave him the following remedies: Rx Merc. Vitae grains 3, Conserv Ros parum. This gave 7 Vomits, and brought away 6 Worms, such as I never

beheld nor read of. The following day I gave an Emetic infusion which gave 5 Vomits and brought up three Worms. The third day, another prescription. This purged well, but brought away no Worms. Thus he was delivered and gave me many thanks. I met him two years after and asked him whether he had any Erosion of the Stomach or an Ejection of Worms and he told me that he had never been troubled with it since."

7) Observation X (Second Century) is a description of a case of scurvy. His description is as follows: "The Lady Brown of Radford was oppressed with these Scorbutic Symptoms, as with binding of the Belly, Melancholy, Watchfulness, troublesome sleep, Obstruction of the Courses, continuing for a year, and by these Obstructions was miserably tormented with Wind and swelling of the Belly, especially about the Spleen. When she broke Wind she was eased; she felt a continual beating at the mouth of her Stomach, so that it might be felt with the hand as though there had been some live thing leaping in her Belly. All these happened from the death of her Daughter, dying in Child-Bed." She was treated with a mixture of scurvy grass, water cress, brooklime, etc. as well as treatment applied to the Spleen which "this discussed the Tumor and eased the pain. Yet although well purged, there remained the Scorbutic Pain of the Belly. After purging, the Urine was troubled and the sediment was various." Beer and leeches were applied and "by the use of these she was freed from the Scurvy, and came to enjoy perfect health." (This sounds like a mixture of scurvy and psychosomatic symptoms with an hysterical identification with her deceased daughter. Although Hall intuitively seems to have connected

some of the symptoms with the death of the daughter in child birth, his treatment was as vigorous as though only scurvy were present. His intuitive awareness of emotional factors was displayed not only in this case but also in the one which follows.)

8) Observation LXXX (Second Century) — "Mrs. Editha Staughton, age 17, was miserably afflicted with Melancholy. Her Courses as yet not having broken forth, as also with the Mother [hysterical seizures]; she was very easily angry with her nearest Friends so that she continually cried out that her Parents would kill her, as also of all others that came unto her. She had been purged well by expert Physicians, yet her Father desired my counsel whether she was curable; to which I answered Very Hardly, being her Constitution was Melancholy. I advised there should be few to trouble her, and so began with Emmolient and discussive Clysters as also such as respected the Humor." Then followed a vigororous course of purging, venesection, application of leeches, clysters, ligatures and finally a drink of rhubarb and senna. For her watching [insomnia] he prescribed a sedative. Hall's final statement in this Observation is "And thus by the blessing of God she was delivered from her Distemper."

9) Observation LXIV (First Century) reads as follows:— "Mrs. Harvey, now Lady, very religious, five weeks after child birth was vexed with a great flux of whites [discharge], as also pain and weakness of the back was thus cured. Rx Dates as many as you please, cut them small, and with purified honey make an Electuary. This she used in the morning. By this only remedy she was cured, freed from her pain which came often,

stayed the whites, and made her fat." This unusual die-
tary treatment çured Lady Harvey's symptoms, but may
have presented a cosmetic problem.

10) Observation XLIV (Second Century) reads as
follows: — "Mrs. Mary Comb of Stratford, aged about 13,
Febr. 15, 1631. Two years before this she had her
Lunar Evacuation sufficient, they beginning to flow
abundantly in the 11th year of her Age; but now they
being stopped, upon which she felt a slight Convulsion
in the right eye (to use her own word, a twitching) as
though her Eyes was pulled inward and presently it
would be gone: after both eyes did suffer with great
pain of the Head for which I administered at bedtime
Pil. Aphel. Fern. Then she became curelly vexed with
the Mother, continuing in the fit for 9 hours, with some
light intervals of ease, from which she was delivered by
the following medicines: she had a fume of Horse-
hoofs." Then follow other medications, and purges for
the next couple of days and a month or so later, when
she again fell into the "Mother with Convulsion of the
Eyes, the said Convulsion having grieved her for two
days before she was afflicted with the Mother." Further
treatment was given and "of this, there was made 5 of
a drachm covered with gold; of these she took 3 at
bedtime. By these she was delivered."

One final case, that of Michael Drayton, though
quoted often, is included here as a fine example of the
conciseness Hall showed in many of his reports.

11) Observation XXII (First Century) — "Mr.
Drayton, an excellent poet, labouring of a Tertian, was
cured by the following: Rx the Emetick infusion Syrup

of Violets a spoonful, mix them. This given, wrought very well both upwards and downwards."

All these cases, together with those more popularly and frequently mentioned, testify to the statement that Dr. Hall's practice was varied, widespread and demanding. It had tremendous range — in the actual physical territory he covered, in the variety of patients he saw, in the diversity of diseases he treated and in the herbs and other therapies he prescribed. It is evident that his treatment was based upon the theory of humors afflicting the body. According to medical science at that time, disease was the result of humors, either displaced or present in abnormal quantities. The rationale, therefore, of Hall's treatment was either to remove the humors or to divert them. To this purpose he employed primarily a multitude of medications, but he also used cupping, leeches and some venesection.

John Hall spent much time with his patients, as the situation demanded, and his schedule was a full one. Within a month, he went twice to Ludlow Castle, 40 miles from Stratford, to see the Earl and Countess of Northampton. He records in regard to Mrs. Finnes that although he attended her initially, "a multitude of business" prevented a return visit. In the case of Mrs. Jackson Junior suffering from a post-partum mental state (Hall feared a "Phrensy"), he was unable to visit "by reason of much business." He prescribed for her, however, and recorded a cure. The fact that all visits to patients would have been made by horseback demonstrates the arduous job that was his. In this regard, his account of his own illness is of interest, inasmuch as he mentions he had to go daily by horseback to patients and the riding aggravated his hemorrhoid condition. As noted in the Observation about his own illness, he did not attend to himself first. Even when he began to develop symptoms of fever, he continued making his appointed rounds on horseback. First and foremost, he was the dedicated healer.

Dr. Hall's Casebook exists today as a testament to the man and physician. The descriptions are short and lucid, and in spite of the present day unfamiliarity with his pharmacopoeia, are highly readable. A chance phrase or description in the Latin of the manuscript lends credence to Fripp's claim that Hall was something of a poet, e.g. in Observation LV (Second Century) when describing the extent and seriousness of Mrs. Woodward's illness, Hall states, "Toward evening she expected her unwelcome Enemy with grief of mind." Also in Observation XLIX (Second Century), his description of the Countess of Northampton, "very fair and beautiful" lying with her baby daughter in her arms, has charm. His simple, moving comment on George Quiney's untimely death (at the age of twenty-four) reads, "Many things were tried in vain; peacefully he sleeps with the Lord. He was a man of good wit, expert in tongues and very learned."

His main literary efforts though are seen in his concise delineative phrases accompanying many of his case reports. For example, Hall refers to Michael Drayton as "poeta laureata" (excellent poet); Esquire Beaufou "qui semper honoris causa nomino" (whose name I have always cause to honour); Lady Beaufou as "pia, honesta" (godly, honest); Lady Jenkinson as "pulcra, pia, casta" (fair, pious, chaste); Lady Rainsford (see Notes on Observations) as "formosa et optima structura, 27 annos" (beautiful and of gallant structure of body, aged 27); Mr. John Trap, Minister "ob insigne pietatis et doctrina nulli secundi" (for his remarkable piety and learning second to none). These are but a few examples of Hall's terseness of descriptive writing.

From his case reports, Hall emerges as human being and physician of his time. He appears a dedicated medical man, independent, conscientious and unbiased, who had time to see patients from all walks of life and to treat all with care. He showed an intuitive understanding of the psychologic needs of his patients. He was moderate in his therapeutic approach, utilizing drastic measures such as venesection only sparingly. He apparently had the courage of his medical beliefs, using a treatment of scurvy which, while successful, was not generally accepted. His participation in community and church affairs indicates his devotion to his fellow citizens, but their first call on him was as medical practitioner. Dr. Bird's comment on Dr. Hall is revealing: "This learned author lived in our time and in the County of Warwick where he practiced physik many years, and was in great fame for his skill far and near."

The Latin inscription, in Hall's own handwriting, at code: "He who practices medicine without a cause and the beginning of his manuscript represents his medical method is as one who navigates without a rudder and oars." This credo could apply to Hall's life, religious, communal and personal.

Lines 2 and 3 in the last paragraph on page 47 have been transposed.

# NOTES ON OBSERVATIONS

The following notes present biographical data on each of Dr. Hall's patients, wherever this is possible. Differences between Hall's original Latin manuscript (freely translated) and the three printed editions (1657, 1679, 1683) are described. It is not always possible to decipher Hall's abbreviated Latin, nor the exact meaning of some of the abbreviations, therefore not all differences are indicated.

Unless otherwise stated, the contents of the three editions are identical to one another and to the manuscript. The first edition is a duodecimo, the second and third editions octavo. In the first edition, the text is within a ruled border.

Differences in spelling in the three editions are not indicated. Spelling, at that time, was in a state of flux, and variations, therefore, are not significant. In general, the spelling in the first edition varies the greatest from the other two. As the first edition appeared in 1657 and the second and third, twenty-two and twenty-six years later, this is not surprising. The second and third editions are practically identical in spelling, text and printing.

No attempt is made in the notes that follow to present a medical diagnosis of each case. Since Hall was under the influence of the humoral theory of illness, his descriptions are in accord with such concepts, and his therapeutic approach primarily that of symptomatic relief. The modern physician finds an absence, in the Observations, of detailed physical findings, of considerations of disordered physiology, and of organic pathology. There is therefore not sufficient information to warrant, in general, an attempt at diagnosing. (See note on Observation LXXIII F.C., Mrs. Boughton for an example of this difficulty.)

N.B.   F.C. represents First Century of Observations
       S.C. represents Second Century

### Observation I

"The Countess of Northampton, aged 44," born 1578, was the daughter of Sir John Spencer, Lord Mayor of London. He apparently opposed her marriage for legend has it that Sir William Compton, K.C., had to carry her off in a baker's basket from her father's home, Canonbury House, to marry her.

Hall used his anti-scorbutic "beer" for the Countess' scurvy condition.

The original manuscript contains descriptive words, "pious, beautiful, chaste," not found in the three printed editions.

Hall, in this Observation, refers to a medication of Crato, identified as Crato von Kraftheim (1519-1586). He studied at Wittenberg with Martin Luther, but gave up literature and theology for medicine. He practised in Augsberg, where he won acclaim.

Additional reference to the Countess: Observation XCIX, F.C.

### Observation II

"William, Earle of Northampton," born 1562, was the son and heir of Henry, first Lord Compton of Compton Wyniates. During Queen Elizabeth's reign, he was a member of Parliament and served on the Privy Council. In 1613, James I appointed him President of the Council within the Marches of Wales, and shortly afterward elevated him to the rank of Earl of Northampton.

In Charles I's reign, William was made Lord President of Wales, Lord Lieutenant of Warwickshire and Knight of the Garter. He died suddenly in 1630 and was buried at Compton. Ludlow Castle was another residence.

The manuscript has the phrase, "most illustrious hero," not found in the printed editions.

Additional Reference: Observation LXVIII F.C.,
Observation LXXII F.C.,
Observation LXXXIII F.C.,
Observation LXXXVII F.C.

### Observation III

"Mrs. Smith of Stratford-Upon-Avon, aged 54" may possibly have been related to Alderman William Smith, who lived in the first house in Henley Street, site of Shakespeare's birthplace.

The manuscript contains the words, "pious and honest," not found in the printed editions.

Observation XXXII S.C. may be a relative.

Observation LXIII S.C. may refer to her daughter.

### Observation IV

"Mr. Wilson, minister of the said Town, aged 40" was most likely Vicar Thomas Wilson, staunch Puritan and friend of Dr. Hall, who joined him in many struggles against the Stratford Corporation.

Vicar Wilson came to Stratford in 1619 following

Vicar Roger's dismissal. He is believed to have received a B.D. from Oxford and was probably the grandson of the Dean of Worcester.

Fripp said of Wilson: "He lived near the Chancel of the Chapel and used it for his children to play in; his servants to dry clothes in; his pigs to lie in and his poultry to roost in."

It is of interest that Hall comments on the fact that the eye drops could be tasted on the palate. Apparently he did not know of the anatomical connection via the lacrimal duct between the eyes and the nasopharynx.

The manuscript, second and third editions, conclude with the words, "By these remedies, he was cured, blessed be God." This is not found in the first edition.

Observation XXI F.C. may refer to his daughter.

Additional reference: Observation XC F.C.

### Observation V
"Mrs. Beats of Ludlow, aged 50" — not identified.

It is of interest that Hall, after carefully curing her "great cough" within a period of five weeks, records her death from cause unknown.

### Observation VI
"A Servant of Mr. Nashes, lying at the Bear in Stratford-Upon-Avon, aged 28" may have been Thomas Jeffs, servant of John Nash, owner of the Bear Inn. By 1622, Thomas Nash, later Elizabeth Hall's husband, appears to have been the owner of the Bear, situated opposite the Swan on Fore Bridge Street.

This patient possibly had malaria.

### Observation VII

"Mr. Powel of Ludlow, aged 50" — not identified.

In this Observation, reference is made to the "amber pills" of Crato. This does not appear in the original manuscript and presumably represents Cooke's knowledge of the nature of Hall's prescription.

See Observation I F.C. for note on Crato.

### Observation VIII

"Mrs. Chandler of Stratford-Upon-Avon, aged 34" may possibly have been the wife, or other relative, of William Chandler, wealthy Stratford property owner and relative of Thomas Greene, friend of Shakespeare.

Within this Observation, Hall records two periods of treatment, three years apart.

The manuscript, second and third editions, lists her age as 34; the first edition as 38.

Additional Reference: Observation XXVIII F.C.

### Observation IX

"Christian Bass of Southam in the County of Warwick, aged 29" — not identified.

The manuscript, second and third editions, lists her age as 29. It is omitted altogether in the first. In the manuscript, her name is "Christina," and has the words "praised be God," not found in the printed texts.

### Observation X

"Mrs. Wincol, the Countess of Northampton's Chamber-maid, aged about 48" — not further identified.

This patient may have had a prolapsed hemorrhoid which Hall replaced manually.

In this Observation, Hall refers to a similar treatment for a servant of Mr. Broad, probably the one mentioned in Observation IV S.C.

### Observation XI
"Mrs. Hamberry" — not identified. See XCI S.C.

### Observation XII
"John Emes of Alcester, aged 15" — not identified.

No doubt this boy had enuresis, a condition for which even today there is no satisfactory physical treatment, since it is usually of psychological origin.

In the manuscript, this Observation is 13.

### Observation XIII
"Mrs. Anne Gibs, aged 19" may have been related to George Gibbes, overseer, who seems to have known the Shakespeare family.

In the manuscript, this Observation is 12.

### Observation XIV
"Frances Reyland of Quenton" — not identified.

### Observation XV
"Mr. Hunt of Stock-green, aged about 46" has been identified by Stopes, Fripp and others as possibly Simon Hunt, outstanding schoolmaster.

However, Hall's manuscript has the word "generosa" before Hunt, denoting the feminine gender. She may have been Hunt's wife.

Hall, in the manuscript, makes a reference to "Joh. Anglici." This is the second and third edition, but not in the first.

Johannus Anglicus (John of Gaddesden, 1280-1360) was a doctor, oculist, poet and grammarian. He attended Merton College, Oxford. He built up a London practice where he "drew his patient's teeth, cut their corns and even killed their lice." In his mid-thirties, he composed "Rosa Medicinae," in 5 parts, chiefly a repetition of others' sayings. It had great success though. He was employed as physician to Edward II and possibly Edward III. He was a great advocate of the ancient belief of the royal touch.

### Observation XVI

"Mr. Dison" — not identified.

This Observation is much shortened in the three editions as compared with the Latin manuscript, for reasons unknown.

### Observation XVII

"Mary Heath of Libington, aged 34" — not identified.

Hall comments, at the conclusion, on the particular effectiveness of the wax remedy prescribed.

### Observation XIII

"Mrs. Lain of Auson, aged 49" — not identified.

The remedy prescribed by Hall was evidently highly regarded for he concludes, "This is excellent, and worth gold."

### Observation XIX

"Mrs. Hall of Stratford, my wife." This is the first of two possible references to Hall's wife. Observation XXXIII S.C. is believed to be Susanna, but as she is only identified there as "Wife," Cooke speculates the case may refer to the wife of the previous case, Smith, of Stratford. He concedes though that it's most probably Susanna Hall.

Susanna apparently was suffering from a "cholick," which Hall treated with the same clyster as used on the Earl of Northampton.

### Observation XX

"Mrs. Herbert" — not identified.

The manuscript contains the words "she was freed" not found in the printed editions.

### Observation XXI

"Mary Wilson, aged 22" possibly was the daughter of Vicar Thomas Wilson (Observation IV F.C.).

The manuscript ends "she sleeps with God," after mention of her death. This is omitted in the printed editions.

### Observation XXII

"Mr. Drayton, an excellent poet" was the English poet, contemporary and friend of William Shakespeare, Michael Drayton. He was born in Hartshill, Warwickshire, 1563, one year before Shakespeare. Not much is known of his education, but some sources say he went to Oxford. He was taken as a page into the household of Sir Henry Goodere of Polesworth. Drayton there met Goodere's daughter, Anne, who became his "Idea" in "Idea's Mirror," 64 sonnets celebrating his love for her.

After Anne's marriage in 1595 to Sir Henry Rainsford of Clifford Chambers, Drayton visited them for many summers and wrote in "Poly-Olbion": "deere Clifford — place of health and sport." He also wrote an elegy on Sir Henry's death in the 1620s. (Several Rainsfords are mentioned in Hall's "Select Observations," including Lady Rainsford, Observation LXVIII S.C.).

Drayton experimented in all poetic forms popular at that time — pastoral poems, sonnets, odes, historical tales, drama, etc. His first volume of poems, "The Harmony of the Church" was seized by the Archbishop of Canterbury and destroyed by public order.

His poems include "England's Historical Epistles," "The Battle of Agincourt," "Nimphidia," and others.

Colville says Hall's description of "poeta laureata" was only intended as an acknowledgement of Drayton's excellence in poetry since Ben Jonson was Poet Laureate at that time.

Drayton died in 1631 and is buried in Westminster Abbey.

### Observation XXIII
"Good-wife Betis, aged 40" — not identified.

### Observation XXIV
"Mrs. Boughton, being with child" is mentioned again in Observation XXVI "three days after a miscarriage in the fifth month." Nothing else is known of her except this fact of her miscarriage, her age (28), and her town (Causon).

The manuscript, second and third editions conclude, "Thus she was cured, praised be God," but this is not found in the first.

### Observation XXV
"Mr. Randolph, aged 35." If Hall is correct in the age given, this cannot be the Thomas Randolph, poet

and friend of Ben Jonson, as suggested by Stopes and others, since the poet died at the age of 30 (1605-1635). This patient suffered so with "coldness of his head that he had to wear *three* caps."

### Observation XXVI

"Mrs. Boughton of Causon, aged 28." See note on Observation XXIV, F.C.

"Praise be God," at the conclusion, is omitted in the first edition, but is found in the manuscript, second and third editions.

### Observation XXVII

"Captain Basset, aged about 50" — not identified.

Though Hall concludes this case, "Thus he was perfectly cured, and continued so for a long time," apparently his hypochondriac melancholy returned for he is mentioned again in Observation XXXIV F.C., still aged 50. This latter case concludes, "Thus he was well cured, and thanked me."

### Observation XXVIII

"Mrs. Chandler, of Stratford-Upon-Avon, aged 36" — possibly the same Mrs. Chandler of Observation VIII, two years later.

### Observation XXIX

"Mr. Fortescue, aged 20" — not identified.

He may have had epilepsy or a form of hysterical seizure.

It is in this Observation that Hall mentions he saw the patient "ten years from the time afflicted," bringing the date of writing the report to at least 1633.

### Observation XXX

"Mrs. Nash, aged 62" may possibly have been Hall's son's-in-law mother, or some other relative. The Nashes were a well-known Stratford family.

### Observation XXXI

"Mr. Kempson, aged 60" was probably a member of the Kempson family of Arden's Grafton. One, Leonard, died young, so this might refer to Edward.

This patient was apparently an extremely sick man, and Hall used all measures at his disposal, including leeches.

In this Observation, Hall refers to the "restorative of Quercitanus," found in all editions.

Quercitanus was the Latinized name of the French physician, Joseph DuChesne, born in Gascony about 1544. He spent a long time in Germany, engaged especially in chemistry. He had some idea of uric acid, and may have known about phosphorous. He graduated from medical school at Basel, Switzerland, about 1573 and resided for a while in Geneva, acting as ambassador on occasion.

In 1593, Quercitanus moved to Paris, where he spent his time trying to upset the Galenic physic theory for chemical remedies. He helped overthrow the humors theory, but still believed in the philosopher's stone. He championed chemistry and alchemy and helped usher in the epoch of iatro-chemistry. In addition to writing books on medicine, he wrote poetry too. He died in 1609.

### Observation XXXII

"Mrs. Garner of Shipson, aged 22" — not identified.

### Observation XXXIII

"Brown a Romish Priest" — not identified.

"Ungarick fever" may have been typhus. Hall's remedies included a decoction of gold leaf, pearl, coral, rubies and other precious stones, a good example of his belief in these as curatives.

The manuscript contains "Blessed be God" not found in the printed editions.

### Observation XXXIV

"Captain Basset, aged 50." See Observation XXVII.

### Observation XXXV

"A child of Mr. Walkers of Ilmington, Minister, aged six months." Not identified further.

The child apparently suffered from seizures of some sort. Treatment included the well-known medieval remedy of hanging peony root around the neck and applying powdered peony on the hair, with good results.

### Observation XXXVI

"Elizabeth Hall, my only Daughter." This is of interest for the light it sheds on Elizabeth. Her father mentions his care of her over several months, including a trip she undertook to London. She had a torticullis on the left side, followed by the same on the right side three months later. In May, she was given full treatment for a serious fever. Her recovery led Dr. Hall to write: "Thus she was delivered from Death, and deadly Diseases and was well for many years. To God be praised."

"To God be praised" is omitted in the first edition, but is found in the manuscript and other two editions.

### Observation XXXVII

"Mrs. Sands" — not identified.

In the original manuscript she is referred to as "Da" (Domina) more commonly translated as "Lady." She is called "Mrs." in all the three editions.

### Observation XXXVIII

"Mr. Queeny" was perhaps George Quiney, brother of Thomas who married Judith Shakespeare. The Quineys were an outstanding old Stratford family. Adrian Quiney was bailiff in 1571 when Shakespeare's father was chief alderman, a justice of the peace and deputy to Quiney.

George took his degree at Baliol, served as curate and usher at Stratford till his death at the age of twenty-four, in 1624. He was regarded as industrious, learned and scholarly, though of delicate constitution.

In the manuscript, Hall writes: "Many things were tried in vain; peacefully he sleeps with the Lord," before "he was a man of good wit, expert in tongues and very learned." The first sentence is omitted in all the printed editions.

### Observation XXXIX

"Joan Chidkin, of Southam, aged 50"—not identified.

### Observation XL

"Mr. Winter, aged 44" — not identified.

His age is given as 40 in the first edition, 44 in the other two. In the manuscript, only the "4" is legible.

There is no way of knowing whether this patient had been the husband of "Mrs. Winter, widow" referred to in Observation XXIII S.C.

### Observation XLI

"Mrs. Fortescue, aged 12" presumably of the same family as Observation XXIX F.C.

Original manuscript has "ga" after Fortescue. Because of her age, she most likely was not married, though the title is translated as "Mrs." in the fashion of the day.

### Observation XLII

"Mrs. Throgmorton, aged 35" was no doubt a member of the very old Warwickshire family, Throckmorton.

In this Observation, Hall refers to the "Mother," an archaic term for hysteria. [King Lear, suffering from the sting of his daughters' rebuffs, cries out:

O, how this mother swells up toward my heart!
Hysterica passio, down, thou climbing sorrow,
Thy element's below!]

Here again, in the original manuscript, she is referred to as "Da" though translated as "Mrs."

### Observation XLIII

"Austin, a Maid" — not identified.

Hall gave this "comely" girl good advice in telling her to keep her face, "full of red spots and pustles," well cleansed.

Hall describes her as "virgo intacta," a maiden.

### Observation XLIV

"Elizabeth Kenton of Hunington, aged 50" — not identified.

### Observation XLV

"Simons of Knowle, aged 40" — not identified.

This cure, Hall describes as acting "cito, tuto et jucundi" — quickly, safely and pleasantly.

### Observation XLVI

"Cooper Marit of Pebworth, aged 48"—not identified.

Her Christian name is "Marita" in the original manuscript. This case is a good example of the "humors" theory. Hall states the patient perceived vapors ascending from her feet into the stomach.

### Observation XLVII

"Mrs. Wagstaff of Warwick, aged 46" may have been related to Timothy Wagstaff of that city.

She suffered from scurvy, along with melancholia, a conjunctivitis and other conditions.

Hall mentions using the same remedy for her "weeping eyes" as in Observation III F.C. Additional reference: Observation LXXVII S.C.

### Observation XLVIII

"Mrs. Symmons of Whitelady-Aston"—not identified.

Hall reports a fifteen year cure of her eye condition. He uses Horst's Vesiccatory remedy and in his manuscript gives the prescription for it. Cooke, however, refers the readers to his own book, "The Marrow of Chirurgery" for details of the prescription.

In the original manuscript, Hall refers to Mrs. Wagstaff of the previous Observation. This is omitted in the three editions.

The Horst he refers to may have been either Jakob Horst (1537-1600) or his nephew, Gregor (1578-1636). Gregor, the better known, studied medicine at Basel and was for a time Professor of Medicine at Wittenberg and Ulm. He published some medical works.

### Observation XLIX

"Julian West, aged 53" — not identified.

In this Observation, Cooke adds a note ("Take this from the Translator") in regard to this woman's menstruation problem.

In the first edition, the note becomes Observation L, but part of Observation XLIX in the other two editions.

### Observation L

"John Smith of Newnam, aged 60" — not identified.

This Observation appears in the original manuscript as number 66. It is omitted altogether in the first edition.

### Observation LI

"Mrs. Sheldon of Bel-end, aged 55" — not identified.

Because Cooke inserted Hall's 66th Observation as the fiftieth in this edition, the numbering from now on differs. It is of interest that Hall numbered his cases in arabic numerals.

This is Observation 50 in the original manuscript.

### Observation LII

"Mrs. Sheldon, wife to the Son" identified only as the daughter-in-law of the patient described in the preceding Observation.

This patient miscarried often, but "brought forth a lusty, hearty son, and after that more," by following Hall's "purging" advice.

This is Observation 51 in the original MS.

### Observation LIII

"Mr. Parker, aged 24" — not identified.

This case is followed by three Observations, inserted by Cooke, on the subject of coughs. He took this material from Thoner, as he found it pertinent to Hall's comments.

Observation LIV pertains to a citizen of Ulm, where Thoner lived; Observation LV to Lord Schellenberg of Kisilect, and Observation LVI to a women citizen of Ulm (spelt "Uline"). None of these are in the original manuscript but are in the three printed editions.

This is Observation 52 in the original MS.

### *Observation LVII*

"Edward Rawlins, aged about two years"—not identified.

He seems to have had a tumor of the testicles or a hernia, which Hall treated.

This is Observation 53 in the original MS.

### *Observation LVIII*

"Good-wife Palmer of Alcester" — not identified.
This is Observation 54 in the original MS.

### *Observation LIX*

"Mrs. Barnes of Tolton" — not identified.
This is Observation 55 in the original MS.

### *Observation LX*

"Talbot, the first-born of the Countess of Salisbury, aged about one year" — not further identified.

This is listed as XL in the 2nd edition, no doubt a typographical error.

This is Observation 56 in the original MS.

### *Observation LXI*

"Mrs. Sheldon of Grafton, aged 24" — not identified.
This is Observation 57 in the original MS.

### Observation LXII

"Mrs. Davis of Quenton, aged 63" — not identified.
This is Observation 58 in the original MS.

### Observation LXIII

"The son of Mr. Bishop, aged 6" — not identified.

This youngster, no doubt weakened from his bout with small pox, was given some of Dr. Hall's gentler remedies — syrup of liquiris, milk, and sugar.

This is Observation 59 in the original MS.

### Observation LXIV

"Mrs. Harvy, now Lady, very religious" — not identified.

The manuscript describes her as "chaste and pious" in addition to "religious." These first two adjectives are omitted in the printed editions.

This is Observation 60 in the original MS.

### Observation LXV

"Mrs. Randolph, aged about 27" may have been the wife of the Mr. Randolph mentioned in Observation XXV F.C.

Hall mentions he used the same powder prescribed for Marit Cooper, Observation XLVI, F.C. Marit Cooper's name is omitted in the printed editions, but is in the manuscript.

This is Observation 61 in the original MS.

### Observation LXVI

"Mrs. Barnes, being great with child"—not identified.
If this is the same Mrs. Barnes of Observation LIX

F.C. she was either pregnant again or this case antedates the earlier.

This Observation has the distinction of having the earliest recorded date, 1617, in the margin of the manuscript. It is omitted in all three editions though.

The manuscript ends with "praise to God, honor and glory in all eternity for the cure in seven days." This has been shortened in all editions.

This is Observation 62 in the original MS.

### Observation LXVII

"Robert Sartor of Stratford-Upon-Avon, aged about 34" — not further identified.

This is Observation 63 in the original MS.

### Observation LXVIII

"Baron Compton, now Earl of Northampton, aged 55 in 1617." See Observation II F.C.

Cooke adds to this Observation some comments of Thoner on pain of the teeth in general. This is part of Observation LXVIII in second and third editions. In the 1st Edition, however, this comment of Thoner's becomes the next Observation, number LXIX.

This is Observation 64 in the original MS.

### Observation LXIX

"The eldest Son of Mr. Underhil of Loxley, aged about 12" was probably a member of the prominent Underhill family.

In this Observation, Hall, in one of his few recorded conferences with the patient's family, talks of the difficulties involved in curing the boy.

In the original manuscript, this Observation is the third to last (176), but the same LXIX in the 3rd Edition. It is Observation LXXXI, S.C., in the first Edition.

### Observation LXX

"Anne Green, the Daughter of Mrs. Green, aged 22" most probably was the daughter of Thomas and Letitia Greene, who lived in New Place around 1609. Greene's children were named Anne (baptized 1603-4) and William (baptized 1607-8).

Dr. Hall's treatment caused her "itch and pustles" to become "fair and smooth."

This is Observation 65 in the original MS.

### Observation LXXI

"John Nason of Stratford-Upon-Avon, Barber, aged 40" — not identified further.

This is Observation 67 in the original MS.

Observation 66 in original MS. is John Smith, Observation L in 2nd Edition.

### Observation LXXII

"Baron Compton, aged 55". See Observation II F.C.

This is the same year (1617) as in Observation LXVIII F.C., as his age is 55 in both. Hall's cure left him free to join King James' campaign into Scotland.

This is Observation 68 in the original MS.

### Observation LXXIII

"Mrs. Boughton, Sister to Mr. Comb of Laufordfair, aged about 36, very handsome" may be the same person as Observations XXIV and XXVI F.C.

It is difficult to determine the nature of this woman's disorder. It had lasted for two years before Hall began to treat her. In view of the extensive nature of her symptoms, the differential diagnosis would at least include various types of neurological disease (such as multiple sclerosis), a possible growth in the throat or esophagus, or a form of hysteria. In the light of Hall's statement that she lived for eight years after his ministrations, this probably was a disorder like multiple sclerosis, hysteria, or a combination of both. If it had been a tumor of the throat, she probably would not have responded. Therefore, a remitting disease was the more likely.

This is Observation 69 in the original MS.

### Observation LXXIV

"Esquire Beaufou (whose name I have always cause honour) about the age of 70" — not identified.

This is Observation 70 in the original MS.

### Observation LXXV

"Esquire Packington" — not identified.

This Observation also contains another method used by Hall to treat anorexia, from which this patient suffered.

This is Observation 71 in the original MS.

### Observation LXXVI

"Mr. Rogers, Clerk, aged about 40" may have been a member of the well-known Stratford Rogers family, as Hall, in the manuscript, refers to Stratford in the use of the word "opidanus."

This is Observation 72 in the original MS.

### Observation LXXVII

"Lady Beaufou, godly, honest, being of noble extract, continuing healthful till the age of 28" may have been the daughter-in-law of Esquire Beaufou, Observation LXXIV F.C.

This Observation is of interest for the continued care Hall gave this patient, and for Cooke's correction of Hall's dosage of laudanum in his prescription.

Additional reference: Observation LXXXVIII F.C.

This is Observation 73 in the original MS.

### Observation LXXVIII

"Mr. Farman" —identified as Lady Beaufou's brother from the case report. Nothing further is known of him.

This is Observation 74 in the original MS.

### Observation LXXIX

"The Lady Rouse of Rouselench, aged 27" — not further identified.

This Observation describes the first of several occasions upon which Hall treated this patient during or after her frequent pregnancies.

The manuscript ends on "Praise be God," not found in the printed editions.

Additional references: Observation XCIII F.C., Observation XCVI F.C.

This is Observation 75 in the original MS.

### Observation LXXX

"William Clavel" — not identified.

This is Observation 76 in the original MS.

### Observation LXXXI

"Richard Wilmore of Norton, aged 14" — not identified.

Hall's original manuscript has "Praise be God" at the conclusion, not found in the printed editions.

This is Observation 77 in the original MS.

### Observation LXXXII

"Mrs. Kempson" possibly a member of the Kempson family of Arden's Grafton.

This is Observation 78 in the original MS.

### Observation LXXXIII

"Baron Compton, President of Wales." See Observation II F.C.

This is Observation 79 of the original MS.

### Observation LXXXIV

"Esquire Rainsford" aged 35, related no doubt to Sir Henry Rainsford, husband of Anne Goodere. As the manuscript gives the date as 1618 (not found in the printed editions) and lists his age as 35, this could not be Sir Henry himself, who married in 1595 and died in the 1620s.

This Observation ends in the original manuscript "he praised God that he was restored to his former health" — not found in the printed editions.

This is Observation 80 in the original MS.

### Observation LXXXV

"Mr. Barns, aged 36" — not identified.

A William Barnes was a friend of Sir Henry Rainsford and Thomas Greene, but it is not possible to identify this patient further.

This condition may have been a varicose ulcer.

This is Observation 81 in the original MS.

### Observation LXXXVI

"Good-wife Sheffeild, a Husbandman's Wife of Old Stratford, aged 48" — not further identified.

Perhaps she was Hall's neighbor, as mentioned in Observation XCII F.C.

This is Observation 82 in the original MS.

### Observation LXXXVII

"The most illustrious Lord, Lord William Compton, President of Wales." See Observation II F.C.

This is Observation 83 in the original MS.

### Observation LXXXVIII

"My Lady Beaufou." See Observation LXXVII F.C.

This Observation has the words "she gave thanks" in the original manuscript, but not in the three printed editions.

This is Observation 84 in the original MS.

### Observation LXXXIX

"Esquire Packington, as he was riding to London." See Observation LXXV F.C.

Hall's diagnosis of gout seems warranted.

This Observation ends with the words "he gave me many thanks" in the manuscript, but not in the printed editions.

This is Observation 85 in the original MS.

### Observation XC

"Wilson of Stratford aged about 48." See Observation IV F.C .

In this Observation, Cooke adds references to Riverius and Thoner on pain in the stomach, in all printed editions.

This is Observation 86 in the original MS.

### Observation XCI

"Mrs. Hanberry of Worcester, aged 30" might be the same patient as Observation XI, as both are spelt "Hanberry" in original MS.

This Observation ends with "praise be God" in the original manuscript, but not in the printed editions.

This is Observation 87 in the original MS.

### Observation XCII

"The sister of my neighbour Sheffeild" most likely the sister-in-law of patient in Observation LXXXVI F.C.

This is Observation 88 in the original MS.

### Observation XCIII

"My Lady Rouse, being in the eighth month of childbearing, aged 28." See Observation LXXIX F.C.

This is Observation 89 in the original MS.

### Observation XCIV

"Mr. Barns of Clifford" may be the same patient as in Observation LXXXV F.C.

This Observation has the date Jan. 1, 1619 in the original manuscript, not found in the printed editions.

Cooke adds, in this Observation, a comment on a similar situation (bleeding) which he treated in London. This Observation is 90 in the original MS.

### Observation XCV
"One Hudson, a poor man" — not identified. This is Observation 91 in the original MS.

### Observation XCVI
"The Lady Rouse, being with child." See Observation LXXIX F.C.

This appears to be this patient's third pregnancy in a relatively short period of time.

This Observation is 92 in the original MS.

### Observation XCVII
"Mrs. Mary Murdin, aged 17" — not identified. May be related to patient in Observation XI S.C. This is Observation 93 in the original MS.

### Observation XCVIII
"Dixwell Brunt of Pillerton, aged 3" — not identified. This Observation has the date, April 27, 1620, in the original manuscript, but not in the printed editions.

This is Observation 94 in the original MS.

### Observation XCIX
"Countess of Northampton, March 6, 1620." See Observation I, F.C.

This Observation occurred two years before Observation I in spite of its appearance much later in the text.

Since the Countess suffered from a generalized

edema, Hall's remedies of purging and sweating helped reduce the swelling.

This is Observation 95 in the original MS.

### Observation C
"Mrs. Goodman, aged 54" — not identified.
This is Observation 96 in the original MS.

## SECOND CENTURY

### Observation I
"Master Penil, Gentleman to Esq. Grevil of Milcot"— not identified.

The Grevilles were a well-known family, of whom Fulke Greville was a member, the man to whom, as Lord Brooke, Cooke dedicated the Second Edition of Hall's "Select Observations."

This is Observation 97 in the original MS.

### Observation II
"Rogers of Stratford, aged 17" perhaps a daughter of the Rogers of Observation LXXVI, F.C.
This is Observation 98 of the original MS.

### Observation III
"Mrs. Randolph, aged 55" perhaps related to the other Randolphs mentioned in Observations XXV F.C. and LXV F.C.
This is Observation 99 in the original MS.

### Observation IV

"Mr. Broad of the Grange" — not identified.

His servant is probably the one mentioned in Observation X, F.C.

Though moderate in his use of venesection, Hall apparently felt its efficacy here and prevailed on the patient to submit to blood-letting.

The manuscript concludes "for which God be praised that can only work wonderfully." This is in the second and third editions but not in the first.

This is Observation 100 in the original MS.

### Observation V

"Mrs. Sadler" no doubt a member of the prominent Sadler family of Stratford, friends and neighbors of the Shakespeare family. Amongst other property, they owned the Bear Inn for a time before selling it to the Nash family.

The manuscript has the date 1621, not found in the printed editions.

This is Observation 101 in the original MS.

### Observation VI

"Mrs. Brown, young, of a very good habit of body"— not identified.

The manuscript ends on "praise to God" not found in the printed editions.

This is Observation 102 in the original MS.

### Observation VII

"Mrs. Mary Talbot, Sister to the Countess, a Catholick, fair" — not identified.

In this Observation, Hall mentions one of his few

conversations with the patient's family when he records reassuring the Countess for her sisterly concern.

The manuscript describes the patient as "chaste," and concludes, "praise be God." These are not in the printed editions.

This is Observation 103 in the original MS.

### Observation VIII

"Mr. Handslop, aged about 61" — not identified.

Hall refers to Horst's medication in this Observation. (See Observation XLVIII F.C.)

This is Observation 104 in the original MS.

### Observation IX

"Lady Puckering" most likely was the wife of Sir Thomas Puckering (Observation XXXIX S.C.) and mother of two daughters.

In this Observation, Hall includes a reference to another case, "Mrs. Iremonger's waiting maid" also afflicted with "trembling" of the heart. He praises his remedy used as "worth gold."

This is Observation 105 in the original MS.

### Observation X

"Lady Brown of Radford" — not identified.

In this Observation, Hall connects some of the patient's distress and symptoms with the death of her daughter in child-birth. In it, he also refers to the treatment of Mr. Handslop, Observation VIII S.C.

This is Observation 106 in the original MS.

### Observation XI

"Mrs. Murden, aged about 53" was perhaps related to Observation XCVII, F.C., Mary Murden.

In this Observation, Hall mentions giving pills to the patient for preventative reasons.

This is Observation 107 in the original MS.

### Observation XII

"Mr. George Underhil, aged about 64" no doubt was a member of the prominent Underhill family who at one time were owners of New Place. This is but one of a number of references to Underhills treated by Hall.

This is Observation 108 in the original MS.

### Observation XIII

"Mr. P. afflicted with a Flux of Semen" — not identified. IIe is the only patient identified by an initial in the manuscript.

In the manuscript, Hall concludes with the words "quickly and safely" in regard to his cure. These are omitted in the printed editions.

This is Observation 109 in the original MS.

### Observation XIV

"Mrs. Kenton of Northampton, aged 48" — not identified.

Hall's remedy here sounds like a patent medicine "good for everything" since he speaks of its use for apoplexy, dropsy, French pox, and other diseases.

This is Observation 110 in the original MS.

### Observation XV

"Mrs. Delaberr of Southam, near Glocester" — not identified.

Hall's treatment eased her sufficiently well for her to travel to Bath for the waters.

The manuscript concludes on the words "glory to God" not found in the printed editions.

This is Observation 111 in the original MS.

### Observation XVI

"Jacob Ballard, aged 60" — not identified.

In this Observation, Hall includes some medical dicta on digestion and dysentery. This is in the manuscript and all three editions.

This is Observation 112 in the original MS.

### Observation XVII

"Mrs. Layton, born of noble stock" — not identified.

In this Observation, Hall refers to two medical men, in regard to epilepsy in this woman. One was Eugalenus, the other Senertus. Eugalenus, identified as Severinus Eugalenus, was born in 1535, and was doctor of medicine at Hamburg and Emden. He wrote on scurvy, epilepsy, arthritis and ulcers.

Senertus, identified as Daniel Sennert (1572-1637) was born in Breslau; studied medicine at Wittenberg, where he graduated in 1601. He was the first to introduce chemistry as a subject of the medical curriculum. He tried to harmonize the doctrines of Galenic medicine with the best in Paracelsus' doctrines. He was a good clinician, interested in scurvy and alcoholism. He wrote numerous works on medicine and natural history. He died in 1637.

This is Observation 113 in the original MS.

### Observation XVIII

"Lydia Trap, the Daughter of Mr. Trap, aged about two years," was no doubt the daughter of John Trapp, Stratford schoolmaster and minister, described in Observation LXXXI S.C. A relative, Simon Trapp, was witness to Hall's will.

In the manuscript, Hall mentions Lydia's father was a schoolteacher. This is omitted in the printed editions.

This is Observation 114 in the original MS.

### Observation XVIX

"The Lady Underhil, aged 53" a member of the Underhill family mentioned in Observation XII S.C.

In this Observation Hall mentions the patient "praised the Apozeme, as if it wrought by inchantment."

This is Observation 115 in the original MS.

### Observation XX

"Esquire Underhil, aged 50." See previous Observation.

The manuscript concludes "praised be God." This is not found in the printed editions.

This is Observation 116 in the original MS.

### Observation XXI

"Mr. Izod." Not identified.

This patient is Mr. Flod in the first edition.

This is Observation 117 in the original MS.

### Observation XXII

"The Lady Smith (a Roman Catholic)" — not identified.

This patient apparently was so pleased with Hall's

remedy that she requested the same for the Countess of Leicester, no doubt a friend.

This is Observation 118 in the original MS.

### Observation XXIII

"Mrs. Winter, Widow (Roman Catholic) aged 28" may have been related to the patient in Observation XL F.C.

In the manuscript her age is given as 29. It is 28 in all three printed editions. The manuscript has the words "glory to God" not found in the printed editions.

This is Observation 119 in the original MS.

### Observation XXIV

"The Lady Jenkinson (fair, pious, chaste)" — not identified.

In this Observation, Hall refers to the "scurvy-beer" prescribed for Mrs. Mary Talbot, Observation VII S.C.

This is Observation 120 in the original MS.

### Observation XXV

"Butler of Stratford" may have been the Robert Butler who in 1611 signed, along with Shakespeare, Hall, Combe, Nash and others, a bill for highway repairs.

This manuscript has the date "1629" in the margin, not found in the printed editions.

This is Observation 121 in the original MS.

### Observation XXVI

"Mrs. Richardson (a Roman Catholic)" — not identified.

This is Observation 122 in the original MS.

### Observation XXVII

"Mrs. Peerse of Auson (Roman Catholic aged about 28)" — not identified.

Hall refers to a "chalybiated Wine" prescribed for Lady Jenkinson, Observation XXIV, S.C.

This is Observation 123 in the original MS.

### Observation XXVIII

"Alice Collins, Servant to my Lady Puckering, aged about 24" refers to Observation IX, S.C.

This is Observation 124 in the original MS.

### Observation XXIX

"Hester Sylvester, Daughter to Mrs. Smith (now Marit) of Burford" — not further identified.

Hall recommends a powder for her worms to be given either in wine, water or the pulp of a roasted apple.

This is Observation 125 in the original MS.

### Observation XXX

"Lynes of Stratford, aged 53" — not identified.

This is Observation 126 in the original MS.

### Observation XXXI

"Mrs. Baker of Stratford, aged 38" may have been related to the Daniel Baker family, kinsmen of Abraham Sturley and friends of Shakespeare.

Hall concludes, in the manuscript, "glory to God." This is not found in the printed editions.

This is Observation 127 in the original MS.

### Observation XXXII
"Smith of Stratford, aged 38" may be related to the patient in Observation III, F.C.

This is Observation 128 in the original MS.

### Observation XXXIII
"Wife". See Observation XIX F.C. on Susanna Hall.

In this Observation, Hall refers to both Sennert and Crato. See Observation XVII, S.C. and Observation I, F.C.

This is Observation 129 in the original MS.

### Observation XXXIV
"Mrs. Combs, aged about 36" perhaps a member of the old Combs family who owned the large stone house in Stratford, called the "College."

In this Observation, Hall makes good use of remedies prescribed in earlier Observations.

This is Observation 130 in the original MS.

### Observation XXXV
"The Lady Clark, aged about 44" possibly the wife of Sir Simon Clark mentioned in Observation XL, S.C.

Hall concludes the manuscript with "gratitude to God." This is not found in the printed editions.

This is Observation 131 in the original MS.

### Observation XXXVI
"Mr. Thomas Underhil, of Lamcot, aged about 39" perhaps related to the Underhills of Loxley, mentioned in Observation LXIX, F.C.

This is Observation 132 in the original MS.

### Observation XXXVII

"Katherine Sturley of Stratford, aged 44, being fat and corpulent" related perhaps to Abraham Sturley.

This is Observation 133 in the original MS.

### Observation XXXVIII

"The Lady Hunks, aged 69" — not identified.

In this Observation, Hall again makes a reference to Quercitanus (see Observation XXXI, F.C.).

This is Observation 134 in the original MS.

### Observation XXXIX

"Baronet Puckering, aged about 38, very learned, much given to study, of a rare and lean constitution" was Sir Thomas Puckering, youngest son of Sir John, Keeper of the Great Seal. He was born in 1592 and was a fellow-student and associate of Prince Henry, James's son, for four years. He was knighted in 1611 and created a baronet in 1612. He served as a member of Parliament and High Sheriff for Warwick in 1625. In 1630 he founded a hospital in Warwick and died in 1636.

Hall refers to earlier-prescribed remedies and the use of leeches in this Observation. In the manuscript he numbers 1 to 5 various forms of remedies.

This is Observation 135 in the original MS.

### Observation XL

"Baronet Clark of Broom-Court, aged about 57" was Sir Simon Clarke, 1st baronet of Salford Priors and Broom Court in Salford. He was born in 1579, the eldest son of Walter Clarke, of an ancient Kentish family. He was a prominent member of a family of antiquarians, contemporaries of Dugdale. He collected manuscripts which he allowed Dugdale to make use of in "Warwickshire." Interestingly enough, he wrote nothing of himself. He was a strong supporter of Charles.

Possibly it is his wife referred to in Observation XXXV, S.C.

This is Observation 136 in the original MS.

### Observation XLI

"Lord Northampton, aged about 29" must be Sir William's son, Sir Spencer Compton, 2nd Lord of Northampton. He was born at Compton Wyniates in 1601. In 1616 he was made Knight of the Bath. He was close to Charles, Prince of Wales, and in 1622 accompanied him to Spain. He assisted at his coronation in 1625. He was accomplished in foreign languages and was employed in royal audiences of foreign ambassadors. He has been described as an uncompromising friend of royalty.

In this Observation, Hall mentions the patient called in a Dr. Clayton of Oxford, whose prescription "delivered him from pain and danger." Hall was generous in his recognition of other medical opinions.

This is Observation 137 in the original MS.

Additional Reference: Observation LXXXII, S.C.

### Observation XLII

"Mrs. Stocken, Servant to Mrs. Sheldon of Weston, aged about 44" — not identified.

This is Observation 138 in the original MS.

### Observation XLIII

"One of Northampton" is identified in the manuscript as Mr. Harvey. He is not identified in any of the three printed editions.

This Observation is of interest for its inclusion of Dr. William Harvey's prescription. Hall's patient saw the "erudissimi" Dr. Harvey in London who prescribed for him. (Cooke omits "erudissimi" in all editions.) The similarity in name between patient and Dr. Harvey may be a coincidence.

This is Observation 139 in the original MS.

### Observation XLIV

"Mrs. Mary Comb of Stratford, aged about 13" was probably the daughter of William Comb of Stratford. Comb was Sheriff of Warwickshire in 1615 and served under Lord Brooke for the Parliamentary Army during the Civil War. Probably the same family is mentioned in Observation XXXIV, S.C.

Hall treated this girl over a period of time with good results for her hysterical seizures.

This is Observation 140 in the original MS.

### Observation XLV

"The First born son of my Lady Harrington" aged 10 may have been  the child of Sir John and Lady Harrington of Leicestershire. (See Addendum, p. 100)

This is Observation 141 in the original MS.

### Observation XLVI

"Margaret Baker, aged 9" — not identified, but might have been a member of the Stratford Baker family.

This Observation is part of the previous one in the original manuscript. In all editions, Cooke made a separate case out of it.

This is Observation 141 also in the original MS.

### Observation XLVII

"My Lady Rainsford (beautiful and of gallant structure of body) near 27" was probably a member of Sir Henry Rainsford's family. See LXVIII, S.C.

In this Observation, Cooke interjects a medical comment, stating he, too, had success with Hall's prescription of "Chamomel, Posset-drink." This is in all printed editions.

This is Observation 142 in the original MS.

### Observation XLVIII

"Mrs. Grace Court, Wife to my apothecary, aged 27" was Richard Court's wife. This is the man who helped Cooke with the translation of Hall's original manuscript.

Hall gave her careful treatment during her pregnancy and gives "honor to the omipotent Lord" on her recovery. These words are omitted in the printed editions.

This is Observation 143 in the original MS.

### Observation XLIX

"The Countess of Northampton, (born of a noble offspring,)" was most likely the wife of Sir Spencer Compton, second Earl of Northampton, mentioned in Observation XLI, S.C.

Hall's treatment extended from the seventh month of pregnancy to the birth of her daughter.

This is Observation 144 in the original MS.

### Observation L

"Mr. Fosset, (a minister) aged about 55" was, along with Wilson, John Trap and others, one of the Nonconformist Divines of that time.

This Observation is shortened, in all three printed editions, to about a half of the original Latin manuscript for unknown reasons.

This is Observation 145 in the original MS.

### Observation LI

"Anne Ward of Stratford" was possibly related to Reverend Ward.

In this Observation, Hall mentions curing two patients, Mrs. Goodyear and Mrs. Savage, in similar manner.

The manuscript has the words "honest, beautifully formed, pious, religious," and "praise be God," not found in the printed editions.

This is Observation 146 in the original MS.

### Observation LII

"Mrs. Fines, aged 22, (wife to the Lord Say's eldest Son, a very religious, excellent Woman)" — not identified further, except for some reference, in Latin, to the Baroness of Wimbelton.

Hall refers to the anti-scorbutic beer used for the Countess of Northampton, Observation I, F.C.

This is Observation 147 in the original MS.

### Observation LIII

"Frances Finch of Stratford, aged 47"—not identified.

In this Observation, Cooke adds a quotation from Riverius on worms.

This is Observation 148 in the original MS.

### *Observation LIV*

"Mrs. Jackson, (Wife to Mr. Jackson Jun.), aged about 24" — not identified, except in the Latin manuscript, Jackson is referred to as "Minister."

In this Observation, Hall mentions one of the few times he could not visit a patient "by reason of much business." Apparently he prescribed for her though, with "happy success."

This is Observation 149 in the original MS.

### *Observation LV*

"Mrs. Woodward of Aven-dasset (a maid very witty and well-bred, yet gibbous) aged 28" — not identified.

In this Observation, Hall refers to earlier successfully used remedies, and when his patient is near death, exclaims, "Towards evening she expected her unwelcome Enemy, with a grief of mind."

In this Observation, Hall makes a reference to Eugalenus. See Observation XVII, S.C.

This is Observation 150 in the original MS.

### *Observation LVI*

"Mrs. Hopper, aged 24" — not identified.
This is Observation 151 in the original MS.

### *Observation LVII*

"Goodwife Archer of Stratford" — not identified.
This is Observation 152 in the original MS.

### *Observation LVIII*

"Mrs. Lewes, Sister to Mr. Fortescue" may be the sister of patient in Observation XXIX, F.C.

This is Observation 153 in the original MS.

## Observation LIX

"Mrs. Vernon of Hanberry, Wife to the Minister, aged about 30" — not further identified.

This Observation is numbered LXI, a typographical error.

Hall calls her "religious, well-formed, beautiful" in the manuscript. This is not found in the printed editions.

In this Observation, Hall mentions curing Mr. Feriman the same way.

This is Observation 154 in the original MS.

## Observation LX

This is Hall's only Observation about his own physical condition. It is of significance for the light it sheds on Hall. His deep sense of religion, his dedication to his patients, his wife's interest in his welfare, are all revealed herein.

This is Observation 155 in the original MS.

## Observation LXI

"Baronet Puckering of Warwick, aged about 44". See Observation XXXIX, S.C.

In this Observation, Hall refers to the "opiat" prescribed by Dr. Lapworth, no doubt a colleague.

This is Observation 156 in the original MS.

## Observation LXII

"Alderman Tyler" may have been Richard Tyler who was elected a burgess to the Stratford Corporation in 1590 and was a friend of William Shakespeare. He died in 1636 at the age of 70.

This is Observation 157 in the original MS.

### Observation LXIII

"Daughter of Alderman Smith, aged about 22." See Observation III, F.C.

This is Observation 158 in the original MS.

### Observation LXIV

"The only Son of Mr. Holy-Oak (which framed the Dictionary)" refers to Thomas Holyoake, son of Francis Holyoake (1567-1653) rector of Southam, Warwickshire. In 1633 Francis published his "Dictionarium Ethmologicum Latinum," which was enlarged by Thomas. Thomas was Chaplain at Queen's College, Oxford, and practiced as a doctor for a time. He died in 1675.

This is Observation 159 in the original MS.

### Observation LXV

"The Lord of Northampton's Gentleman." Not further identified.

This is Observation 160 in the original MS.

### Observation LXVI

"Mrs. Boves of Kings-Cotton, aged 46" — not identified.

In this Observation, Cooke adds a comment from Thoner on curing a six-year-old girl, and it is in all three editions.

This is Observation 161 in the original MS.

### Observation LXVII

"The Lady Brown of Radford, aged 49". See Observation X, S.C.

In this Observation, Hall discusses in some detail

how this patient's "scorbutic fever" differs from others, strengthening the belief that he was a keen observer. The fever was more gentle, and there was less thirst and restlessness.

This is Observation 162 in the original MS.

### Observation LXVIII

"The Lady Rainsford, aged about 62" has been identified as Anne Goodere, born around 1571 and married to Sir Henry Rainsford of Clifford Chambers in 1595. She met Michael Drayton (See Observation XXI, F.C.) when a young girl and became his "Idea," as seen in Drayton's poem "Idea's Mirror."

In the manuscript, Hall describes her as "modest, pious, friendly, devoted to sacred literature and conversant in the French language." None of this is found in the printed editions.

This is Observation 163 in the original MS.

### Observation LXIX

"Doctor Thornberry, Bishop of Worcester, aged about 86, Feb. 1, 1663." (This date is a typographical error in this edition. It should be 1633.) He has been identified as a companion of Lyly at Oxford.

In this Observation, Hall shows his understanding of geriatrics in his cautious treatment of this patient. He intuitively connected the patient's physical condition with his mental distress.

This is Observation 164 in the original MS.

### Observation LXX

"Mr. Simon Underhil, aged about 40" was perhaps the son of William and Mary Underhill, born in 1589. If the date 1633 given in the original manuscript, and omitted in the printed editions, is right, the patient would be 44 at that time.

This patient had such discomfort, he begged Hall either "to cure him perfectly or kill him." Hall records he "became perfectly well."

This is Observation 165 in the original MS.

### Observation LXXI

"Mrs. Swift (dwelling with Baronet Brook at Warwick Castle, a Maid) aged about 20" — not identified.

The manuscript describes her as "chaste, and of exceptional structure," omitted in the printed editions.

This is Observation 166 in the original MS.

### Observation LXXII

"Mrs. Finnes" — not identified.

In this Observation, Hall mentions a Midwife was with the patient, and discusses her fever following the birth of her child.

This is Observation 167 in the original MS.

### Observation LXXIII

"Mr. Fortescue, (Catholic) of Cook-hil, aged 38, (a great drinker, of a very good habit of body)" — not identified.

Hall again in this Observation refers to earlier, successfully-used remedies.

This Observation ends on "glory and honor to God" not found in the printed editions.

This is Observation 168 in the original MS.

### Observation LXXIV

"Mr. Kimberly, aged about 26" — not identified.

In this Observation, Hall says the patient called him "Father" for delivering him from death.

This is Observation 169 in the original MS.

### Observation LXXV

"Mrs. Editha Staughton, aged 16" — not identified.

Hall mentions using the same treatment as for Mrs. Boves in Observation LXVI, S.C.

Additional Reference: Observation LXXX, S.C.

This is Observation 170 in the original MS.

### Observation LXXVI

"Mrs. Wilson" probably was the wife of Vicar Wilson (See Observation IV, F.C.).

Hall mentions she travelled to Bristol for her health; and then on to Bath, where Dr. Lapworth prescribed for her.

The manuscript describes her as "honest, pious and religious." This is not found in the printed editions.

This is Observation 171 in the original MS.

### Observation LXXVII

"Mrs. Wagstaff of Warwick (a Widow) aged about 48." See Observation XLVII, F.C.

The patient, two years older, is a widow in this Observation.

This is Observation 172 in the original MS.

### Observation LXXVIII

"Mrs. Cooks, near 48 of a thin body"—not identified.

The manuscript concludes on "Praise be God" not found in the printed editions.

This is Observation 173 in the original MS.

### Observation LXXIX

"Nurse Degle of Bengwort, aged 29"—not identified.
This is Observation 174 in the original MS.

### Observation LXXX

"Mrs. Editha Staughton, aged 17." Same patient as Observation LXXV, but now a year older.

Hall recognized the hysterical nature of the girl's distress and advised her parents to have "few trouble her."

This is Observation 175 in the original MS.

### Observation LXXXI

"Mr. John Trap, Minister, (for his piety and learning, second to none)." See Observation XVIII, S.C. Trap was born in 1601 and graduated from Oxford. He settled in Stratford and became schoolmaster of the Grammar School after Alexander Aspinall. He was very celebrated in his lifetime as teacher and divine. He died in 1669.

This is Observation 177 in the original MS, and Observation LXXXII in the first edition.

Observation 176 in the original MS, is son of Mr. Thomas Underhil, Observation LXIX, F.C. in this edition and Observation LXXXI in the first edition.

### Observation LXXXII

"The Earl of Northampton, aged about 32, following his hounds in a cold and rainy day." See Observation XLI, S.C.

This is Observation 178 in the original MS.

This brings Hall's Observations to a conclusion.

It should be noted again that Hall's original manuscript contained 178 medical observations. As pointed out in the Introduction, Cooke obtained an extra case by dividing one of Hall's Observations into two, making a basic 179 cases in all editions. To this, Cooke added three pertinent cases from Thoner, bringing the number of case histories to 182.

In the first edition, however, one full case, John Smith of Newnam, is omitted. But Cooke added two new cases based upon his own and Thoner's medical experiences. These follow Hall's Observations on Julian West (Observation XLIX, F.C.) and Baron Compton (Observation LXVIII, F.C.). Thus, in spite of the omission, the first edition ends with 183 cases in all.

The second (and third) edition reinstates Hall's Observation on John Smith. The two medical comments of the first edition are incorporated into the specific cases of Julian West and Baron Compton, so that Cooke returns to the 182 for these two editions.

# FOOTNOTES

1. Quoted with the permission of the Folger Shakespeare Library, Washington, D.C. [Ms X.d 164 (3)], owners of the original letter.

2. Wing, Donald: *Short-Title Catalogue of Books.* New York, New York, printed for the Index Society by Columbia University, 1948, Vol. II, p. 152. Wing lists some twenty-one copies altogether for all three editions of the "Select Observations." The New York Academy of Medicine has an additional copy (first edition).

3. Venn, John and J. A.: *Alumni Cantabrigienses.* Cambridge, England, Cambridge University Press, 1922, Part I, Vol. II, p. 286.

4. British Museum, Egerton Ms. 2065.

5. James Cooke (1614-1688), physician, had a large practice in and around Warwick. He was surgeon to many leading families of that day, including Lord Brook of Beauchamp-Court, to whom he dedicated the second edition of Hall's "Select Observations." He wrote a treatise on medical, surgical and obstetrical subjects entitled "The Marrow of Chirurgery," (1648). During England's Civil War, he was surgeon to the Parliamentary forces at Stratford. Cooke, in his Preface to the second edition of Hall's "Select Observations," describes himself as a "friend to the friendly and an enemy to none of mankind." (Although Cooke's name is generally spelt "Cooke," it appears as "Cook" in the second edition, where, after his signature to the Preface, he has also added "Sen.", distinguishing himself from his son.)

6. Wing, Donald: *Op cit.* Wing lists two editions of Hall's "Select Observations" for the date 1683. The Folger Shakespeare Library has a copy of the 1683 edition with the imprint: "By H.H. and are to be sold by Samuel Eddowes, 1683." Another copy in the Osler Library, McGill University, Montreal, has the imprint: "For William Marshall and S. Eddows, 1683."

7. Rolleston, Sir Humphrey: *Cambridge Medical School.* Cambridge, England, Cambridge University Press, 1932, p. 217. Rol-

leston states Dr. John Bird's identity is doubtful, but that he was probably an Oxford graduate. He lists him as a Linacre Lecturer for 1644. (A personal survey at Cambridge University did not reveal his name.) Dr. Bird's letter to the readers in the first edition is signed from Sion College, July 1, 1657. The British Museum General Catalogue lists a work by John Bird of Sion College with the title, "Ostenta Carolina", London 1661.

8.    Bedfordshire Parish Register lists Susan, Sara, Martha, Mary, Damaris and William.

9.    Eccles, Mark: *Shakespeare in Warwickshire.* Madison, Wisconsin, University of Wisconsin Press, 1961, p. 112. Eccles records five additional Hall children: Elizabeth, Samuel, Dive, *John* and Frances.

10.    Gray, Irvine in the *Genealogists' Magazine,* Vol. VII, Sept. 1936, p. 350.

11.    Gray, Irvine: *Op cit.* p. 345-346.

12.    Scarlett, E.P.: "Shakespeare's Son-in-law: Dr. John Hall." *Canadian Medical Association Journal,* Vol. 43, Nov. 1940, p. 483.

13.    Jerome Cardàn (1501-1576), graduate in medicine from Padua, was an Italian astrologer, mathematician, and physician. He stressed the relation of astrology to the origin of life. His work included treatises on cubic equations, astrology and methods of teaching the blind to read.

14.    Fripp, Edgar I.: *Shakespeare's Stratford.* London, England, Oxford University Press, 1928, p. x.

15.    Pensioner is the second of the three ranks in which students were matriculated: Fellow Commoner, Pensioner, Sizar. The rank of Pensioner connoted a certain degree of social standing.

16.    As checked personally in the Archives, Cambridge University.

17.    Fox, Levi: *Hall's Croft, the Home of Susanna Shakespeare.* Norwich, Jarrold and Sons, Ltd. n.d.

18.    "Profession of Physic in England." *Edinburgh Medical and Surgical Journal,* Vol. 16, 1820, p. 484. In the third year of Henry VIII's reign (1511), bishops were given the right to grant medical licenses. In the fifteenth year, this right was taken away and given to the Royal College of Physicians. The bishops however

continued to grant licenses in the provinces for approximately the next 150 years. A letter dated 1686-1687 from the Royal College of Physicians to all bishops points out that they no longer have this right which they apparently were continuing to exercise.

19. Chambers, E.K.: *William Shakespeare.* Oxford, England, Clarendon Press, 1930, Vol. 1, p. 9.

20. Eccles, Mark: *Op cit.* p. 91.

21. Lee, Sir Sydney: *A Life of William Shakespeare.* New York, New York, MacMillan Co. 1924, p. 462.

22. Halliwell-Phillipps, J.O.: *Outlines of the Life of Shakespeare.* London, England, Messr. Longmans, Green & Co., Fifth Edition, 1885, p. 35.

23. D.N.B., Vol. VIII, p. 954-955.

24. Letter quoted with the permission of the Director, Trustees and Guardians of Shakespeare's Birthplace, Stratford-upon-Avon, England.

25. Fripp, Edgar I.: *Shakespeare Studies.* Oxford, England, Oxford University Press, 1930, p. 169.

26. Fripp, Edgar I.: *Ibid.,* p. 169.

27. Simpson, R.R.: *Shakespeare and Medicine.* Edinburgh and London, England, E & S Livingstone Ltd., 1959, p. 101-104.

28. Elton, Charles I.: *William Shakespeare, His Family and Friends.* London, England, John Murray, 1904, p. 245.

29. John Hall's will is in the Registry of the Prerogative Court of Canterbury.

30. Eccles, Mark: *Op cit.* p. 114. Eccles identifies John Bowles as Joseph Bowles of Chapel St., Stratford. He was M.A. from Emmanuel College, Cambridge, 1634.

31. Susanna Hall died on July 11, 1649 at the age of 66.

32. Judith Shakespeare Quiney died in her seventy-seventh year 1661-1662. All three sons predeceased her, the last dying in 1638.

33. Mitchell, C. Martin: *The Shakespeare Circle.* Birmingham, England. Cornish Bros., Ltd., p. 43. Mitchell states Thomas Greene, barrister of Middle Temple, lived in New Place from about 1600-1610 with his wife, Letitia, Shakespeare's wife and presumably Judith. Two of his children were christened William and Anne. Greene was Town Clerk of Stratford 1603-1616.

34.   Lee, Sir Sydney: *Op cit.,* p. 463-464.

35.   Simpson, R.R.: *Op cit.,* p. 116.

36.   Nielsen, W.A. and Hill, C.J.: *Complete Plays and Poems of William Shakespeare.* Cambridge, Mass., Houghton Mifflin Co. The Riverside Press, 1942, p. 425.

37.   Garrison, F.H.: *History of Medicine.* Philadelphia and London, England, W & B Saunders, 1929, Fourth Edition, p. 236.

38.   Elton, Charles I.: *Op cit.,* p. 244.

39.   Personal communication from H.W. Rickett of the New York Botanical Garden.

40.   Roddis, Louis: *James Lind, Founder of Nautical Medicine.* New York, New York. Henry Shuman, 1950, p. 45. Roddis states that the great Elizabethan surgeon, William Clowes, recommended an ale in which water cress had been cooked. Scurvy grass was also frequently mentioned by writers of that time, and earlier.

41.   Flack, Isaac (pseud. Graham, Harvey): *Eternal Eve.* London, England, William Heineman Medical Books Ltd., 1950, p. 254.

42.   This reading of Sid Davenport's letter is by the present editor. It agrees in substance with that of R.R. Simpson in his book: *Shakespeare and Medicine,* pages 99-100. The variations are in spelling, Davenport's erasures and principally the date. *See also* note 24.

43.   Ricci, James V.: *The Genealogy of Gynaecology.* Philadelphia, Pa., Blakiston Co., p. 359. Ricci states Lazarus Riverius (1589-1655) was physician to the King of France, and first professor of iatro-chemistry at Montpellier University. Riverius compiled an anthology of medicine and surgery entitled "The Practice of Physick."

44.   *Biographisches Lexikon des Hervorragenden Aertze.* Wien und Leipzig. Urban und Schwarzenberg, 1887, Vol. 5, p. 669. Augustin Thoner lived in the seventeenth century. He was deacon and director of the Medical College in Ulm, Germany. Shortly before his death at the age of 82, he published the results of his medical observations and experiences, showing his indebtedness to Galen.

45.   In Hall's original Latin manuscript, the word "generosus" looks like "generosy."

## ADDENDUM

Re-examination of the original Latin manuscript shows another variation between it and the printed text. The Observation XLV, Second Century, which starts "the first-born son" of Lady Harrington in the three printed editions actually reads, as written by Hall, "filia primogenita" or "first-born daughter." This may have been a simple mistake in translation by Dr. Cooke, and perpetuated in all three printings, or it may have been deliberately changed on the advice of Hall's apothecary, Richard Court, who assisted Cooke.

# SELECTED BIBLIOGRAPHY

References marked with * indicate those used in the preparation of Notes on Observations. The remainder are selected for their general interest. Others recommended are found in the Footnotes, pp. 96 ff.

Adams, Joseph Quincey: *A Life of William Shakespeare.*
Boston and New York, Houghton Mifflin Co., 1923.

Aubrey, John: *Brief Lives.* Edited by Oliver Lawson Dick.
Ann Arbor, University of Michigan Press, 1957.

*Bashford, H. H.: *The Harley Street Calendar.*
London, Constable & Co., Ltd., 1929.

Brooke, Charles Frederick Tucker: *Shakespeare of Stratford.*
New Haven, Yale University Press, 1926.

Brown, Ivor: *Shakespeare.*
Garden City, New York, Doubleday, 1949.

Brown, Ivor: *Shakespeare in his Time.*
Edinburgh, Thomas Nelson & Sons Ltd., 1960.

Bucknill, John: *The Medical Knowledge of Shakespeare.*
London, Longman & Co., 1860.

*Cambridge History of English Literature.* Book IV.
Cambridge, Cambridge University Press, 1950.

Chute, Marchette: *Shakespeare of London.*
New York, E. P. Dutton & Co., Inc., 1949.

Cohen, R. A.: "Documents Concerning James Cooke, Surgeon of Warwick." *Medical History* Vol. 1, No. 2, April 1957.

*Colville, Frederick: *The Worthies of Warwickshire.*
London, Henry T. Cooke & Sons, 1869.

*Eccles, Mark: *Shakespeare in Warwickshire.*
Madison, University of Wisconsin Press, 1961.

*Ferguson, James: *Bibliotheca Chemica.* Vols. 1 & 2.
Glasgow, James Maclehose & Sons, 1906.

Fox, Levi: *The Borough Town of Stratford-upon-Avon.*
Published by the Corporation of Stratford-upon-Avon, 1953.

*Fripp, Edgar I: *Shakespeare Studies.*
Oxford, Oxford University Press, 1930.

*Fripp, Edgar I: *Shakespeare's Stratford.*
    London, Oxford University Press, 1928.

Halliday, Frank Ernest: *Shakespeare, a pictorial biography.*
    New York, T. Y. Crowell Co., 1956.

Harrison, G. B.: *Introducing Shakespeare.*
    New York, Penguin Books, Inc., 1947.

Hill, Frank E.: *To Meet Will Shakespeare.*
    New York, Dodd, Mead, 1949.

Lindley, Walter: "Dr. John Hall — Shakespeare's Son-in-law."
    *The Medical Record,* May 20, 1916.

Moschowitz, Eli: "Dr. John Hall: Shakespeare's Son-in-law."
    *Johns Hopkins Hospital Bulletin,* Vol. 19, No. 328, June 1918.

Neilson, W. A. & Thorndike, A. H.: *Facts about Shakespeare.*
    New York, Macmillan Co., 1913.

Rolfe, William J.: *A Life of Shakespeare.*
    Boston, D. Estes & Co., 1904.

*Stopes, Charlotte: *Shakespeare's Environment.* London,
    G. Bell & Sons, 1914.

*Styles, Philip: "Sir Simon Clarke." *Birmingham Archaelogical
    Society's Transactions,* Vol. LXVI, 1950.

Tillyard, Eustace: *The Elizabethan World Picture.*
    New York, Macmillan Co., 1944.

Traversi, Derek: *The Last Phase.*
    New York, Harcourt Brace, 1955.

Trevelyan, G. M.: *Illustrated English Social History.* Vol. 2.
    London, New York, Longmans, Green, 1949.

Trevelyan, G. M.: *History of England.* Book 3 (3rd edition reissue).
    London, New York, Longmans, Green, 1952.

Wilson, John Dover: *The Essential Shakespeare.*
    Cambridge, Cambridge University Press, 1937.

FACSIMILES AND TRANSCRIPTS

# Select Observations
## ON
# *ENGLISH*
# BODIES:
### OR,

Cures both Empericall and
Historicall, performed upon very eminent Per-
sons in desperate
Diseases.

**First, written in Latine**
by Mr. *John Hall* Physician,
living at *Stratford* upon *Avon*
in *Warwick-shire*, where he
was very famous, as also in
the Counties adjacent, as ap-
peares by these Observations
drawn out of severall hun-
dreds of his, as choysest.

Now put into English for com-
mon benefit by *James Cooke*
Practitioner in *Physick* and
*Chirurgery*.

*London*, Printed for *John Sherley*, at the
*Golden Pelican*, in *Little-Britain*. 1657.

# DR. JAMES COOKE'S PREFACE TO
# THE FIRST EDITION

## TO THE
## FRIENDLY
## READER.

FRIENDS,

Being in my Art an Attendent to parts of some regiments to keep the pass at the Bridge of Stratford upon Avon, There being then with me a Mate allyed to the Gentleman that writ the following observations in Latin, he invited me to the house of Mrs. Hall Wife to the deceased, to see the Books left by Mr. Hall. After a view of them, she told me she had some Books left, by one that professed Physick, with her Husband, for some mony. I told her, if I liked them, I would give her the mony again; she brought them forth, amongst which there was this with another of the Authors, both intended for the Presse. I being acquainted with Mr. Hall's hand, told her that one or two of them were her Husband's, and shewed them her; she denyed, I affirmed, till I perceived she begun to be offended. At last I returned her the mony. After some time of tryall of what had been observed, I resolved to put it to suffer according to perceived intentions, to which end I sent it to London, which after viewed by an able Doctor, he returned answer, that it might be usefull, but the Latin was so abbreviated or false, that it would require the like pains as to write a new one. After which having some spare hours, (it being returned to me) put it into this garb, being somewhat acquainted with the Authors concisenes, especially in the Receipts, having had some intimacy with his Apothecary. To compleat the number to 200. I have given the Observations of some others, wherein for your advantage, ye may observe severall under one head. It seems the Author had the happinesse (if I may so stile it) to lead the way to that practice almost generally used by the most knowing, of mixing Scorbuticks in most remedies: It was then, and I know for some time after thought so strange, that it was cast as a reproach upon him by those most famous in the profession. He had been a Traveller acquainted with the French tongue, as appeared by some part of some Observations, which I got help to make English. His practice was very much, and that amongst most eminent Persons in the County where he lived, and those adjacent, as may appear by his Observations. If my pains in translating for the common good may be any wayes advantagious, it is all I look after, which shall be earnestly prayed for by

an unworthy friend<br>James Cooke.

Post Script.

I had almost forgot to tel ye that these Obser. were chosen by him from all the rest of his own, which I conjectured could be no lesse than a thousand, as fittest for publique view.

# DR. JOHN BIRD'S INTRODUCTION TO THE FIRST EDITION

## TO THE
## JUDICIOUS
## READER.

A Word or two is thought fit to be said first to you Reader, for your encouragement and direction, before you begin, touching both the Author, and the Work. This Learned Author Lived in our time, and in the County of Warwick, where he practised Physik many years, and in great Fame for his skill, far and near. Those who seemed highly to esteem him, and whom by Gods blessing he wrought these cures upon, you shall finde to be among others, Persons Noble, Rich and Learned. And this I take to be a great Signe of his Ability, that such who spare not for cost, and they who have more than ordinary understanding, nay such as hated him for his Religion, often made use of him. Many Indigent Persons, through penury, and the Brutishly foolish, through want of understanding, trust their lives to any who professe skill, and yet when oftentimes they see their own errour, and finde not according to their expectation, many will to others not discover this, lest they should be derided, but praise their deceivers, which brings more into the toil. Nor is this, if we well consider, to be wondered at; and take notice, that Sicknesse is commonly a punishment for Sin, which when God sends, although he deal favourably with some, it is not to be thought that Diseases are laid on onely to be taken off again. For God having determined that sicknesse shall be a Punishment, sometime it is of one nature, other times of another; now it goes away of it self, sometimes not without help, and when the Almighty will not have Diseases Curable, sometimes they are so in themselves, and then no Physician can cure them, as the Leprosy under the Law, and oftentimes they become so by the Patient, and often by the Physician. And so much touching the Author.

For the Book, I have this to say, That as Practice is the last and chiefest part of Physik, so is Observation the surest, and most demonstrating part of Practice. Hence it cometh to pass through defect of Observations, that so many Prescriptions we meet with in the Works of the most learned Practicioners, fall often short in performing the cures they promise, and we took them up for; they so often delivering up as their own and approved, what they took from other men upon Trust, thorow how many hands we know not; and likewise giving us as approved, such things as had no other ground than their own Imagination. But Observations are the Touch-stone for the trying of what ever is not good, and what Current in Physik. True it is, that the Rules of Physick in any part thereof, are hardly Demonstrable, not onely because such multitudes of experiments are to be gathered, and such variety of circumstances to be most exactly weighed before we ought to make a firm Thesis; Insomuch that the great Master of Medicine Hippocrates, after so many signs of life and death in sundry places of his works given by him, is forced to confesse that the signes of life and death are uncertain; but because God Almighty as his peculiar often pardons whom we give over to death, and takes away whom we acquit, for so saith the Lord, Deuteron.32:39. I kill, and I make alive; I wound, and I heal: and none can deliver, out of my hands. Yet what demonstration can be made touching the cure and incurability of diseases, as ordinarily to fall out so, plainly ariseth from Observation, even as the Art it self took its beginning (as Quintilian did truly speak) from the Observation of things, some which did good, others that did hurt. Particularly for this Work, it is wholly New as for the peculiar argument, Observations from English Bodies never yet extant, though very necessary. Next the Observations more General than those of most other Writers; here you meet with all sorts of diseases, there in them most commonly some of the rarest. Lastly, as I willingly give this Testimony touching their worth, so shall I be as ready to maintain my opinion, if need be, They are equal to the best published; which may the rather be believed because others commonly write such as they intended to, and have published while they have been living, and are probably unwilling to part with their best at such times; this was intended by the Author not to be published til his decease, when men more willingly part with what they have. And now Reader pardon the Translators haste, and give good heed to the escapes of the Press, and much good may it do you. Farewel.

Johannes Bird pridem in Academia Cantabrigiensi Medicinae Praelector Linacerianus.

E Colleg. Sionis.
Julii 1. 1657

## Explanatory Note

The complete title page to the second edition of Hall's "Select Observations" is reprinted here, including its reference to Dr. Cooke's "Counsels" and "Advices," and to Dr. Stubbs' "Directions." The actual facsimile reprint, however, consists solely of Dr. Hall's known medical Observations, with three additional cases (Observations LIV, LV and LVI, First Century), inserted by Cooke as an integral part of the body of the printed text.

The Table of Contents pages after Page 179 do not apply to this reprint.

# SELECT

# OBSERVATIONS

## ON

# Englifh Bodies

### OF

Eminent Perfons in defperate
DISEASES.

Firft written in Latin by Mr. *John Hall*,
Phyfician : After Englifhed by
JAMES COOK, Author of the
*Marrow of Chirurgery.*

To which is now added, an hundred like
*Counfels* and *Advices*, for feveral Honourable Perfons: By the fame Author.

In the Clofe is added, Directions for drinking of
the *Bath-Water*, and *Ars Cofmetica*, or Beauti-
fying Art : By *H. Stubbs*, Phyfician at *Warwick*.

*LONDON*,
Printed by *J. D.* for *Benjamin Shirley*, under the
Dial of St. *Dunftan*'s Church in *Fleet-ftreet*, 1679.

## TO THE

# Right Honourable,

# F U L K, Lord Brook,

## Baron  B R O O K

### O F

## *Beauchamp-Court,*

*Right Honourable,*

HE great and undeſer-
ved Favours for many
years conferred on me
by your noble Ance-
ſtors, with thoſe which I
ſtill receive from your ſelf,  and o-
her their Survivors,  encourage me

A 3

to

to prefent to your Lordſhip this Piece, now called to be made public a ſecond time ; humbly begging your acceptance and protection of what I tender in acknowledgment of my Duty and Service. The Part formerly printed, and what is added thereto, are moſt fit to be laid at your Honour's Feet, having received allowance from your Honourable Family to be made public, and moſt of it practiſed among them, for the ſpecial uſe of thoſe Noble Perſons, who are now gone from us ; and for whoſe memory I could not tranſcribe with dry eyes. What their Loſs vvas to the Public, is vvell known, and no leſs lamented ; and ſo great to me, that I can never forget it.

The Right Honourable, your Father, was pleaſed to ſhew me greater Favour than I do pretend

to deferve. Your Right Honourable Mother was feldom ill at home
or abroad, without commanding
my attendance: The fame have the
Right Honourable your Brothers and
your Lordfhip done. By whom
fcarce any thing was taken without
my thoughts, from the moft eminent
Phyficians, till they became acquainted with their Bodies. In all
which Services it pleafed God, I fo
ordered my felf, that I have had
from your Phyficians,not only thanks
but commendation. Which I have
always looked on as proceeding more
from the Favour of your Honour's
Family, than my Deferts.

Thefe Obligations under which I
lie, have given your Lordfhip the
trouble of this Dedication, and this
poor Piece, which I here prefent with
my hearty and humble Prayers for all
and each of your Honourable Family,
that

that they may receive the greateſt of God's Favours here, and the full enjoyment of Himſelf in Bliſs hereafter: Which is and ſhall be the continued Petitions of,

My Lord,

Your Honour's moſt

humble Servant

in all Duty,

*Warwick,*

March 25.

1 6 7 9.

*J AMES COOK,* Sen.

THE

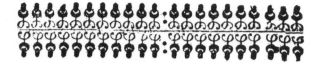

# THE

# PREFACE

## TO THE

# READER.

Courteous Readers,

*O you it is that I now address my self, to give you some small account of what is added in this Impression.* To the Select Observations on English Bodies, *you have an hundred* Counsels and Advices, *by very eminent Physicians, on several Honourable Persons, and others of no inferior Rank and Repute in this and other Counties. The Honourable Family which I have attended, and do still, hath always commanded me, as to receive all Prescriptions, so to see them made up in several places where*

# The Preface

*where I have attended, both to see them taken, and to observe their Success. Their favourable allowance I have for what is done. Their Honours, when Physicians were with them, were always ready to engage them to be helpful to their sick Neighbours; the Advices for such being for most part entrusted in my hands. I hope what is made publick can be no wrong to any of those Physicians, having for their Pains, Prescriptions, and Directions, received generous Pay and noble Entertainment. If there necessarily occur any thing concerning those living, I humbly beg their Pardon, and if I had not feared giving offence, I had named them as well as those dead : But this is not all, for as I have a due rememembrance of those deceased, (whose freeness I always found in communicating to me what they kept private from most ) so I give hearty thanks to those living, who have been like minded, and by whose Directions I have received no small advantage. Something there is intermixed, and something also in the Close, of Dr. Stubbs's, whose Civilities and Openness I cannot but remember. He was not a Person greedy of Gain. Not many months before he died, he said to me, "We must " study all ways possible to find out and appoint " Medicines of cheap rate, and effectual; for " Money is scarce, and Country-People poor :*

## to the Reader.

*To which I answered, That it had been, and should be my constant Course as long as I lived. I have heard it was said by one, over whom none is supreme in these Nations, ( whom God preserve and continue here, and crown with Himself in Glory hereafter ) That if* Dr. Stubbs *had but some of* Saturn *to poize his* Mercurial Brain, *he would make a good Statesman. And not a few famous Practitioners have said the like of him, as a* Physician. *But he is gone, and I cannot but say, Seldom comes a better. But to pass this, I hope my Service in this Impression will be civilly accepted, which is all, save to crave leave to subscribe my self always a Friend to the Friendly, and an Enemy to none of* Mankind.

JAMES COOK, Sen.

Warwick,
March 25.
1679.

An

## An Alphabetical

# TABLE

## OF

# DISEASES

### AND

# MEDICINES.

### A.

# An Alphabetical Table

         *Burning*

# of Diseases and Medicines.

Contusion

# An Alphabetical Table

Distil-

## of Diseases and Medicines.

a        *Electua*

## An Alphabetical Table

### F.

Fever

## of Difeafes and Medicines.

## G.

# An Alphabetical Table

                                                          I.

# of Diseases and Medicines.

## I.

## K.

## L.

M.

## M.

## N.

## O.

Oxymel

## of Diseases and Medicines.

# An Alphabetical Table

Pills

## of Diseases and Medicines.

## An Alphabetical Table

                           *Steel'd*

## T.

Tumors

# of Diseases and Medicines.

# An Alphabetical Table

Wine

## Y.

Characters

## Characters for brevity used herein.

| | | | |
|---|---|---|---|
| ℔ | a pound. | M. | an handful. |
| ℥ | an ounce. | ß. | half. |
| ʒ | a dram. | q. ſ. | quantity sufficient. |
| Э | a scruple. | *quar.* | a quart. |
| gr. | a grain. | *f.* | make. |
| p. | as much as may be | *pul.* | a pouder. |
| | held between the | ā | each. |
| | Thumb and two | *Miſc.* | Mix. |
| | firſt Fingers. | *C.C.* | Harts-horn. |

| | | | |
|---|---|---|---|
| Twenty grains | ⎫ | | a scruple. |
| Three scruples | ⎬ make | ⎰ | a dram. |
| Eight drams | ⎭ | ⎱ | an ounce. |
| Twelve ounces | | | a pound. |


Health

Health is from the L O R D.

# C U R E S Hiſtorical and Empirical, experienced on Eminent Perſons in ſeveral Places.

## Observ. I.

THE Counteſs of *Northampton*, aged 44. on *March* the 6th, 1622. as ſhe was walking in her Bed-chamber, ſuddenly fell into a ſwoon, without either ſenſe or motion for half an hour, ſhe fell with her face on the frame of a Table, which cauſed a Wound with contuſion, whence aroſe Inflammation, as alſo a great and troubleſom Flux of Rheum, which diſtilling from her eyes, excoriated the whole face with exulcerations; the habit of her Body was Scorbutick and Cacochymick: her reſidence then was at *Ludlow-Caſtle*: To whom being called, I cured perfectly, by God's aſſiſtance, with

B

the

the fol'owing Medicines. She was purged with
the following, ℞ *Sena* ʒj. *Agarick* ʒ iij. *Rubarb*
ʒii. *Cinnamon* ʒiſs. *Infuſe them all for twelve hours
in three pints of White-wine on warm embers, after it
was ſtrained through an Ippocras bag, ſix or ſeven times,
and ſweetned with half a pound of Sugar.* Doſe ʒv.
twice a day, *viz.* in the morning faſting, and at
four a clock in the afternoon. This gave five or
ſix ſtools a day without gripings, it was continued four days. Her face was anointed with *white
Ointment camphorated*, which cured it in four days.
The Body being not ſufficiently emptied, the following Pills were uſed, ℞ *Pil. Ruffin. & Succin.
Crato.* of each equal parts ; of ʒi, were made ſeven
Pills, three of which ſhe took when ſhe went to
bed, the next day ſhe had ſix or ſeven ſtools. But
this was obſervable, that inſtead of ſwallowing the
Pills, ſhe chewed them, and ſo let them down,
ſaying ſhe could not ſwallow them, though never
ſo little; withal, that ſhe thought it the beſt way.
She took of theſe twice a week. Thoſe days ſhe
took not the Pills, I adminiſtred the following:
℞ *Elect. Chalyb, Crat. mixed with the ſalts of Scurvy-
graß, Wormwood and Coral.* In her Broth was
boiled theſe Scorbutick Herbs, *viz. Scurvy-graß,
Water-Creſſes,* and *Brook-lime.* After all, ſhe took
this Scorbutick Beer, ℞ *Scurvy-graß* M iv. *Water-
creſſes, Brook-lime,* each M ii. *Wormwood, Fumitory,
and Germander,* each M. j. *Roots of Fennel, Borage,
Succory,* each ʒi. *Root of Elicampany* ʒſs. *Liquoris*
ʒi. *Flowers of Borag. Bugloſſe, Roſemary,* each p ii.
*Bovl them all in five gallons of Beer, till one be waſted.
After having the following Ingredients in a bag, viz.
Sarſaparilla, Calamus aromaticus, Cinnamon, Mace,*
Seeds

*Seeds of Anis* and *Fennel,* each ℥ß. *Juniper-berries*
℥ viii. *Let them be infused in the hot liquor, well co-*
*vered till it be cold, after put it up, hanging the bag in*
*it.* After fifteen days she drank of it, using no
other; this she drank in *April.* Till it was ready, she
took the following; ℞ *Sarsaparila* ℥ ii. *Guaicum*
℥i. *Sassafras roots* ʒii. *Slice aud bruise them, after in-*
*fuse them in* ℔ xv. *of Spring-water for twelve hours.*
*After add* S*curvy-grass* M ij. *Brook-lime, Water-*
*cresses,* each M i. *Betony, Agrimony,* each M ß. *Cur-*
*rants* ℥ii. *Boyl them all till* v ℔ *be wasted; after take*
*it from the fire, adding presently of Cinnamon bruised*
ʒi. *after let it pass through an Hippocras bag.* Dose
℥ vi. taken hot, being in bed, composing the Body
to sweat gently; cover the Head and Neck with
hot linnen clothes: after sweating, the sweat was
rubbed of gently with fine dry warm linnen. An
ordinary Drink was made of the second Decoction, which was used in those days she did not
sweat, with which was taken the juice of Scurvy-
grass rightly prepared, six spoonfuls in one
Draught; in her Broths was used the Salt of the
same. By the blessing of the Almighty, she was
by these Remedies perfectly cured, beyond the expectation of her Lord and Friends.

---

## Observ. II.

WIlliam, Earle of *Northampton,* labouring of
the heat of Urine, *April* 4. 1622. was
cured as followeth. ℞ *Cassia new drawn* ℥i. *Ter-*
*bentine washt* ʒi. *Rubarb* Ɔi. *Liquoris powdered* Ɔß.

*make them in a bole with Sugar.* The next day and the following he took this, ℞ *Malloes* Mi. *Liquoris* ℥i. *Boil them in a quart of Milk, after strain it, and add Syrup of French Mallowes* ℥vi. Dose ℥iv. or v. every morning; at night when he went to bed, he took ℥ß. of *Cyprus Terbentine,* in the form of a Pill in a rosted Apple. Thus was he presently and perfectly cured, being at *Ludlow,* at that time being President of *Wales,* and Councellor to the King.

---

## OBSERV. III.

Mrs. *Smith* of *Stratford* upon *Avon,* aged 54, being miserably afflicted with a hot Distillation in her Eyes, so that she could not open them in the morning, was cured thus. First there was administred for four nights together when she went to bed, ℥ß. of *Pil. de Succin. Craton.* made in three Pills. These gave five or six stools without pain the following days. In the interim, to the Eyes was applied the following, ℞ of the *Juyce of Housleek* a spoonful, *White-wine* two spoonfuls, *mix them together* : Of which there was dropt one or two drops into the Eyes, laying upon them all night a double linnen Rag wet in the same; this mitigated the heat. After I commanded to distill one or two drops of the following into the eyes twice or thrice a day :

*Collyrium* for the Eyes. ℞ *Sarcocol* wash'd. ℥iij. *Prepared Tutty* ℥ij. *Aloes* ℥i. *White Sugarcandy* ℥iß. *Saffron* gr. iv. *Rosewater* ℥iv.

iv. Mix them, letting them stand a day, sha-
ing them oft. By these she was cured.

---

## Observ. IV.

MR. *Wilson*, Minister of the said Town, aged
40, being grievously vexed with a Rheum
in his Eyes, was cured by the following Medicines.
℞ *Pil.Succin.* ʒi. *Aurear.* ʒß. *Troch. agar.* ϶i. *cum
Syr. Betonic. f. Pil.* N° 10. He took five of these
when he went to bed, which gave him the next
day six stools; the other five he took the following night. Outwardly was applied to the forehead and Temples the following Plaster, ℞ *Bole
Armoniack* ʒß. *Gypsum* ʒiii. *Dragons blood, Acaciæ,*
each ʒii. *Pomgranate-Pills, Galls,* each ʒi. *Pouder
them all, and with the whites of Eggs, and a little
Vinegar make a Plaster.* Behind the Ears was laid
*Bole* and *Gypsum,* framed into a Plaster as the former. Upon the Eyes were applied *Whites of Eggs
well beaten with Rosewater and Womans milk.* Into
the Eyes were dropp'd twice or thrice a day some
of our *Opthalmick Collyrium,* prescribed in the former Observation. This is remarkable, that a
while after it was used, he found the taste of the
*Sarcocol* on his Palat. By these Remedies he was
cured, blessed be God.

## Observ. V.

Mrs. *Beats* of *Ludlow*, aged 50, who being troubled with a great Cough, *Asthma*, and grievous Pain in the Side, was thus cured. First, I administred this Electuary, ℞ *Conserve of red Roses* ℥ij. *Raisins of the Sun* (stoned, *Sugar-candy, each* ℥i. *make them into an Electuary: To which was added Oil of Vitriol, and Sulphur, sufficient to make it sharp.* Dose morning and night the quantity of a Nutmeg. For a Fume was prescribed the following: ℞ *Frankinsence, Mastich*, each ℨiß. *Brimstone* ℨiiß. *Juniper* Əii. *Storax* Əi. *Terbentine sufficient to make a Past.* which frame into what figure pleaseth. Some of which being cast on some embers, the Fume was received into her Mouth by a tunnel, her Head being covered ; this dried up the superflous humidities of the Brain. For a pain in her Stomach, I applied the following; ℞ *Labdanum* ℥i. *Wax* ℥ii. *Species Aromatic. rosat.* ℨiii. *Caranna* a little, make a Plaister *S. A.* spred upon Leather. For the Pain of her Side I used this, ℞ *Ung. Dialthæa* ℥ii. *Oil of sweet Almonds* ℨii. Mix them, and with it anoint the Part pained, hot ; upon it I laid a linnen Cloth dipped in Butter, hot ; this gave her some ease. For a long time following she used this Drink : ℞ *of the Water distilled from Coltsfoot, Ground-Ivy, Mullin, Speedwel, Elicampany, Knapwood, Scabious, Hyssop, Herb Trinity, Great Figwort,* both *Maiden-hairs, Horehound, the*
                                                                    *cordial*

*cordial Flowers*, Roots of *Oris*, *Angelica*, *Sopewort*,
and *Water-Betony*, ℔xij. *Guaiacum* ℥xij. *Sarsaparila* ℔ß. *Oris roots* ℥ij. *China sliced* ℥iij. *Elicampany
roots* ℥iij. *Maiden-hair*, *Speedwel*, each M i. *Liquoris* ℥ij. *Aniseed* ℥i. *Raisins of the Sun stoned* ℥vi.
*Boyl them in a double Vessel well stopt, after strain and
clarify it.* Dose two or three good Draughts every day. Each night I gave at Bed time the quantity of a walnut of this: ℞ *Conserve Roses* ℥i. *Bole*
Ɖi. *mix them.* She also took of the following Julep oft in a day. ℞ *prepared Snails* ℔i. *Pieces of
white Bread* ℔ß. *Whites of Eggs* 30. *Cream* ℔iv.
*Cinnamon* ℥ii. *Best Sugar* ℔ij. *Muscadine* ℔ij. *Distil
them all in B. M.* It was drunk with *Manus Christi
perlat.* (now called *Sacchar. Tabuli perlat.*) and
sometime with the following Lohoch. ℞ *Loh. San.
& expert* ℥ii. *Penidies* ℥ij. *Syrup of Maiden-hair*,
*Hyssop*, *Liquoris*, and *Coltsfoot*, each ℥i. *Roots of Angelica and Elicamp. candied*, each ℥ß. *Roots of Oris* ℥i.
*mix them*; to ℥iv *of which add Flower of Brimstone* ℥ii.
These in the space of five weeks cured her; afterward she died, but of what Disease I know not.

## Observ. VI.

A Servant of Mr. *Nashes*, lying at the Bear in
*Stratford* upon *Avon*, aged 28, having the
Yellow Jaundice, with a Tertian Ague, was thus
cured: ℞ *Wine of Squils* ℥ß. *Oxymel of the same* ℥i.
*Our emetick Infusion* ℥ß. *mix them.* This exhibited
gave seven Vomits. After I purged him with this,
℞ *Rubarb powdered* ℥i. *Elect. Diaphæn.* ℥iij. *Pul.*

*Sen.*

*Sen. lax.* ℥ß. *Syrup of the Juice of Roses* ℥i. *Celendine water* ℥iij. *mix them.* It gave him eight stools for four mornings. After I administred to him fasting the following; ℞ *of the inner Rind of the Barbery Tree, Turmerick, Shavings of Ivory and Hartshorn, of each alike quantity. Saffron half the quantity of one of them: make a Powder of all.* Dose ℥i, in a rear Egg. These cured him perfectly, although the Jaundice was very much all over his Body.

## Observ. VII.

MR. *Powel* of *Ludlow*, aged 50, having an *Opthalmia*, accompanied with a continual Defluxion, so that his whole face was excoriated, neither could he endure to see the light, was cured as followeth. There was given him ℥ß. of *Amber Pills of Crato's*, made in three Pills four nights together; the first three gave him six stools the next day. Outwardly was applied the following, ℞ *Mastick, Frankinsence, Myrrh, each* ℥iß. *Dragons blood* ℥i. *Bole, Bean-meal, each* ℥ß. *Saffron* ℈i. *with White of Eggs, Oil of Roses, and a little Vinegar, make a Frontal,* which was applied. Into the Eye was distilled the following Collyrium. ℞ *prepared Tutty* ℥iß. *Camphire, Saffron. each* gr. xij. *Tie them up together in a fine Rag, and hang them in Rose water and White-wine, each* ℥ß. Of this there was dropt into his Eyes, he lying on his back, two or three drops three or four times a day. Whiles this was doing, was used the Decoction of *Sarsaparilla, and Guaiacum,* &c. without the Herbs prescribed,

*Observ.*

*Obſerv.* 1. And ſo in twenty days he was cured beyond all expectation.

## Observ. VIII.

Mrs. *Chandler* of *Stratford* upon *Avon,* aged 34, after long Sickneſs, and a great Flux of her Courſes, falling into an ill habit of Body, was cured thus; Firſt, ſhe took the Decoction of *Sena,* &c. preſcribed *Obſerv.* 1. for five days; after being let blood, her Courſes ſtayed to admiration, and ſhe became well.  Three years after being extremely weakned with the like Flux in the time of her lying in, ſo that Death was expected, ſhe was cured by bleeding.

## Observ. IX.

CHriſtian *Baſs* of *Southam* in the County of *Warwick,* aged 29, was miſerably tormented with Wind and Phlegm in the Stomach, which although by the taking of *Aqua Vitæ* ſhe was for preſent eaſed, yet it preſently returned with more violence, yea almoſt to ſtrangling; after which followed the Cholick.  She was cured as follows, ℞ *Emetick Wine* ʒv. *Wine of Squils* ʒſs. *mix them.* This given wrought very well by Vomits and Stools.  The next day I gave this, ℞ *Laurel prepared with Vinegar, the weight of 6 d. with Syrup of Violets, and Poſſet-drink, make a Potion.* It gave
ſeven

feven ftools. The Body thus emptied, I prefcribed this, R London-*Treacle*, *Mithridate*, each ʒi
*Conferve of Wormwood* ʒiii. *mix them*. For three
mornings fhe drunk the Decoction of Mints and
Balm in fteeled Water. And fo fhe was perfectly
cured, for which fhe gave me many thanks, and
never was molefted with the like pain.

## Observ. X.

Mrs. *Wincol*, the Countefs of *Northampton*'s
Chamber-maid, aged about 48, afflicted
with a *Tenefmus*, and falling out of the Fundament,
was cured as follows: R *Camomel* M i. *Sack* ℔ifs.
*infufe them on hot coals for an hour or two*: After
with linnen Clothes doubled, the *Anus* was fomented as hot as could be endured. After the Fundament was put up with ones finger, and a Spunge
dipt in the faid Decoction, and wrung out, was
applied thereto, on which fhe fate. Note, the
Flowers of *Camomel* are much better. Thus was
fhe delivered from both the aforefaid Evils.
After the fame manner was cured a Servant of
Mr. *Broads*.

## OBSERV. XI.

Mrs. *Hamberry* was cured of her Face that was full of Pustles, Itch, and Excoriations, and deformed as a Leper, with the following Medicines. I purged her Body with *Amber-Pills* ℥i. given when she went to bed, at twice; using to her Face *Aq. Mercurial. Penot.* with the Emulsion of white Poppy-seeds, Borax, and white Sugar-candy.

## OBSERV. XII.

JOhn *Emes* of *Alcester*, aged **15.** was cured of pissing in bed thus, ℞ *the Windpipe of a Cock dried, and made into powder, and with Crocus Martis* given in a rear Egg every morning.

## OBSERV. XIII.

Mrs. *Anne Gibs*, aged 19, cured of an Apostem in the Stomach. After its breaking, first I prescribed her this Lincture, ℞ *Syrup of Hyssop, and Coltsfoot, each* ℥i. *Vinegar of Squils* ℥i. *make a Lincture:* Of which with a Liquoris stick she licked often. After she was purged with this; ℞ *Cassia new drawn with Endive water* ℥i. *Rubarb*
*powdered*

powdered ʒi. *Scabious Water* ʒiv. *Syrup of Chichory
with Rubarb* ʒi. *make a Potion.* This gave eight
Stools. To the Stomach I outwardly applied
this hot. ℞ *Wormwood, Roses, Buglosse, each a
sufficient quantity; which make into a Pultis with the
Oil of Roses, Mastick and Violets.* Last of all I
used this, ℞ *Roots of Flower-deluce, and Lillies,*
each ʒi. Boil them in a Pint of White-wine to
the half. Dose ʒiv. in the morning. Thus she
became well, and of a good colour.

## Observ. XIV.

FRances *Reyland* of *Quenton,* taking cold in the
time of her Courses, there arose Tumours both
in her hands and feet, so that she could not move
her self. She was cured as followeth; first, she
received this. ℞ *Elect. Caryccostin.* ʒ iii. *Crystal.
Tartar.* ℈i. *cum Sacch. f. Bol.* It gave her six
stinking Stools. After I caused a Vein to be
opened, and so she was freed.

Twenty days after she relapsed, then I caused
her to be purged with Laurel prepared, and after
used the following Potion. ℞ *Guaiacum* ℔ß. *A-
grimony, Brook-lime, Water-cresses, Sage, Betony,
Rosemary,* each Mi. *Boil them in* ℔ viii. *of Spring-
water, till half wasted. In the end of the boyling, add
Cinnamon and Annifeed,* each ʒii. *after strain them.*
Dose ʒviij in the morning, which procured sweat.
At her going to bed she used this Bath. ℞ *Oak
leaves* M xx. *Camomel, Sage, Rhue,* each M ii.
*Salt* ℔ii. *Allum* ℔i. *Quick Brimstone* ʒ iv. *Boyl*
them

*them all in a sufficient water for a Bath.* Often the Member was anointed with this: ℞ *Vnguent. Martiat.* ℥i. *Ol.Lumbric. & Terebinth.*ana ℥ß. *misc.* Thus she was perfectly cured.

---

## OBSERV. XV.

MR. *Hunt of Stock-green,* aged about 46. labouring of a grievous Scab and Itch, was thus helpt: ℞ *Fumitory, Borage, Buglofs, Scabious, Wormwood, of each a like quantity, as much as you please; draw out the Juyces, of which take* ℔iii. *boyling it in Whey to the Confumption of the Whey, always fcumming of it; after it is boyled fuffer it to settle.* Drink every day a good draught of it cold with Sugar. This is the *Syr. Scabious. Joh. Anglici,* and a Secret by which he cured many of the Scab, with which I have cured many alfo.

---

## OBSERV. XVI.

MR. *Difon,* who was grievoufly tormented with a Pain at the mouth of the Stomach ( ufually called the Heart-ach ), fainting, as alfo Illnefs in a morning till he eat, was cured thus: ℞ *Pil. Ruffi. de Succin. Stomac. Hier. fimpl.* ana ℈i. *f. Pil.* 7. Thefe purged freely. After I gave him the following every morning: ℞ *Conferv. Rofar. & Mithrid.* ã ℥i. *Conferv. Abfynth.* ℥iii. *Theriac. Lond.* ℥vi. *Misc.* Dofe ℥iß. By thefe he was wholly freed.

OBSERV.

## Observ. XVII.

MAry Heath of *Libington*, aged 34, being cruelly vexed with a *Dysentery Catarrh*, Pain in the Back, Worms, casting out a thick stinking matter by Urine, having been before fat, but now grown lean, was thus cured; ℞ *Rubarb powdered* ʒiß. *Syrup of Roses solutive* ℥i. *Borage Water* ℥iij. *make a Potion.* This was given in the morning. Afterward this Clyster was cast in : ℞ *the Decoction of torrified Barly* ℔i. *Oil of Roses* ℥iii. *two Yolks of Eggs, red Sugar* ℥iß. *make a Clyster.* After the Clyster this was exhibited, ℞ *Yellow Wax* ℥ß. *Crocus Martis* ʒi. *Make of them a Ball like a Nutmeg, after put it into the midst of an Apple, the Core taken out ; after roast the Apple under hot Ashes, so that they may be melted into the substance of the Apple* ; and so she eat it fasting. Her Drink was steeled, her Diet was *Panados*, made of French Barly dried, and Crums of Bread, with steeled Water and Sugar. With these Remedies she was perfectly cured. *I have also cured many with Wax so prepared.*

## Observ. XVIII.

Mrs. *Lain* of *Aufon*, aged 49, much troubled with Pain in her Breaft, and great difficulty of breathing, was cured as followeth: ℞ *Troches of Agarick* ℨii, *with Honey of Rofes, and Syrup of preferved Ginger, make a Bole.* This was taken for three days; the firft day it gave four Stools, the fecond day fix, and third three. The fourth day was taken a Spoonful of the following, as often as difficulty of breathing required, fwallowing it by degrees. ℞ *Raifins* ℥ ſs. *Hyffop, Origanum, Horehound, Penny-royal, Speedwel, Germander, Scabious, Coltsfoot, Carduus benedictus, Nettles, each* Mſs. *Oris Roots fliced, Calamus Aromaticus, each* ℥i. *Agarick* ℨiij. *Sena* ℥ii. *Ginger* ℥ii. *Of thefe make a Decoction in* ℔ij. *of Wine-Vinegar, pouring in a third part of* Water, *andboil it to the third part. After ftraining, add of the beft Honey* ℥ xii. *after boyl it to the thicknefs of an Oxymel.* You may hang in it afterward thefe things following in a little fine Rag, viz. *Cinnamon, Cloves, Calamus Aromaticus,* all powdered, Dofe a fpoonful at a time. This is excellent, and worth Gold.

## Observ. XIX.

Mrs. *Hall* of *Stratford*, my Wife, being miſerably tormented with the Cholick, was cured as followeth. ℞ *Diaphœn. Diacatholic.* ana ℥i. *Pul. Holand* ℨii. *Ol. Rutæ* ℥i. *Lact. q. ſ. f. Clyſt.* This injected gave her two Stools, yet the Pain continued, being but little mitigated; therefore I appointed to inject a Pint of Sack made hot. This preſently brought forth a great deal of Wind, and freed her from all Pain. To her Stomach was applied a Plaiſter *de Labd. Crat. cum Caran. & Spec. Aromat. roſat. & Ol. Macis.* With one of theſe Clyſters I delivered the Earle of *Northampton* from a grievous Cholick.

## Observ. XX.

Mrs. *Herbert*, miſerably vexed with a Pain of her Side, was thus eaſed: ℞ *of Spirit of Wine,* or *Aqua Vitæ* ( which is next hand ) ℥vi. *Camphire* ℥i. *boyl them a little till the Camphire be diſſolved, adding whilſt hot,* red *Saunders* pulverized ℨiſſ. A Cloth was wet in this Liquor, and applied.

## Observ. XXI.

MAry Wilson, aged 22, afflicted with a Hectick Feaver, with a Cough, Obstructions of her Courses, and Weakness, was thus cured : There were appointed Meats boiled, as Veal, Hens, Capons, fed either with Barley, or crammed with Past made of Barly Meal , Frogs, Snails, and River-Crabs were also exhibited ; by this she got Flesh. Our Restorative was a Caudle made of the yolks of Eggs, Wine, and Sugar. She also used the following Panatella ; ℞ *Crums of Bread moistned with Milk, and after mixed with Almond Milk, Rose-water, and Sugar.* A *Ptysan,* or Cream of Barly was thus prepared: ℞ *Barly* ℥ii. *Purslain, Borage, each* Mß. *Boil them in* ℔x *of Water, till a fourth part be wasted; after strain it, and drink of it.* She frequently used Sugar of Roses. For a Clyster this was used : ℞ *Chicken-broth* ℥x. *in which was boyled Seeds of Poppies, Flowers of Water-Lillies, Violets, Lettice, Mallowes, each* Mß. *Being strained, there was added Oil of Violets* ℥iß. *White Sugar* ℥ii. *Honey of Violets* ℥iß. *Common Salt* ʒiß. *the Yolk of one Egg; mix them.* She sucked Womens Milk, nourished with cooling and moistning Diet, as Lettice. A year after this she died.

---

## Observ. XXII.

MR. *Drayton*, an excellent Poet, labouring of a Tertian, was cured by the following: R̲ *the Emetick Infusion* ʒi. *Syrup of Violets a spoonful: mix them.* This given, wrought very well both upwards and downwards.

---

## Observ. XXIII.

GOod-Wife *Betis*, aged 40, who once a month ( yea sometimes twice or thrice ) was grievously pained on the right side of her Head, which often ended with vomiting, and in her Fit could neither walk nor stand : was cured thus : First, she took this Vomit : R̲ *the vomiting Infusion* ʒi. This wrought six times. For the next day was provided the following Pills : R̲ *Pil. de Succin.* ʒii. *Cephal. Fernel.* ʒi. *f. Pil.* N° xv. She took three of them before supper, every day till they were spent. After I caused a Vein to be opened to ʒvi. After she took this Decoction: R̲ *Sarsaparilla* ʒiv. *Water* ℔x. *being sliced, let them infuse for twenty four hours, after boyl them till half be wasted, strain it.* Dose a draught morning and night, when she went to bed. For ordinary Drink, she took the second Decoction, which was made of the same Wood, adding ℔xv of Water, boyling it without infusion till the third part be wasted.

OBSERV.

## OBSERV. XXIV.

Mrs. *Boughton*, being with Child, and troubled with Vomiting, and a Flux of the Belly, was thus freed: Rx *Sack* ℥vi. *Oil of Vitriol six drops.* She took an Ounce of it every morning fasting as long as it lasted. Her *Stomach* was anointed with the following: Rx *Oil of Wormwood, and Mace,* each ℥ß. *Spec. aromatic. rosat.* ℥ß. *mix them, and make an Ointment.* As she pleased she took of this Julep: Rx *Syrup of Poppies* ℥iii. *Waters of Scabious and Mints,* each ℥ii. *of Borage* ℥vi. *Oil of Vitriol to sharpen it for taste: mix them, and make a Julep.* Thus she was cured, praised be God.

## OBSERV. XXV.

Mr. *Randulph*, aged 35, troubled with Pain of the Head, great Distillation, and continual Spitting, with coldness of his Head, so that he was constrained to wear three Caps, was delivered from all in seven days by the following: Rx *the Emetick Infusion* ℥i. This gave six Vomits, and three Stools. The next morning were taken the following Pills. Rx *Pil. Coch.* ℈i. *Aurear.* ℈ß. *Troch. Alhand.* gr. vi. *cum Syr. Betonic.* f. *Pill.* 7. Thus purged, there was taken away ℥vi of Blood. Afterward there was taken morning and evening ℥i of the following Powder: Rx *Powder of Sena* ℥vi.

*Rocket*

*Rocket Seed* ʒß. *Long Pepper* ʒiß. *Make a Powder of these.* After the taking of it seven days he became altogether well.

---

## Observ. XXVI.

Mrs. *Boughton* of *Causon*, aged 28, three days after Miscarriage in the fifth month, fell into a Feaver, accompanied with abundance of After-fluxes, Vomiting, Loathing, Thirst, Swooning, and in danger of Death, was speedily helped as follows: ℞ *burnt Hartshorn finely powdered* ʒi. *Boyl it in three quarts of Spring water, till a quart be wasted, then remove it from the Fire; after add Syrup of Limons* ʒii. *Rosewater* ʒiv. *Sugar a sufficient quantity.* This she drank constantly instead of Drink, which gave great ease. The following Decoction was given morning and evening, which did cleanse, cut, cast out, and extinguish Thirst. ℞ *French Barly* Miv. *Violets* p. ii. *Liquoris* ʒß. *Jujebs* ʒi. *Sebestens* ʒii. *Carduus benedictus* Miß. *Make a Decoction in a sufficient quantity of Water to* ℔xij. *To the straining add Sugar of Violets* ʒiv. *and make a Drink.* By these Medicines alone she was cured beyond all expectation, praised be God.

Observ.

## Observ. XXVII.

CAptain *Basset,* aged about 50, afflicted with a Tertian, was thus cured : ℞ *Emetick Infusion* ʒv. *Wine of Squils* ʒii. *Syrup of Violets a spoonful* ; *mix them.* This was given an hour before the Fit, which wrought by vomit and stool sufficiently. At the end of vomiting he took this : ℞ *Elect. de Gem. frigid.* Əii. *Diascord.* ʒß. *Syr. Papav. erratic.* ʒi. *Aq. Scabios.* ʒiii. *Misc.* The next day he was free from his Fit, he took the following : ℞ *Diaphænic. Diacathol.* ā ʒii. *Rhab. Pul. Pul. Sen. laxat. Ruland.* ā ʒß. *Pul. Holand* ʒi. *Syr. Cochl.* ʒi. *Aq. Card. benedict.* & *betonic.* ā ʒii. *Misc.* This purged and cured him.

Three months after he fell into a Dropsy, with a swelling in his feet, which was removed by the following : ℞ *the Emetick Infusion* ʒß. *Wine of Squils* ʒii. *Barly water, and Syrup of Violets, each* ʒß, *mix them.* This gave seven Vomits, and three Stools. The next day, and for three mornings, he took the following : ℞ *Leaves of Succory, Borage, Bugloss, Violets, Strawberries, each* M. i. *Seeds of Anis and Caraway, each* ʒi. *Roots of Smalage and Sharpdock, each* ʒi. *Flowers of Borage, Bugloss, Violets and Roses, each* p. i. *Boyl them in a quart of Water to* ʒxij. *Of the straining thereof,* ℞ ʒiiij, *in which infuse Troches of Agarick, Rubarb, each* ʒi, *Mecoachan* Əii. *Ginger* Əiß. *Spicknard* gr. iv. *Cinnamon* ʒß. *In the morning strain them again, to which Expression add Syrup of Roses* ʒiß. *Manna* ʒß, *Mix*

*them*

*them for one Dose, and so for four mornings.* This being done, there was administred the following Pills : ℞ *Pil. aggregat.* ℈i. *Gambog.* gr. v. *Ol, Anis.* gut. v. *Syr. Cichor. cum Rhab.* q. s. f. *Pill.* ii. These gave seven Stools, the next day one Pill gave five Stools, and with happy event, for thereby he could both better breath and walk. After he took this sweating Potion : ℞ *Sarsapar.* ʒii. *Saſſafras* ʒi. *Bul. in Aq. fontan.* ℔viij. *ad Conſumpt. dimid.* ( this muſt be after they have been infuſed 24 hours ). *Towards the end of the boyling was added bruiſed Cinnamon* ʒii. *Seeds of Anis, Carraway, Coriand.* ā ʒ ſſ. *Doſe* ʒvi. in a morning taken hot. After he uſed this laxative Drink : ℞ *Sarſaparilla* ʒii. *China* ʒi. *Saſſafras* ʒvi. *Guaiacum* ʒii. *Sena* ʒiiſſ. *Rubarb* ʒi. *Agarick* ʒiii. *Mecoachan* ʒi. *Shavings of Ivory and Hartshorn, each* ʒſſ. *Seeds of Fennel, Nutmegs, Cloves, each* ʒii. *Leaves of Violets, Roſemary, Fumatory,* ā M i. *put them into a Bag, and hang them in* 3 *gall. of Beer.* Theſe perfectly cured him. In *August* he laboured of an Hypocondriack Melancholy, with Pain of the Head, for which was uſed the following : ℞ *Pill. de Succin.* ʒii. *Spec. Hier. ſimp.* ℈ii. *cum. Syr. Chicor. cum Rheo.* f. *Pil.* N xi). He took three of theſe at the hour of Sleep, theſe eaſed him of his Head-ach. After which was uſed *Pil. aggregat. cum Cambog.* &c. as before ; only they were made up with the Syrup of Apples into two Pills, which gave eight Stools with a great deal of eaſe. After to the Stomach was applied this : ℞ *Origanum, Wormwood, Mints, each* M ſſ. *Seeds of Milium, Anis* toſted, *each* ʒſſ. *Flowers of Camomel, Roſemary, and Coltsfoot, each* p. i. *Bay-berries* ʒi. *Nutmegs* ʒſſ.

ʒß. *make a gross Pouder of them all, and stitch them in Sarsanet, and make a Bag in form of the Stomach, which was besprinkled with Sack, and applied and reiterated as oft as there was occasion.* Thus he was perfectly cured, and continued so for a long time.

## Observ. XXVIII.

Mrs. *Chandler*, of *Stratford* upon *Avon*, aged 36, five days after Labour, fell into an Erratick Feaver, with horror, heat, and shaking often day and night, was thus cured : ℞ *the Decoct. of Harts-horn* (as *Obs.26.*) ℔iij. Of this she drank continually, shaking the Glass as she was to take it. After she took the following : ℞ *Hartshorn prepared* ʒiiʲ. *Rain water* ℔ß. *Boyl them to* ℥iv. *After add Syrup of red Poppies* ℥ii. *Rose water* ℥i. *Spirit of Vitriol sufficient to make it acid :* It was for two doses : After which she was very well.

## Observ. XXIX.

MR. *Fortescue*, aged 20, was troubled with the Falling-sickness, by consent from the Stomach, as also Hypochondriack Melancholy, with a depravation of both Sense and Motion of the two middle Fingers of the Right-hand ; his Urine was much clear, like Spring-water, and heavy. Being called to him, I thus proceeded : The fifth of *June* 1623. were administred these

Pills:

Pills: ℞ *Pil. sine quibus* ʒi. *Fœtid.* ℈ii. *Castor* ℈i.
*Aq. Borag. q. s. f. Pil.* 7. Thefe exhibited gave
three Stools. At the conclufion of its working,
the Senfe and Motion of the Fingers were returned. The fixth day there was drawn ʒviii of
Blood from the Cephalick Vein; the fame night
at bed-time was given *Pil. Succin.* N° iii; the fe-
venth day he had three Stools. The eighth day
the following was prefcribed: ℞ *Caftor. opt. Affæ
fœtid.* ā ʒſſ. *Rad. Pæon. fubtilif. pul.* ʒi. *Aromat.
rofat.* ʒii. *Mifc. cum Syr. de Menth. f. Pil.* 7. He
took one of them when he entred his Bed. The
next morning was given the quantity of a Nutmeg of the following: ℞ *Conferv. Bugloff. Borag. Anthos,* ā ʒiſſ. *Confect. Alkerm.* ʒii. *Lætific.
Gal. & de Gem.* ā ʒſſ. *Pul. Rad. Pæon. Ariftol.* ā ℈i.
*Rafur. Ebor. C. C. Coral.* ā ℈ii. *cum Syr. de Hyffop.
q. f. f. Opiat.* In the very inftant of the Fit the
following Fume was ufed: ℞ *Benzoin. Mum. Pic.
nigr.* ā ℈i. *Mifce cum Succ. Rut. f. Suffit.* You may
alfo anoint the Nofe with the fame more liquid.
Obferve that in the morning before the *Opiat,* was
ufed this neezing Powder: ℞ *Pyreth. Rad. Pæon.*
ā ℈ii. *Hell. nigr.* ℈ſſ. *f. Pul. fubtilif.* By thefe
means, through the mercy of God, he was in a
fhort time cured; and now ten years from the
time afflicted he hath been very well.

## Observ. XXX.

Mrs. *Nash*, aged 62, having of a long time laboured of a Consumption, and now afflicted with Wind of the Stomach, as also Heat thereof, with sweating from the Pit of the Stomach to the Crown of the Head, having great Pain of the Head, especially after Meat, was thus cured : ℞ *Loaf-sugar* ʒiv. *Cubebs, Grains of Paradise, Galangal, Ginger, each* ʒi. *Long Pepper* ʒß. *Cinnamon* ʒiii. *White-wine* ℔ii. *Let them stand to infuse for twenty four hours, after strain them through a Bag, and make a Drink commonly called Hippocras* : Of which she took ʒiii in a morning. There was used a Clyster of Linseed Oil with good success. Lastly she took ʒiii of the following Syrup : ℞ *Cinnamon grosly beaten* ʒiij. *Calamus Aromaticus* ʒi. *Infuse them in* ℔ii *of Sack for three days in a Glass Vessel, near the gentle heat of the Fire. To the straining add Sugar* ℔ iß. *Boyl them gently, and make a Syrup, S. A.* These freed her from Wind, and she was able to eat, and said she was very well for a long time after.

## Observ. XXXI.

MR. *Kempson,* aged 60, oppreſſed with Melancholy, and a Feaver with extraordinary
heat, very ſleepy, ſo that he had no ſence of his
Sickneſs, was cured as followeth : ℞ *Leaves of
Mallowes, Beets, Violets, Mercury, Hops, each* M iſs.
*Borage* M ii. *Epithymum* ℥ſs. *Peny-royal* p. ii. *Rhue,
Wormwood, Cammomel, each* Mſs. *Seeds of Anis,
Rhue, Carraway, Cummin, Fennel, Nettles, Bay-berries,
each* ℥ſs. *Polypod.* ℥iſs. *Sena* ℥i. *Bark of black Ellebore* ℥i. *Boyl them all in* ℔iii *of Whey, till half be
waſted. Of this ſtrained, take* ℥x. *Confect. Hamech,
Diaphænic. each* ʒv. *Salt* ℥i. *Mix them, and make
a Clyſter.* This brought away two Stools with
a great deal of Wind ; it was given in the morning, and again at night. After theſe there were
applied to the Soals of his Feet, *Radiſhes ſliced,
beſprinkled with Vinegar and Salt,* renewed every
third hour. This hindred the Recourſe of Vapours, and drew them back, and ſo he ſlept far
more quietly, without ſtarting and fear. The
following was prepared for his ordinary drink, ℞
*Spring water* ℔iv. *Syrup of Limons* ℥i. *Julep of
Roſes* ℥iſs. *Hartſhorn burnt and powdered finely* ℈iv.
*Spirit of Vitriol, ſo many drops as ſufficed to make it
tart.* After the Leeches being applied to the A-
nus, there was drawn forth ℥viii of Blood. After which was exhibited this : ℞ *Lap. Bezoar.* gr.
v. *Tinct. Coral.* gr. iv. *mix them ; it was given in
Poſſet-drink.* After this the Urine was very frothy,
with

with a great fediment, and he was much better.
The Clyfter, Drink, and Powder was repeated
with defired Event. To remove Sleepinefs, he
ufed to neeze only with Tobacco. The *Reftora-*
*tive of Quercitanus,* fol. 187. of his *Diæteti. poly-*
*chreft.* fect. 4. chap. 8. was ufed. But yet his
Stomach being ill, I gave him this ; ℞ *Emetick*
*Infufion* ʒvi. *Syr. Violets* ʒii. *Oxymel of Squils* ʒi.
This gave four Vomits and nine Stools: After
which he was well for five days, and then relap-
fing into a fhaking Ague, a Clyfter being injected,
he became well, bidding farewell to Phyfick, and
fo was cured beyond all expectation, and lived
for many years.

## Observ. XXXII.

Mrs. *Garner* of *Shipfon,* aged 22, miferably
weakned with the Whites, was cured as
followeth : ℞ *Caffia newly drawn with Parfley wa-*
*ter* ʒvi. *Terbentine wafhed in Parfley water* ʒii. *Gum*
*of Guaiacum* ʒii. *With Sugar make a Bole.* The
next day this Plafter was applied ; ℞ *Ung. Comi-*
*tif.* ʒi. *Gypf. Bol. Arm.* ã ʒſſ. *cum Alb. Ovi f. Empl.*
It was applied to the Back. After I prefcribed the
following : ℞ *Coriander Seeds prepared, Seeds of*
*Sorrel, Plantain, and de Agn. Caft.* each ʒi. *Sealed*
*Earth, and Bole Arm.* each ʒſſ. *Spec. Diatrag. frig.*
ʒi. *Make a very fine Powder, and with Sugar diffol-*
*ved in Plantain water make Rouls or Tablets ( add*
*Gum Tragac.) weighing* ʒii. Of thefe fhe eat one
before dinner and fupper, and prefently after
drank

drank a spoonful of red Wine. This is admirable in Uterine Fluxes. By these she was healed.

## Observ. XXXIII.

BRown, a Romish Priest, labouring of an *Ungarick Feaver*, in danger of Death, was cured as followeth: ℞ *the Emetick Infusion* ℥vi. *Syrup of Violets* ℥ii. *Oxymel of Squils* ℥i. *mix them.* Being given, it gave five Vomits, and four Stools. The next day there was removed ℥vi of Blood. After which was prescribed the following: ℞ *Springwater* ℔iij. *Syrup of Pomgranats, Julep of Roses,* each ℥iß. *Hartshorn prepared* ℥iii. *Spirit of Vitriol, as much as will make it a little tart.* In Broths he took *Tinct. of Coral* ℈i. And at Bed time there was a Clyster injected, made of emollient Herbs, *Pul. Sen. lax.* and course Sugar, it gave three stools. In the day and night was taken the quantity of a Walnut of the following, often: ℞ *Rob. rib. Confer. Rosar. Confer. Car. citrior.* ā ℥i. *Cortic. Citr. condit.* ℥ß. *Aurant. condit. Spe. liberant.* ā ℥ii. *C.C. præp,* ℈ iv. *Lap. Smaragd. rub. Hyacinth. præp.* ana gr. vi. *Flor. Sulphur.* ℥i. *Coral. rub. præp.* ℈i. *Succ. Granat.* ℥ß. *Syr. acetof. Citr. q. f. f. Elect. liquid.* This I have used with happy success without the precious Stones, to corroborate the Heart. I gave the following at thrice: ℞ *Conserve of Roses* ℥i. *Tincture of Coral* ℈ii. *C.C. præp.* ℥i, *Diascord.* ℥ß. *Flor. Sulphur.* ℈ii. *mix them.* The following was prescribed to quench thirst: ℞ *Barly* ℥ii. *Liquoris* ℥iß. *Borage, Succory,* each M i. *Boyl them*

*them in* ℔iii *of Water to* ℔ii. *Add Sal. Prunel.* ℥ß.
*Burnt Hartshorn* ℨiii. *after boyl them a little.* He
took of this thrice a day. His Meat was besprinkled with this Cardiac and Alexipharmic Powder : ℞ *prepared Pearl, prepared Coral, burnt, Harts-
horn, prepared Granats, each* gr.viij. *The Fragments
of* Jacynt. *Smardines and Rubies, each* gr. iij. *One
leaf of Leaf-Gold ; mix them, and make a Powder.*
The former Julep being spent, this was used : ℞
*Spring water* ℔ii. *Burnt Hartshorn, and Crude, each*
℥iii. *Species liberant.* ℈iv. *Boyl them to the consumption of half a pint, add the Juyce of Limons, a sufficient quantity to make it tart, boyl them again, scum
it, and clarify it with Whites of Eggs.* He took of
this thrice a day. By these beyond all expectation
the Catholick was cured, especially with the Decoction of Hartshorn, with which I have cured
these and other Feavers in a short time, very many.

## Observ. XXXIV.

CAptain *Basset,* aged 50. afflicted with Hypochondriac Melancholy, with trembling
and pricking of the Heart, as also with Pain in
the Head, and tumour about the Ancles, was cured as followeth : ℞ *the Leaves of Succory, Borage,
Buglose, Violets, Strawberries, each* Mi. *Root of
black Ellebore* ℨii. *Liquoris, Polypody, each* ℥ii. *Citron
seeds* ℥iß. *Seeds of Anis and Caraway, each* ℥ß. *of
all the Myrobalans each* ℨii. *Beat them all grosly, and
rub them with your hands with Oil of sweet Almonds,*
After infuse them *for twenty four hours in* ℔ß of
*Fumitory*

*Fumitory water.* *After take Roots of Parfly, Buglofs,*
each ℥i. *Flowers of Borag. Buglofs, Violets, Rofes,*
each M i. *Boyl them all in five pints of Water, till
two pints be wafted; ftrain it, and add Sena, Epithymum, Tamarisk, each* ℥ii. *Boyl them again to
two Pints. In the ftraining, infufe for a night Troches
of Agarick, Rubarb, Mechoacan, each* ℥ii. *Ginger*
Ɖiv. *Spikenard* ℨſſ. *Cinnamon* ℨi. *Strain it again,
and boyl it with Sugar to the confiftence of a Syrup;
to which add Syrup of Rofes folutive* ℥iv. *Manna*
℥ii. *and referve it for four Dofes.* This purged
well, with happy event. At the end of purging,
he took for a whole week one of the following
Morfels, morning and evening, two hours before
meat: ℞ *Spec. Lætifican. Gal. Diamofch. dulc. A-
romat. rof.* ana ℨi. *Cinnamon* ℨſſ. *Piftach. mund.* ℥ſſ.
*Confeƈt. Alker. Croc. off. de Cord. Cervi, Coral. rub.
margarit.* ana Ɖi. *Chalyb. præp.* ℨii. *Sacch. diffol.
in Aq. Cinam. q. f. f. Morful.* pond. ℨiiſſ. On the region of the Stomach this was applied; ℞ *Labd.*
℥ii. *Ceræ* ℥ſſ. *Ol. Macis* ℨii. *Spec. aromat. rof.* Ɖii.
*mifc. f. Emplaft.* It is to be fpread on Leather. I
ufed a Clyfter framed of Emollients and Carmina-
tives with Sugar. After meat he ufed the following: ℞ *Coriander feed prepared* ℨii. *Seeds of Fennel
and Anis,* each ℨi. *of Carraway* ℨſſ. *Liquoris* ℥ſſ.
*Ginger* ℨii. *Galangal, Nutmegs, Cinnamon, Cloves,*
each ℨi. Make a grofs Powder, or they may be
made into Tablets with Sugar diffolved in Rofe-
water. Thus he was well cured, and thanked
me.

## Observ. XXXV.

A Child of Mr. *Walkers* of *Ilmington*, Minister, aged six months, afflicted with the Falling-sickness, by consent was thus freed : First, I caused round pieces of Piony roots to be hanged about the Neck. When the Fit afflicted, I commanded to be applied with a spunge to the Nostrils the Juyce of Rhue mixed with White-wine-vinegar; by the use of which it was presently recovered; and falling into the Fit again, it was removed in the same manner. To the Region of the Heart was applied the following; ℞ *Theriac. ven.* ℥ii. *Rad. Pæon. pul.* ℥ß. *Misc.* The Hair was powdered with the powder of the Roots of Piony. And thus the Child was delivered from all its Fits.

## Observ. XXXVI.

E*lizabeth Hall*, my only Daughter, was vexed with *Tortura Oris*, or the Convulsion of the Mouth, and was happily cured as followeth: First, I exhibited these Pills: ℞ *Pil. Coch. & Aurear.* ana ℥i. *f. Pil.* 10. She took five the first day, which gave her seven Stools; the next day with the other five she had five stools. I fomented the part with *Theriac. Andromac.* and *Aq. Vitæ.* To the Neck was used this: ℞ *Unguent. Martiat.*

*Martiat. magn.* ℥i. *Ol. Laurin. Petrolei, Castor. &
Terebinth.* ana ℥ß. *de lateribus* ℥ß. *Misc.* By this
she had great advantage, her Courses being ob-
structed. Thus I purged her: ℞ *Pil. fœtid.* ℥i.
*Castor.* ℥i. *de Succin. Rhab. agaric.* ana ℈iß. *f.
Mass.* She took of this five Pills in the morning,
of the bigness of Pease; they gave eight stools.
The next day she took *Aq. Ophthalm.* see *Obser.* 3.
as ℞ *Tutiæ,* &c. her Courses flowed. For an
*Ophthalmia,* of which she laboured, I used our
Ophthalmick Water, dropping two or three drops
into her Eye. Her Courses staying again, I gave the
following Sudorific Decoct. ℞ *Lign. Vitæ* ℥ii. *Saf-
safras* ℥ß. *Sassap.* ℥i. *Chin.* ℥vi. *macerat. per* 24 *hor. in
Aq. fontan.* ℔ viii. *After boyl them to* ℔iv. After the
use of these, the former form of her Mouth and
Face was restored ( there was not omitted *Ol.
Sarsap.* which was above all to anoint the Neck )
*Jan.* 5. 1624

In the beginning of *April* she went to *London.*
and returning homewards, the 22d of the said
Month, she took cold, and fell into the said Dis-
temper on the contrary side of the Face , before
it was on the left side, now on the right ; and
although she was grievously afflicted with it, yet
by the blessing of God she was cured in sixteen
days, as followeth : ℞ *Pil. de Succin.* ℥ß. *Aurear.*
℈i. *f. Pil.* v. She took them when she went to
bed. The same night her Neck was anointed
with Oil of *Sassafr.* In the morning I gave ℥ß
of *Pil. Ruffi.* and again used the said Oil with
*Aqua Vitæ,* and dropped into her Eye the Ophthalmick Water. The aforesaid Oil being
wanting, I used the following : ℞ *Pul. Castor.
Myrrh.*

*Myrrh. Nuc. Mosch. Croci.* ā ℈i. *Ol. Rutæ, Laurin. Petrol. Tereb.* ā ℥ii. *Ungu. martiat.* ℥ß. *Ol. Costin. de Peper.* ā ℥i. *Misc.* But first the Neck was fomented with *Aqua Vitæ,* in which was infused *Nutmegs, Cinnamon, Cloves, Pepper.* She eat Nutmegs often. To the Nostrils, and top of the Head was used the Oil of Amber. She chewed on the sound side, Pellitory of *Spain,* and was often purged with the following Pills : ℞ *Pill. fœtid.* ℈i. *Castor pul.* ℈ß. *Pil. Ruffi. & de Succin.* ā ℈i. *f. Pil.* N° v. And thus she was restored.

In the same year, *May* 24. she was afflicted with an Erratick Feaver ; sometimes she was hot, and by and by sweating, again cold, all in the space of half an hour, and thus she was vexed oft in a day. Thus I purged her : ℞ *the Roots of Parsly, Fennel, each* Mß. *Elder Bark* M ii. *Roots of the vulgar Oris, of Madder, each* M . *Roots of Sparagus* M ii. *Boyl them in sufficient quantity of Water to six pints. To the straining, add Rubarb, Agarick, each* ℥ß. *Sena* ℥vi. *Mechoacan* ℥ii. *Calamus Aromaticus* ℥i. *Aniseeds* ℥i. *Cinnamon* ℥ß. *Infuse them in a Vessel well stopt according to art : strain it again, and to the straining, add Sugar sufficient to make a Syrup. of this take* ℥iv. *Rubarb infused in* ℥v *of Cichory water* ℥ii. *Mix them, and give seven spoonfuls every day fasting.* It gave seven or eight stools without pain. ℞ *Sarsap.* ℥i. *Sassafr.* ℥ii. *Guaiac.* ℥i. *Liquoris* ℥ß. *Herb of Succory, Sage, Rosemary, each* M ß. *Boyl them in ten pints of Water till half be wasted.* Of which she took a draught hot in the morning. The following was used to anoint the Spine : ℞ *Gum. Galban. Bdel. dissol. in Aq. Vit.* a ℥ß. *Benzoin.* ℥i. *Styrac. liquid.* ℥i. *Fol. Rut. Chamæpith.*

D

*mxpith. Flor. Stæchad. Lavendula,* ā ʒii. *Rad. costi.*
Ʒ ß. *Castorei* Ɔi. *infund. misc. & pulverisat. in Aq.*
*Vitæ.* It is to be infused in some hot place for
some days. Before it was used, the Spine was
rubb'd. An hour after it was used, all the Symptoms remitted daily till she was well. Thus was
she delivered from Death, and deadly Diseases,
and was well for many years. To God be praise.

---

## Observ. XXXVII.

M rs. *Sands* after her Purification was miserably afflicted with a Tumor, and pain of the
Hemorrhoids. I appointed they should first be
anointed with *Ung. Populeon.* After there was
applied the *Yolk of an Egg,* well beaten with Oil
of Roses, and added a little Saffron powdered.
In Winter may be used *Oil of sweet Almonds,* &c.
This mollified their hardness, and removed their
pain.

---

## Observ. XXXVIII.

M R. *Queeny,* labouring of a grievous Cough,
with vomiting abundance of Phlegm and
Meat, having a gentle Feaver, being very weak,
and had red Urine without sediment, was thus
cured : ℞ *Troches of Agarick* ʒiß. *Olibanum, Mastic.*
each ʒß. *Terbentine sufficient to make a Mass of* ʒi,
*make five Pills.* These he took at Bed-time. In
his

his Sauces he used Saffron, because profitable for
the Breast; and he eat Mustard and Honey, which
caused spitting in abundance. ℞ *Hydromel simplex,
newly prepared with the best Honey* ℔iß. *add Raisins
of the Sun stoned* ʒi. *Figs* 10. *Oris Roots, Calamus
Aromaticus, each* ʒi. *Boyl them altogether, after strain
them, to which add Sugar-candy and Penidies, each*
ʒiii. *Cinamon bruised* ʒß. *So make an Hydromel.*
He took of this morning and evening ʒviij or ix.
To the Head I applied this: ℞ *Roots of Oris, Galangal, Ciperus, Angelica, each* ʒii. *Roots of Pelli-
tory of Spain, Agarick, Rubarb, Squils, each* ʒi.
*Sena* ʒii. *Marjoram* ʒi. *Coriander seeds, Bay ber-
ries, Cloves, Nutmegs, Mace, each* ʒi. *Gith seeds,
Mustard seeds, each* ʒß. *Benjamin, Storax, each* ʒiii.
*Chalcanth. alb.* ʒß. *Lapis Calaminaris* ʒii. *Alum* ʒi.
*Oyl of Nutmegs some drops, Oil of Marjoram and
Sage distilled, Rosin and Wax sufficient to make a
Plaster.* The Head was first shaved. The days
he rested, in the morning I gave the following in
White-wine: ℞ *Saffron* ℈j. *Musk* gr. i. For his
hoarsness I gave the following: ℞ *the Juyce of
Liquoris* ʒi. *Myrrh.* ʒß. *Gum Tragacanth* ℈i. *Sugar-Candy, and Penidies, each* ʒß. *of which make
Morsels.* Hold one of them in your Mouth, lying
on your back, to the end it may dissolve of it self.
There was also given an *Emulsion, or Milk of Almonds Pine-nuts, and some new Goard-seeds, expressed to* ʒiv. *in it was dissolved Sugar of Roses* ʒii.
And it was drunk every other morning warm,
fasting; it was continued fourteen days. Being
not wholly freed from it, he fell into it again
the next year, and all Remedies proving suc-
cesslefs, he died. He was a Man of a good

wit,

Wit, expert in Tongues, and very learned.

## O b s e r v. XXXIX.

JOan *Chidkin* of *Southam,* aged 50, being troubled with trembling of the Arms and Thighs, after felt Vapours ascend to the Heart, thence to the Throat, and after thought her self suffocated, was thus cured: ℞ *Merc. vitæ* gr. v. *Diaphœnic.* ʒſs. *Misc.* This exhibited, gave two Vomits and two Stools. After she took *Theriac. Andromac.* ʒi. in Posset-drink. I purged her with the former again, only adding one grain of the *Mercury,* which gave four Stools. After which she had the foreiner *Theriac.* with the shavings of *Hartshorn,* for four days. By which she was helped miraculously, all Symptoms vanishing.

## O b s e r v. XL.

MR. *Winter,* aged 44, cruelly tormented with the Worms and Feaver, was cured as followeth: He first had a Suppository made of Honey, drank the Decoction of prepared and crude Hartshorn, had an Emplaster applied to the Navil against the Worms. I purged him with ʒſs of *Manna dissolved in Broth* ; with which there came forth many dead Worms, with stinking Excrements. He also took in his Drink and Meat the following Powder : ℞ *Coral* gr. viii. *Pearl, Hartshorn,* born, *Granats,* all prepared, gr. viij. *Fragments of Jacinth, Smardine, Rubies,* each gr. iii. *one leaf of Gold: mix them for use.* For his Cough he used Syrup of Poppies, with Syrup of Maiden-hair. By these, with God's blessing, he was cured in three days.

## Observ. XLI.

Mrs. *Fortescue,* aged 12, having a most vehement Cough, and cruelly troubled with the Worms, was thus cured: First there was used a Suppository of Honey; to the Navil was applied the Emplaster against Worms. For her Cough this was used: R *Flos Sulphur.* ʒß. *Benzoin. vel Assæ Odorat.* Ɔß. Make them into very fine Pouder, and divide it into twelve parts: there was given every morning one part, and at night Hartshorn, with which the Cure was perfected.

## Observ. XLII.

Mrs. *Throgmorton,* aged 35, being afflicted with pain at her Stomach, Melancholy, and the Mother, was thus cured: She first took the following Purge: R *Rubarb* ʒi. *Agarick* Ɔii. *Sena* ʒß. *Cinamon* a little. *Make an Infusion* in ℔ß *of Wormwood wine, to* ʒvi. *strain it.* Of this she took six spoonfuls, with two spoonfuls of the Syrup of Succory, with Rubarb, and so for three days,

D 3       which

which gave fix ſtools a day. The third night ſhe had a greater *Flux* of her Courſes than in many years before, and ſo for that time I was diſmiſs'd in *March*. She ſent again the firſt of *April*, I purged her with theſe Pills : ℞ *Pil. ſine quib. & Ruffi.* ā ʒi. *f. Pil.* 9. She took three at a time when ſhe went to ſleep. The Body being purged, there was given of the following ſteeled Wine two ſpoonfuls, and ſo to four and ſix, increaſing it by degrees. ℞ *prepared Steel* ʒi. *the middle Bark of Aſh, Tamaris, Roots of Cappars, each* ʒß. *Saſſafras, Juniper, each* ʒvi. *roots of Elicampana, Angelica, Galangal, Calamus aromaticus, each* ʒii. *Shavings of Hartſhorn, and Ivory, yellow Sanders, each* ʒiii. *Fol. Wormwood, Ground-Pine, Spleenwort, Dodder, Balm, Germander,* ā p.ii. *Flowers of Bugl. Borag. Scab. Broom,* ā p.i. *Cinam.* ʒß. *Cloves, Ginger, Mace, Nutmegs,* ā ʒii. *Beat them very groſly, and mix them by degrees in four pints of White-wine, and infuſe them in* Bal. Mar. *in a Veſſel well ſtopt for* 3 *or* 4 *days ; after ſtrain them through an Ippocras bag.* After it is exhibited, exerciſe is to be uſed. After meat ſhe uſed this Pouder : ℞ *Coriander ſeeds prepared* ʒi. *Seeds of Anis, Fennel,* ā ʒß. *Carraway,* Ði. *Cordial Flowers, each* ʒi. *Marjoram* ʒß. *Liquor. Elicamp. Ginger, each* ʒi. *Galangal, Nutwegs, Cloves, each* ʒß. *Beat them into groſs Pouder, adding Sugar, make a Pouder.* The Stomach and Sides were anointed with the following, thrice a week. ℞ *Oil of Dil. Nard. Capars, each* ʒß. *Vinegar of Squils* ʒi. *Boyl them to the waſting of the Vinegar, add Gum. Ammoniacum diſſolved in Vinegar* ʒii. *Roots of Aſarabacca* ʒi. *Gith ſeeds* ʒß. *Saffron* Ði *Wax ſufficient to make a Liniment.* Thus in the ſpace of little more than twenty days ſhe was cured.

OBSERV.

## Observ. XLIII.

A *Uſtin*, a Maid, had her Face full of red ſpots, with red Puſtles, very ill favoured, although otherwiſe very comely, and of an excellent wit, was thus cured: Firſt, ſhe was thus purged: ℞ *Elect. Diacathol.* ʒv. *Confect. Hamech.* ʒii. *Aq. fumariæ* ℥iii. *Syr. Cichorii cum Rhab.* ʒvi. *f. pot.* It purged her very well. The following day ſhe took theſe Pills: ℞ *Pil. fœtid. de Hermod.* ā ʒſſ. *Aurear.* ℈ii. *Miſc.* Theſe emptied plentifully. The Body thus purged, her Face was anointed with the following Liquor: ℞ *Litharge of Gold powdered* ℥i. *Alum* ʒi. *Borax* ʒiii. *Ceruſſ* ℥ſſ. *Vinegar* ℥ii. *Roſewater, and Plantain water, each* ℥iii. *Boyl them to the waſting of the third part, after ſtrain them, and add the Juyce of Limons* ℥ſſ. Before the uſe of this ſhe was let blood. I adviſed her morning and night (the Puſtles opened, broken, and cruſhed) ſhe ſhould waſh the Puſtles daily with the ſaid Water, which ſhe continued, and was wholly delivered from them in few days, and became well coloured.

## Observ. XLIV.

ELizabeth *Kenton* of *Hunington*, aged 50, troubled with a Flux of Blood from her Mouth,
was thus cured : ℞ *Syrup of red Poppies* ℥ii. *Scabious water* ℥iii. *Rosewater a little: mix them.* She
took one half in the morning, the other at night.
℞ *Conserve of Roses* ℥i. *Bole Armoniack, Blood-stone,
red Coral, sealed Earth, each* ℈i. *make a mixture
with Syrup of Poppies.* She took of this the quantity of a Bean after the Julep, and so she was
cured.

## Observ. XLV.

SImons of *Knowle,* a Vein being broken, vomited Blood, aged 40, was cured thus : ℞ *Rubarb powdered* ℨii. *Syrup of Maiden-hair* ℥i. *Succory water* ℥iv. *mix them.* This he took. After
there was taken this : ℞ *Philon. Persic.* ℥i. *Syrup of
Myrtles* ℥i. *Plantain water* ℥iv. *mix them.* There
was also drunk Goats milk with Sugar. And at
night going to bed was given Conserve of Roses
℥i. By these few Medicines the Cure was performed quickly, safely, and pleasantly.

## Observ. XLVI.

COOper *Marit* of *Pebworth*, aged 48, perceived
Vapours or Wind ascending from her Feet
into the Stomach, and so ill, that she could scarce
be kept from swooning, was cured as followeth :
℞ *Pil. Fœtid. Ruffi.* ā ℈iv. *misc. f. Pil.* N. *9.* She
took three at the hour of Sleep. Afterward the
following Powder was given after meals : ℞ *Sha-*
*vings of Hartshorn and Ivory,* each ʒi. *Spec. Aromat.*
*Ros. Gabriel.* ʒß. *Seeds of Coriander, Fennel, Anis,*
each ʒi. *Carraway* ʒß. *Cordial Flowers* ʒi. *Marjo-*
*ram* ʒß. *Roots of Liquoris, and Elicampane,* each
ʒi. *Ginger, Galangal, Nutmegs, Cloves,* each ʒß.
*Saffron* ℈i. *beat them grosly, and add Sugar of*
*Roses the weight of all.* Dose half a spoonful. She
said it was worth Gold. On the Stomach was
applied a Plaster of *Labdanum, Wax, Caranna,*
*Spec. Aromat. ros. and Oil of Mace.* By these
alone she was delivered from all the Symptoms,
and cured.

## Observ. XLVII.

Mrs. *Wagstaff* of *Warwick*, aged 46, afflicted
with Hypochondriac Melancholy, the Scurvy, beating of the Heart, Pain of the Head and
Joynts, Ophthalmia, Vertigo, Morpheu, was
cured as followeth, although they were Chronic,
and

and she almost wasted with them. Her Urine
was one day clear as Spring-water, otherwhile
thick and filthy, often changing, a discovery she
laboured of a Scurvy, with livid and purple spots
scattered on the Arms, &c. ℞ *Roots of Succory,*
*Bugloſs, each* ℥i. *Fennel, Oris, Bark of Tamaris,*
*each* ℥ſſ. *Elicampana, Worwwood, each* ℨiii. *Mar-*
*joram, ground Pine, Germander, Fumatory, each* ℨii.
*Cordial Flowers, each* ℨi. *Seeds of Anis, Fennel,*
*Parſly, each* ℨiſſ. *Sena* ℥iſſ. *Carthamus bruiſed* ℥i.
*beat them, aud put them into a quart of Whitewine,*
*boyl them to a pint ; to the ſtraining, add Syrup againſt*
*the Scurvy by* Foreſtus ℥iii. *It is to be uſed for five*
*days.* Doſe ℥iv. with which she had six, sometimes
seven, eight stools. And thus she was freed from
the Heart-beating. The Body rightly purged, I
advised the Wine following: ℞ *the opening Roots*
*each* ℥ſſ. *Wormwood* ℨii. *Marjoram* ℨiſſ. *Cordial*
*Flowers, each* p. i. *Bark of Tamaris, and Capars,*
*each* ℨi. *Seeds of Fennel, Anis, each* ℨii. *Carraway*
*ſeeds* ℨi. *Spike* ℈i. *Tops of Centaury* ℨiſſ. *Steel*
*prepared* ℨiii. *put them in a quart of White-wine.*
Take of it three hours before meat, and an hour
after dinner take the Juyce of Scurvy graſs prepared in Wine, Doſe four or five ſpoonfuls twice or
thrice if need be. To keep the Belly always
open, take a Doſe of the following Pills : ℞
*Aloes* ℨii. *Myrrh.* ℨſſ. *Gum. Ammoniac. in Acet. diſſol.*
℈i. *Agarick, Rhab.* ā ℨiſſ. *Rad. Aſari. Gentian.*
ā ℨſſ. *Maſtic.* ℈i. *Spicæ, Sem. Petroſelin.* ā ℈ſſ.
*cum Succ. Abſynth. inſtar extract. inſpiſſ. f. maſ.*
She took ℨſſ once a week or oftner, two hours before dinner. If you would have them work better,
mix them with *Pil. aggregat.* For after meat, uſe
the

the following Powder : ℞ *Cloves, Galingal. Nut-megs, Cinamon,* each ʒ ſ. *Seeds of Coriander prepared, Roots of Elicampana,* each ʒi. *Seeds of Anis, Fennel,* each ʒſſ. *Carraway* Ͽi. *Liquoris* ʒii. *Ginger* ʒi. *Powder them grosly, and add Sugar of Roſes* ʒ ii. *Mix them.* The Region of the Heart was anointed with this: ℞ *Succ. Cardiacæ, Ol. Nardin.* ā ʒ ſ. *boyl them a little, and add Sugar of Cloves* Ͽſ. *Camph.* Ͽi. *Saffron* Ͽſſ. *Wax a little to make a Liniment.* Being after troubled with the ſwimming of the Head, the reſt of the Symptoms ending by degrees, I counſelled to uſe theſe Tablets : ℞ *Pul. Diacydon. ſine Spec. Nuc. Moſch.* ā ʒi. *Fol. Euphraſ. Majoran. Flor. Lavendulæ,* ā Ͽi. *Coral. rub.* Ͽii. *Raſ. Ebor.* Ͽi. *Sacch. diſſolut. in Aq. Roſ. f. Tab.* Take them in the Morning, after take ſome Broth wherein is boiled Marjoram and Mace, or in a rear Egg, adding Carraway ſeeds with ſalt. The Leeches were applied to the Hemorrhoid Veins. For the Morpheu, which was very filthy, it was removed by the following : ℞ *White Sope* ʒii. *Quick Sulphur* ʒi. *Verdigreaſe* ʒi. *Camphire* Ͽi. *with Oil of Tartar make a Globe, and moiſten it in a little Vinegar, and anoint the Face with it, and let it dry by it ſelf, the morning after waſh it off with Milk.* With this ſhe was delivered, the which I have experienced an hundred times. For her weeping Eyes was uſed our Opthalmick Water, ſet down Obſerv. 3. to the Temples. For ſtaying the Rheum was applied this : ℞ *Bole Armoniack* ʒii. *Maſtick* ʒ ſ. *Dragons blood* ʒi. *Powder of Galls* ʒ ſ. *with Whites of Eggs and Vinegar make a Plaſter, which apply to each Temple.* By theſe ſhe was ſpeedily cured.

 OBSERV.

## Observ. XLVIII.

**M**rs. *Symmons* of *Whitelady-Aston,* troubled
with a Diſtillation of the right Eye, for a
year, without pain and redneſs, by reaſon of
which there was diminution of ſight, was cured
by me for fifteen years, by the following courſe :
For the removing the watering of the Eye, this
was uſed : ℞ *Fumatory, Sena,* each ʒiij. They
were boiled in Whey for one draught, which was
often repeated. After was uſed *Pil. ſine quib. eſſe
nolo.* To the Neck was applied *Horſtius's Veſic-
catory,* which I have a long time uſed with moſt
happy ſuccceſs ( the preſcript of which you have
in the *Marrow of Chirurgery* ) above the Eye effected. On the Temples I appointed to be applied *Empl. contra Rupt.* or in place of it, that preſcribed of Bole in the former Obſervation. In the
following *Collyrium* were dipt two little Spunges,
after wrung out, and applied to the Eye, and
there bound till dry ; it is moſt efficacious and approved. ℞ *Pomgranate Pills* ʒi. *boyl them in Water of Roſes, Plantain, Nightſhade, each* ʒiij. *In
the ſtraining diſſolve Bloodſtone* ʒii. *Stir it till it be
red, after caſt away the Fæces, and add Myrrh.* ʒſs.
*Sarcocol waſhed in Milk* ʒi. *Ceruſſ. Tutia, each*
ʒi. *White Vitriol, Starch, each* Əi. *Powder them
all finely, and mix with the Collyrium.* There may
be alſo prepared the Mucilage of the Seeds of
Line and Fenugreek, and when you would uſe
the

the *Collyrium,* mix a little with it, or in want of
these, the White of an Egg. And thus she was
cured.

---

## Observ. XLIX.

JUlian *West,* aged 53, troubled with an immoderate Flux of her Courses, was cured as followeth: ℞ *Sena* ℥i. *Troches of Agarick* ℥iii. *Sugar* ℥vi. *Ginger* ℥i. *Currants* ℥ii. *boyl them on a
gentle Fire in two quarts of Whey till half a pound
be wasted.* Of this Decoction take ℥iß. morning and night for three days, which emptied her
Body from ill humors. The fourth day was
given the following: ℞ *Crocus Martis in red Wine*
℥iß. After was given the following: ℞ *the Yolk
of an Egg, with a little Sallet-Oil, mix them with
the following Herbs,* viz. *Motherwort, St. Johns-
wort, Milfoil,* and *Celendine,* and *make a Fritter.*
Take one a day made thus for nine days. To
the Back was applied an Emplaster framed of
Creta and Whites of Eggs, by which she was delivered.

Take this from the Translator, which hath
been often experimented by him on several Persons. ℞ *Plantain water* ℥ii. *Rubarb powdered* ℈ii.
*Yellow Myrobalans powdered* ℈i. *Syrup of dried Roses* ℥iß. mix them, and give it at seven a clock in the
morning, two hours after, taking some broth. The
next day was opened the Liver-vein of the right
Arm,

Arm, and there was removed ℥vi of Blood or more, often stopping it. After bleeding was given the following : ℞ *Conserve of Roses* ℥iv. *Magistral of Coral, and Pearl, of each* ℨi. *Confection of Jacynts* ℨi. *mix them, and make an Electuary.* The Dose was the quantity of a Nutmeg, five or six times a day, taking every morning and evening an hour after it a spoonful of the Tincture or Syrup of Coral, with the Waters of Roses and Plantain, of each three spoonfuls. The following hath been proved as successful: ℞ *the Pulp of Tamarinds* ℥ß. *Mace* ℈i. *Yellow Mirobalans* ℨii. *Rubarb.* ℨi. *Schænanth.* p ß. *boyl them in Plantain water to three ounces ; to the straining add Rubarb torrified powdered* ℈i. *Syrup of dried Roses* ℥i. *make a Potion.* Which was given in the morning. The next, six Ounces of Blood were removed, that is, two ounces at a time, by repetition, so much distance of time betwixt, as one might go a stones cast. After bleeding was taken the following : ℞ *Crocus Martis, Troches de Carab. each* ℨ ii. *Conserve of Roses, Marmalad of Quinces,* ℥i. *Syrup of Myrtles, so much as may make an Electuary.* There was given of it ℨi morning and night so long as was necessary, drinking after it of *Plantain water* ℥iij. *Sugar, and a spoonful of the Tincture of Coral.*

OBSERV.

## Observ. L.

JOhn *Smith* of *Newnam*, aged 60, was miserably tormented with the retention of Urine for three days, caused by the Stone, in which fell out a total Suppression with hazard of Life. For his ease many things were used without any advantage. At last they sent for me, to whom I successfully gave the following : ℞ *Winter Cherry berries* N. vj. *Parsley seed* ʒiij. *boyl them in sufficient quantity of Milk, with which make Posset-drink, of which he took* ʒvi. *Syrup of Marshmallows* by Fernelius ʒi. *Holland Powder* ʒii. *mix them.* He drank White-wine, wherein Winter Cherries bruised were infused. To the Region of the Bladder, and between the Yard and Anus was appl ed hot the next : *Take a good big Onion, and Head of Garlick, fry them with Butter and Vinegar.* These thus used, procured Urine within an hour, with some stones and gravel ; and so was he delivered from that long, pernicious and eminent Danger, for which God be praised.

## Observ. LI.

Mrs. *Sheldon* of *Bel-end*, aged 55, was miserably affl cted with an old Cough, and withall, dulness of hearing, was cured as followeth : ℞ *Pil. de Succin.* ʒß. *Pil. Aurear. sine quib.* ā ℈i.

ā ℈i. f. *Pil.* 5. She took three at night, and two in the morning. The day after was exhibited the following Powder, from ℈i to ʒi. for every day, morning and night, with white Wine, Broth, or other grateful Liquor. ℞ *Card. Bened. Sinap. Sylveſt.* ā ℈ij. *Piper. long.* ℈i. *Sen.* ʒii. *Sem. Aniſ.* ʒſſ. *Diagrid.* ℈ſſ. *miſc. f. Pul. ſubtiliſ.* It was taken for three days. The Cough being very urgent, were given the following Troches, holding one in the Mouth till jt be diſſolved. ℞ *Diatragac. frigid.* ʒiſſ. *Sem. Hyoſc. alb.* ℈i. *Sacc. penid.* ʒi. *Opii diſſol. in Vin. gener.* gr. vi. *cum infuſ. Gum. Tragac. fačt. in Aq. Roſ. f. Troch.* They are very profitable between ſleep in the Night. By theſe ſhe was altogether freed from her Cough. For her dulneſs of hearing was uſed in the morning a Fume received into the Ear by a Tunnel. It was framed of the Decočtion of *Origanum, Rhue, Marjoram, Spica Celtic. Bay berries, Juniper berries, ſeeds of Fennel, Carraway, Cummin, boiled in Wine.* After which was put in Musk with Wooll in the night ; but in the day Garlick, being firſt perforated, and after macerated in Honey. In the day time alſo was drawn into the Noſe the juice of *Pimpernel, Burnet and Beets,* which was very profitable, a like quantity of each mixed. By theſe, with God's bleſſing, ſhe was cured.

## Observ. LII.

Mrs. *Sheldon, Wife to the Son,* being corpulent, well coloured, was wont to miscarry often, the second month after conception, yet suffered no other accident with it, required my counsel. I advised her to purge, and strengthen the Womb, for which she took *Sage* in her drinks and meats, also a little of the following Powder in a rare Egge. ℞. *Gran. tinctor. Margarit. Tormentil. ana* ℥ i. *Mastic.* ℥ ß. *Mis. f. pul.* There was given as much as would lie on a groat. For the retaining the Infant, this is the best Plaster. ℞. *Labd. puris.* ℥ i ß *Gallar. Mos. Quercin. Bol. Arm. Nuc.Cupres.Ter. Sigil. Mirtil. Ros. rub. Sang.Dracon. Balaust. ana.* ℥ß. *pic. Naval.* ℥ ii. *Tereb.* ℥ vi. *Malax. omnia simul, f. Empl.* Part of which spred on leather, and applied to the Loins, *Os sacrum,* and the bottom of the Belly. This she used all her time, and after brought forth a lusty hearty Son, and after that more.

## Observ. LIII.

Mr. *Parker* aged 24, greivously vexed with a long cough ; by divine assistance was cured as followeth. ℞. *Venice Terbintine washed in Hyssop water* ℥ i. *dissolve it according to Art with the yolk of an Egg,* to which add ℥iii *of Hyssop water, as also*

E ℥i *of*

℥ i. *of Syrup of Liquoris.*    This purged him. After he took every morning the following Mixture: ℞ *Flower of Sulphur* ℥ii. *Roots of Elicampana, Oris, Liquoris,* each ℥i. *Hony sufficient to make an Electuary,* add *Oil of Sulphur* ten drops, *and make a Licking.* When he went to bed, he used this Fume: ℞ *Storax, Mastich, Terbentine,* red *Arsnick,* each ℈iv. *Incorporate them with the Yolk of an Egg:* After with it anoint little Bits of Juniper, and dry them; the Fume of which is to be received into the Mouth by a Tunnel.

## Observ. LIV.

REceive two or three brief Observations of *Thonerus,* as to the former Disease, which I could not pass, because much approved; of which this is the first:

A Son of a Citizen of *Ulm,* being fourteen years old, was molested with a long Cough by the flowing of a thin Catarrhous matter, so that there was a Consumption feared; the Counsel of other Physicians proving fruitless, he was cured as followeth: ℞ *Roots of Elicampana, Polypody of the Oak, Oris,* each ℥ii. *Hyssop, Betony, Carduus benedictus,* both the *Maiden-hairs,* each p. i. *Liquoris* ℥ii. *Figs, Jujubes, Sebestens,* each ℥ii. *Sena* ℥vi. *Troches of Agar. Mechoac.* ā ℥ii. *Ruharb* ℈iv. *Cinam.* ℥i. *Galang.* ℥ii. *Make a Bag for* ℔ii *of Hydromel.* Of which take ℥i every day.   Being it was a dry Cough, and conjectured to be produced from a
thin

thin ſerous matter, there was preſcribed this : ℞
*Syrup of Jujubes, Corn-Poppies, each ℥iſs. Olibanum
℈iiſs. Myrrh ℈i. Liquoris ℈ii. White Sugar candy,
Penidies, each ℥vi. mix them.* Of this was taken
a ſmall ſpoonful morning and evening, upon a
White-bread Toaſt moiſtend in Sack. Thus he
was wholly cured, although there was no ſmall
danger of a Conſumption.

---

## Observ. LV.

ANother was of the Noble Lord of *Schellenberg,* dwelling in *Kiſelect,* aged 80, who
was grievouſly tormented with a Cough, abhor-
ring Medicament ; for whom was preſcribed the
following : ℞ *Spec. Diair. ſimp. Diatrag. calid. ā
℥i. Sacch. in Aq. Salu. diſſol. ℥iv. f. Confect. in
Rotul. oblin. Ol. Cinamom.* They promoved abundance of Phlegmatick Excretion by Cough. He
commended them for their Affects and Pleaſant-
neſs.

---

## Observ. LVI.

A Certain Woman of *Uline,* being troubled
with a long Cough from a ſalt Rheum, was
thus cured : ℞ *Coriander ſeeds prepared ℥ſs. Spec.
Aromat. Roſat. ℥i. Dianth. ℥ſs. Spec. Diatrag. frig.
℥i. Aniſeeds ℈ii.* the Tablets of Sugar of *Roſes
℥v. make a Paſt, and of it Troches,* which are to
E 2 be

be taken. ℞ *Spec. Diair. S. Diatrag. calid.* ℨi.
*Extrac. Liquor.* ℨſſ. *Sacch. in Aq. Farfar. diſſol.* ℥iv.
*Aq. Aſthm.* ℨii. *& f. Rot.* By theſe was expecto-
rated abundance of viſcid matter, ſhe was delivered, and praiſed the Medicines.

## Observ. LVII.

EDward Rawlins, aged about two years, had
a hard Tumor of one of his Stones to the big-
neſs of a Hen's Egg, which was cured as followeth: ℞ *Linſeeds, powder them, and with Linſeed
Oil make a Pulteſs, which was applied hot.* After
there was a little Bag made of Cloth to keep it up
in, with which he was cured.

## Observ. LVIII.

GOod-wife *Palmer* of *Alceſter,* afflicted grievouſly with Pain of the Head and Heart, from
obſtruction of the Courſes, was delivered by the
following: ℞ *the Syrup of the five Roots* ℥i. *Rubarb powdered* ℈i. *Diacath.* ℨvi. *Manna* ℥ſſ. *Mugwort water* ℥iv. *mix them.* This gave eight ſtools
after the *Saphæna* was cut. After ſhe took the
following: ℞ *Troches of Myrrh* ℈ii. *Cinamon, Caſtory, each* ℈i. *Syrup of Mugwort and White-wine,
each* ℥ii. *mix them.* This is moſt excellent for the procuring of the Courſes,
often proved.

Observ.

## O B S E R V. LIX.

Mrs. *Barnes* of *Tolton*, being troubled with the over-flowing of her Courses a month after Birth, was cured only by the following Remedy : ℞ *the Shavings of Hartshorn ʒß. taken in drink, in the morning for four days.* She felt present ease, and was altogether restored and cured.

## O B S E R V. XL.

*Albot,* the First-born of the Countess of *Salisbury,* aged about one year, being miserably afflicted with a Feaver and Worms, so that Death was only expected, was thus cured. There was first injected a Clyster of Milk and Sugar. This gave two stools, and brought away four Worms. By the Mouth was given *Hartshorn burnt,* prepared in the form of a Julep. To the Pulse was applied *Ung. Populeon* ʒii. *mix'd with Spiders webs, and a little Powder of Nutshels.* It was put to one Pulse of one Wrist one day, to the other the next. To the Stomach was applied *Mithridate* ; to the Navel, the Emplaster against Worms. And thus he became well in three days, for which the Countess returned me many thanks, and gave me a great Reward.

O B S E R V.

## Observ. LXI.

Mrs. *Sheldon* of *Grafton*, aged 24, was miserably troubled with vomiting her Meat, and Feaver, fourteen days after Birth ; as also she was afflicted with Fits of the Mother, and cold Sweats, was thus delivered : ℞ *Posset drink of rasped Hartshorn, and Marygold flowers.* For the Mother was given ℈ii *of the white of Hens dung, Tincture of Coral* ℈iiſ. *Bugloſs water* ℥iv. It was given oft in a day, a spoonful or two. To the Navel was applied an Emplaster of *Caranna*, in the midst of which was put three grains of Musk. To the Stomach was applied this : ℞ *Labdan.* ℥i. *Wax* ℥ii. *Cloves, yellow Sanders, each* ℈i. *Mastick* ℥i. *Myrrh* ℥ſ. *with Oil of Wormwood and Mace make a Plaster.* By these she was cured.

## Observ. LXII.

Mrs. *Davis* of *Quenton*, aged 63, long tormented with Pain in the Stomach by Wind, helped as followeth : ℞ *Spec. Aromat. Rosat. Gabr.* ℥ii. *Rad. Enul. Camp.* ℥iii. *Cal. Aromat.* ℥ii. *Liquoris* ℥v. *Turbith. præp.* ℥ſ. *Sena* ℥ii. *Sem. Aniſ.* ℥ſ. *Santon* ℥ii. *Rad. Gentian.* ℥iſ. *Sacch. q. ſ. f. Pul.* Dose, as much as will lie upon a shilling, given in Wine. With this she was cured.

Observ.

## Observ. LXIII.

THE Son of Mr. *Bishop*, aged 6, being delivered a month before safely from the Small Pox, fell into a grievous Cough and Feaver, with Worms. ℞ *Manna* ℈ii. *Diacatholicon* ℥ss. *Flower of Cassia* ℥ii. *mix them with Syrup of Liquoris.* This he licked of often. I gave also burnt *Hartshorn* in Milk. His Breast was anointed with the Pectoral Ointment. There was given him our Julep of Poppies, and a Clyster of Milk and Sugar, and so he was cured.

## Observ. LXIV.

Mrs. *Harvy*, now Lady, very religious, five weeks after Child birth, was vexed with a great Flux of Whites, as also Pain and Weakness of the Back, was thus cured: ℞ *Dates as many as you please, cut them small, and with purified Honey make an Electuary.* This she used in the morning. By this only Remedy she was cured, freed from her Pain which came often, stayed the Whites, and made her fat.

E 4     Observ.

## Observ. LXV.

Mrs. *Randolph*, aged about 27, troubled with Wind in the Stomach, and too much Flux of her Courses, being discolour'd with torment of her Stomach after Meat, was thus cured: To the Back was applied this Emplaster: ℞ *Bole Armoniac. Creta, with the Whites of Eggs make a Plaster.* For the staying of the Flux of the Courses was given a Penny-weight of *Allum* in red Wine. There was also used the Powder prescribed *Observ.* 46. Thus in the space of four days she was cured.

## Observ. LXVI.

Mrs. *Barnes*, being great with Child, and near delivery, fell into a Tertian Feaver, which was accompanied with Thirst, Watching, Pain of the Head, a miserable pricking Pain on the left side. She was aged about 28, was cured as followeth: ℞ *the Powder of white Hellebore a sufficient quantity, apply it with slit Figs to the Pulse of each Wrist:* It was removed every four and twenty hours. For ordinary drink, ℞ *Barley* ℥iii. *Succory* M i. *Roots of Succory* ℥iii. *Syrup of Roses and Violets, each* ℥i. *Liquoris sliced* ℥iii. *Figs* iii. *Currants* ℥ii. *Sugar-candy* ℥ii. *Boyl them all in eight quarts of Water, till a quart be wasted, after strained, it was drank cold.* To the Side was used this Ointment,

ment: ℞ *Ung. Dialth.* ℥i. *Ol. Amygd. dulc.* ℥iii. *Misc.* The Side being anointed with it, there was applied a Linnen Cloth spread with Butter, it was applied hot. There being very great pain of the Head, there was used the following Ointment: ℞ *Ointment of Alabaster* ℥ß. *Opium* gr.vii. *mix them.* With this were the Temples anointed, and to them some of it applied. By these means she was cured, and delivered from danger of Miscarriage. She was cured in seven days space.

## Observ. LXVII.

Robert Sartor of *Stratford* upon *Avon*, aged about 34, fell into a violent bleeding at the Nose, which intermitted for four hours, and returned again, was stopt as followeth: I caused Tents made of new Cloth, often dipp'd in *Frog-spawn* in *March*, and dried, to be put up his Nostrils, made strong Ligatures below the Shoulders. After the following Plaster was spread upon Linnen, and applied to the Forehead, Temples, and Neck very often, cold; ℞ *burnt Argil, and powdered*, M ii. *Wine vinegar* ℔ß. mix them to consistence of an Emplaster: And thus within half an hour the Flux was stayed.

## Observ. LXVIII.

BAron *Compton*, now Earl of *Northampton*, aged
55, in 1617, was cruelly tormented with
Pain of his Teeth, and very much molested with
swelling of his Gums, which was removed by the
following Remedies : ℞ *Pil. de Succ. Crat.* ℥iii. *f.*
*Pil.* N° 18.    Of these he took three every morning and night for three days, which purged very
well.    This *Gargarism* was used : ℞ *the Decoction*
*of the Bark of Guaiacum, and of Barley, each* ℥iv.
*Syrup of Mulberries, and Honey of Roses, each* ℥ii.
*Spirit of Vitriol so many drops as will make it taste*
*sharpish.*   In this also was there often in a day a
piece of Spunge, applied to the pained Gums, and
there it was held the whole day.    By these Medicines he was delivered from all his Symptoms ;
the second day he could eat meat, and the third
day he was perfectly healed.

*Thonerus* hath some short Observations concerning Pain of the Teeth, which receive here :
I have (saith he) tryed on my self, if the Tooth
be hollow, as also on many others to stop the
Tooth with a little *Camphire* : But if they be not
hollow, then he boiled ℥ß *of Camphire in half a*
*pint of Vinegar,* which was held hot in the Mouth.
Both which he found successful.
One who had Pain of the Teeth, and Tumor
of the left Jaw, from a hot defluxion, was thus
cured : ℞ *Mas. Pil. Aurear. Cochear. sine quib.* ā ℈i.
*Extract.*

*Extract. Catholic. Theophr.* gr. vi. *cum Aq. Betonic.* f. *Pil.* 27. which was taken.   The middle Vein of the left Arm was opened, and the outward Jaw anoint with the following : ℞ *Camphire* ℥i. *dissolved, Oil of sweet Almonds.* By the use of these was a desired effect.

---

## Observ. LXIX.

THe eldest Son of Mr. *Underhil* of *Loxley*, aged about 12, having laboured the summer before of a *malign Spotted-Feaver,*after fell into the*Measels,* of which he was cured *Jan.* 1. 1634. Being sent for to him, I found him grievously afflicted with the Scurvy ; on the right side he had a Tumor without discoloration, so that I judged there was a Tumor of the Liver.   He was grown as lean as a Skeleton, was Melancholy, with black and crusty Ulcers appearing in the Legs.   He had a loathing of Meat, a disposition to Vomit, and an Erratic Feaver ; his Urine was red, as in a burning Feaver, yet without thirst or desire to drink.   The Pulse was small, weak, and unequal, scarcely to be perceived with the Finger ; all Signs of a confirm-ed Scurvy.   His Parents were very earnest with me to cure him ; I told them, I would do my ut-most to do it, but it would require some time, and it would be difficult.   I proceeded as follows: ℞ *Cryftal.Vener.* ℥ii. *Spec. Diatrion. Santal.* ℥i. *Pul. Holland.* a ℥ii. *M. f. Pul.* for four doses.   It gave him every day three or four stools without any gripings.   The affected Part was anointed with
*Unguent.*

*Unguent. Fido variol.* To the Ulcers was used *Diapalm.* After for three days was given *Cream of Tartar* ʒi, in the morning; and an hour after was taken the following: *Take of our steeled Wine* ʒiiij. *the Essence of Fumitory and Germander*, ( which you have in *Bald. Ronf.* fol 259. with *Senertus in 8vo*) each ʒſs. *Syrup of Brooklime* ʒii. *of Water-cresses* ʒi. *Juyce of Scurvy-grass prepared* ʒvi. *mix them.* The Dose given was four spoonfuls, after which to use exercise : With which he had two stools, and cast up by vomit the first day some Phlegm. The next day in the morning he took *Diacurcum* ʒſs. after the steeled Wine. Every third day he purged with *Diatart. Quercet.* Ǝſs. in the pap of a rosted Apple. After he used our Antiscorbutic Beer. To his Spleen was applied *Empl. de Ammoniac. Foreſt.* Sometimes he used the next : *Take Juyce of Scurvy-grass* ℔ſs. *Syrup of Brook-lime and Water-cresses, each* ʒiſs for three mornings. The *Chalibiat* Wine was continued for a whole Month, with the Juyce of Scurvy-grass, *&c.* as before. He purged with *Pil. Ammoniac. River.* Of ʒſs. was made three Pills, one of which he took every third day, which gave him two or three stools. The Side swell'd and pained, was anointed with the following : ℞ *Unguent. Splanch. Magiſtr. Dialth.* ā ʒi. *M.* morning and night. In the use of the Scorbutic Beer all other was forbidden. After the use of the former Pills twice, there fell out a painful Tumor of the Foot, which hindred his Sleep by night, and moving by day; with which were joined Faintings. Therefore to corroborate was used the following : ℞ *Pul. Pannon. rub.* Ǝi. *Magiſt. Coral.* Ǝſs. *Lap. Bezoard.* gr. iij. *M.* To

the

the Foot was used the next : *Take Brook-lime,*
M iv. *Wormwood, Melilot, Chamomel, Sage,* each
M i. *Boyl them in sufficient quantity of Beer for a
Bath.* Which used for three days, he was almost
altogether freed from the Pain and Tumor. Then
I purged him with the following : ℞ *Pill. Ruffi.
Stomach. Hier. cum Agaric.* ã ℈i. *f. Pil.* 6. He
took one at Bed-time. The Foot being well,
there fell out a miserable Pain in the right Shoul-
der, which he was freed from in twenty four hours,
by the use of *Ung. Fido.* He never left off the Steeled Wine, except those days he purged. After meals
he took of the next so much as would lie upon a
shilling : ℞ *Plerisar.* ℥ß. *Sacch.* ℥ii. *Misc.* Especially
he purged twice with *Pil. River.* And sometimes
he took in a morning two of the following, which
gave three or four stools : ℞ *Pil. de Ammoniac.* ℥i.
*Gum Gamb.* pp. gr. ix. *sine quib.* ℥ß. *M. f. Pill.* By
this method he was cured, God be praised.

## OBSERV. LXX.

ANne Green, the Daughter of Mrs. *Green,* aged
22, was troubled with Pain of the Head,
sometimes a vivid Colour through all the whole
Body, after that white, with an universal Itch
over the Body, with painful Pustles, so that she
could not walk without great Pain, was thus
cured : ℞ *Sarsaparilla* ℥ii. *Hermodactiles* ℥iß. *Guaicum, Liquoris,* each ℥i. *Polypody of the Oak, Sena,*
ã ℥ii. *Agaric.* ℥ii. *Roots of Fennel, Parsly,* each ℥i.
*Betony, Sage,* each Mß. *Rosemary* p. i. *The Seeds of
Anis,*

*Anis, Carraways,* and *Coriander,* each ℥ß. *Cinamon*
℥i. *Boyl them in eight pints of Water, till half be*
*wasted ; after strain it, and of the strained Liquor*
*take* ℥iiß. *Syrup of Roses solutive* ℥i. *Oil of Vitriol*
*so much as will make it sharpish.* It was given, and
procured five stools. This being continued five
days, the Body was well purged. After was given
this Decoction : *Take of China sliced* ℥iii. *Infuse it*
*in three pints of Spring water for twenty four hours,*
*after boil them on a gentle Fire till half be wasted.*
After being strained, there was given a Draught
in a morning five hours before Dinner, and also
three hours before Supper, hot, till all was
drunk. It was given every third day. After the
use of this *Sudorifick Decoction,* the following Bath
was used : ℞ *Oak leaves* M xx. *Fennel* M xv. *Roots*
*of Briony, Elicampane sliced,* each M iv. *Brimstone,*
*Allum, Sea salt,* each ℔i. *Boyl them in sufficient Wa-*
*ter for a Bath.* From the Bath she went into her
Bed, and sweat. After, her Body was anointed
with the following : ℞ *Roots of Elicampane, Brio-*
*ny, each as much as pleased, Alum a little, make an*
*Ointment with May Butter.* By these means she became fair and smooth.

# Observ. LXXI.

JOhn *Nason* of *Stratford* upon *Avon,* Barber, aged
40, always after Meat suffered most bitter
Pains of the Stomach, as also cruel Misery in the
Loins, so that he had seldom any Sleep at nights,
was entring into the Yellow Jaundice; his Urine
was

was thin, red, the Crown yellow and frothy. Ɽ *our Emetick Infufion* ʒi. It gave fix Vomits, and four Stools. The following day, Ɽ *Horehound* ʒii. *Hops* ʒi. *Roots of Buglofs, Elicampane, and Eupatory,* each ʒfs. *Rubarb grofly fliced* ʒi. *Wood of Aloes* ʒifs. *Boyl them all in three pints of White-wine, till the third part be wafted; after ftrain it without expreffion; to the ftraining add the Juyce of Goofe-dung half a pint.* Of this he took ʒiii with *white Sugar* ʒii. This quantity he drunk betimes in the morning. And thus in few days fpace he was cured, and well coloured.

## Observ. LXXII.

BAron *Compton,* aged 55, was infefted with bitter Pain by the heat of Urine, was cured by the following Water, often proved by me in this Difeafe : Ɽ the *Whites of eight Eggs well beat, Cows milk* ℔i. *Red Rofe water* ℔fs. *diftill them in a common Still.* Of this *Water* Ɽ ʒiv. *Syrup of Alth. Fernel.* ʒi. *mix them.* It is to be given cold, fafting. And fo he was perfectly cured, fo that he rode with King *James* in his Progrefs into *Scotland.*

## Observ. LXXIII.

Mrs. *Boughton*, Sister to Mr. *Comb* of *Lauford-fair*, aged about 36, very handsom, was afflicted with a most grievous Disease, and bitter Symptoms, for above two years; and although many expert Physicians did lend their help, yet there was no Profit, yea rather all was more bitter and grievous. She could scarce swallow or breath, she felt something hard in her Throat to the bigness of a Dove's Egg, so that she could scarce swallow either Meat or Drink. This was caused from Wind; for she felt it move, and in its motion it was sometimes more and less painful. The tumor of the Almonds was not great, from a Rheum which distilled from the Head, which vexed her most in the night. Her Illness and Pain hindred her Sleep, and she feared she should be choaked; yet her Head was afflicted with a notable numness, and an incredible proneness to sleep; her Body was so also afflicted, by which she could scarce walk, and natural Action was deprived; hence there were a long time of Symptoms. By intervals her Hands would be livid, not without coldness; the Thighs tumified, and a *Scorbutick Dropsy* broke forth; all these being caused from the Spleen, Liver, and suppression of the Courses. ℞ *Sena* ℥iiß. *Cream of Tartar* ℥ii. *the best Turbith, Hermodactils, each* ℥i. *Rubarb, Troches of Agarick, each* ℈ii. *Scamoni* ℈p. ℥ß. *Mace, Cinamon, Galangal, each* ℥iii. *Sugar of Violets the weight*

of,

*of all, make a Powder.* Dose from ʒi to ʒii in Broth, wherein was boiled *Peniroyal, Mugwort, Horehound, Sage, Betony.* This ended, the next Decoction was taken: ℞ *China sliced* ʒi. *Sassafras* ʒiii. *Spring water* ℔vi. *Juyce of Limons* ʒii. *Infuse them for twenty four hours, after boil them till a third part be wasted, and then let it pass through an Ippocras bag.* Of which there was drunk ʒv morning and night, with ʒii of the *Juyce of Scurvy-grass prepared.* Every third day, if the Body was not open, was given a Clyster framed of ʒxii *of the former Decoction, red Sugar* ʒii. *and Honey of Rosemary flowers* ʒiii. For her Mouth, ℞ *Spring water* ʒii. *Oil of Vitriol so many drops as made it very sharp, in which Water was dipp'd a Feather, and so conveyed to the swell'd Fauces.* This was done often in each hour, by the use of which there ran out, and was spit forth continually very much Phlegm. After was used a Fume of Amber, which was received by a Tunnel into the Mouth. To the Stomach was applied our Plaster for the Stomach, *Observ.* 19. ℞ *Diamor. simp.* ʒv. *Mel Rosar.* ʒiv. *Succ. Matris sylvæ* ʒviii. *Aq. Hord.* ʒxii. *Ol. Sulph. q. s. ad gratam acidit.* This Gargarism was often used in a day. Thus she was cured, and lived eight years after.

F

OBSERV

## Observ. LXXIV.

ESquire *Beaufou*, (whose Name I have always cause to honour ) at the end of his Supper eating great quantity of Cream, about the age of 70, after his first sleep he found himself very ill, and so continued. The second day he sent for me, I found his Pulse quick, and his Urine red and little, often pissing, his Stomach full of Phlegm and Choler, as appeared: for falling into a voluntary vomiting, there came up a great quantity of Choler, like the Yolks of Eggs putrified. This considered, I gave him an ℥ of our *Emetick Infusion*, which gave ten Vomits and three Stools, which answered desire. To drink, he had prescribed the Decoction of Hartshorn with Sugar and Limon. And thus he was cured in four days.

## Observ. LXXV.

ESquire *Packinton* was troubled with want of Appetite, to whom I prescribed the following Powder, which was taken for many days: ℞ *Sena* ℥iii. *Ginger, Mace,* each ℈i. *Cinamon* ℥ß. *Cream of Tartar* ℥ii. *mix them, and make a Powder.* Dose ℥i in Broth. This restored his Appetite, for which he thanked me, desiring the Receipt. The next year after he also used it with good success.

The

The following hath cured many of the like Affect : Firſt purge with a Potion framed of the Decoction of *Wormwood* and *Agrimony,* and ℥ß of *Diaphænicon.* After was drunk the following : ℞ *Leaves of Agrimony, Wormwood,* and *Centaury,* each M i. Boil them in water to ℔ß of the ſtraining ; add a little Sugar, drink it every morning for three or four mornings.

## Observ. LXXVI.

MR. *Rogers,* Clerk, aged about 40, was troubled with Pain in the Throat, Tumor of the Tonſils and Palat ; he could hardly either ſwallow or breath, and was almoſt ſtrangled, to whom I coming preſcribed the following : ℞ *Figs, Liquoris, Raiſins, Aniſe ſeeds,* each ℥i. *Spring water* ℔iv. *Boyl them till half be waſted, and uſe it for ordinary drink.* Take the Fume of Amber oft in a day. To the Neck and Tumor appearing, I commanded this Cataplaſm : ℞ *Green Wormwood* M ii. *Hogs greaſe as much as will make a Pultis, being well beat together.* In one nights ſpace he was cured, and had his ſwallowing again. This was proved an hundred times.

## Observ. LXXVII.

THe Lady *Beaufou*, godly, honeſt, being of a
noble Extract, continuing healthful till the
age of 28, which was 1617, *July* 1. fell into
a burning malign continual Feaver, with great
Pain of the Head, moſt vehement Heat, Pain
in the Stomach ; the Body all over, eſpecially the
Arms, was full of ſpots ; the Urine was red and
little. It was then called the *New Feaver*, it invaded many, I was called the third day of its In-
vaſion. The Stomach being ſtuffed and burdened
with ill humors, as I perceived, I adviſed the
following Vomit : ℞ *Emetick Infuſion* ℥ix. This
gave twelve Vomits without any great trouble.
The day before ſhe had (unknown to me) drunk
much Milk to quench her thirſt, by reaſon whereof the Vomit at firſt drew forth a wonderful
quantity of curdled Milk, ſo that ſhe was almoſt
choaked, after came Choler mixed with Phlegm,
afterward burnt Melancholy. She had alſo ſix
Stools Phlegmy, mixed with green Choler and
much Seroſities. Her vomiting ending in three
hours, I gave a Pill of *Laudan. Paracelſi* gr. vii.
(ſure he miſtook her, for four is a good Doſe) after
which ſhe ſlept four hours, the Pain of her Head
ceaſing. Then to me unknown her Servant gave
her a draught of Whey, which being drunk, ſhe
preſently had three Vomits of black Stuff without
any trouble, and two ſuch like Stools, and was
cruelly afflicted with the Hiccough, to allay which

I

I gave Claret wine burnt with Aromatick, which succeeded ; she was quieter the rest of the Night, but did not sleep well. In the morning I gave Chicken-broth, made with appropriate Herbs, and so for four hours she rested. At the end of that time I gave a draught of the Decoction of Hartshorn hot. On Munday morning having some evacuation, I appointed the same Decoct. should be given cold. She was miserably afflicted with *Pustles*, with great heat of the Tongue and Throat, that she could not drink without great difficulty, for which she used the following Gargarism : ℞ *Diamoron. simp.* ℥iv. *Honey of Roses* ℥ii. *Rosewater* ℔j. *Oil of Sulphur, so much as made it sharpish.* After the use of the *Hartshorn Decoction,* the seventh day, the Pox appeared, yet the foresaid Gargarism was used for the Throat, and she drunk of the Decoction of Hartshorn cold four times a day, and so she was cured. I ordered that the Pox after the eighth day should be anointed with this: ℞ *common Oil, and Carduus water,* well shaked together, and so there were left no Scars.

## Observ. LXXVIII.

MR. *Farman,* afflicted with the Small Pox, whilst being at my Lady *Beaufon's,* so that he could not go to his Father's at *Leicester.* To expel them, I gave him this : ℞ *Diascordium* ℥i. *Mithrid.* ℥ß. *Croc.* ℈ß. *Aq. Dracuncul.* ℥iii. *Corn. Cervi* ℈i. *f. Haustus.* This caused him to sweat, and the same day began to appear his Pox. This

caused

caused no small joy to his Sifter, and thankfulnefs to God, that he was delivered from the Jaws of Death. For his thirft, he drank at his pleafure the Decoction of Hartshorn, and ufed the fame Gargarifm prefcribed for the Lady *Beaufou*; as alfo anointed hi face often in a day, when it began to dry, with this: ℞ *Carduus water* ℥ii. *Sallet Oil* ℥ifs. *Stir them much together*. This removed the Pits.

## Observ. LXXIX.

THE Lady *Roufe* of *Roufelench*, aged 27, fell into a Quotidian Feaver two days after Child birth; in the very Fit fhe was moft violently afflicted with the Head-ach, as alfo cruel Pain in the Neck, was thus cured: ℞ *Diafcord.* ℥i. *Magift. Perlar. Tinctur. Coral.* ā gr. xii. *Aq. Card. benedict.* ℥ii. It was given two hours before the Fit, it was reiterated before the next Fit, and fo for two days. She was delivered from the Pain of her Neck with this Plafter: ℞ *Caran.* ℥i. *diffol. in Vino Hifpan. Pic. alb.* ℥i. *f. Empl.* Spread it upon Leather, and apply it to the Neck. And thus fhe was delivered from her Pain and Feaver.

## OBSERV. LXXX.

WIlliam Clavel, troubled with a virulent *Go-norrhea*, and extream heat of Urine, ha-ving been under anothers hands for a month with-out Profit, was cured with the following Reme-dies in fifteen days space, being in the Month of *November* : ℞ *Gum. Guaiac. pul.* ℥i. *It was given in Beer.* It gave five stools. Afterwards he took a pint of the following Decoction, morning and night: ℞ *Sarsaparilla* ℥ii. *Hermodactils* ℥iß. *Guai-acum, Liquoris, each* ℥i. *Sena* ℥ij. *Seeds of Anis, Carraway, and Coriander, each* ℥ß. *Boyl them in eight pints of Water, till half be wasted.* After the strained Liquor was taken, Dose ℥iv. there was given the following Electuary: ℞ *Gum. Tragacant.* ℥ß. *dissolve it in sufficient quantity of Plantain water, strain it, add Gum. Guaiacum powdered* ℈ii. *Ter-bentine burnt* ℈i. *mix them. Dose* ℈iß. By the use of the Decoction of *Sarsaparilla* he was very well purged, and delivered altogether from the pains of the Loins, and the heat of Urine in four days, and by the use of the Electuary he was altogether cured of his *Gonorrhea.*

## Observ. LXXXI.

RIchard *Wilmore* of *Norton*, aged 14, vomited black Worms, about an inch and half long, with six feet, and little red heads, when he was to vomit, he was almost dead, but in a little time after he revived, I gave him *Merc. Vitæ.* The next day after his Father brought some wrapped up in Paper, they crept like Earwigs, and were very like, save in colour, he earnestly desired my best advice. I considering the state of the Disease, the strength of the Party, and that for most part he was thus cruelly afflicted every New Moon, unless he devoured abundance of Meat, insomuch that he was ready to tear himself in pieces, I gave the following Remedies : ℞ *Merc. Vitæ* gr. iii. *Conserv. Ros. parum.* This gave seven Vomits, and brought away six Worms, such as I never beheld or read of. The following day I gave this : ℞ *the Emetick Infusion* ℥v. It gave five Vomits, and brought up thrice Worms. The third day I gave the following : ℞ *Spec. Diaturb. cum Rhab.* ʒi. *Pul. Sen. lax.* ʒß. *Aq. Portulac.* ℥ iii. *Syr. Ros. sol.* ℥ii. *Ol. Vitriol. gut.* 8. *Misc.* This purged well, but brought away no Worms. Thus he was delivered, and gave me many thanks. I met him two years after, and asked him whether he had any Erosion of the Stomach, or an Ejection of Worms, and he told me he had never been troubled with it since.

## Observ. LXXXII.

Mrs. *Kempson*, being for many days and nights cruelly tormented with a hollow Tooth, and had used many Medicines, as also Charms, and yet not profited, came running to me, to whom I prescribed the following Water, which being used, removed the Pain, provoking a great deal of spitting, which was very thin : ℞ *Water of Corn Poppy* ʒii. *Oil of Vitriol so much as made it sharp, being well mixed.* There was dipp'd in it Lint, and applied to the hollow Tooth, it was reiterated often. This speedily removed the Tooth-ach, yet Pain in the Head continued, for which was prescribed the following Pills : ℞ *Pil. Coch.* ʒß. *Aurear.* ʒi. *Troch. Agaric.* ℈ß. *cum Aq. Betonic.* f. Pil. 7. These gave ten Stools, and three Vomits, and brought away four great long Worms by stool. And thus was she delivered from her foresaid Symptoms.

## Observ. LXXXIII.

Baron *Compton*, President of *Wales*, being much afflicted with swelling of the Face arising from Rheum, which made his Face very ill-favoured, was thus cured : ℞ *Vnguent. Dialth.* ʒß. *Ol. Chamomel. Viol. Amygd. d.* ā ʒii. *Axung. Gallin.* ʒi. f. *Vnguent.* With this his Face was anointed, and a
double

double Linnen Cloth laid upon it. He took ℥iſs of *Amber Pills*, when he went to bed, by which the Tumor of the Face was removed. There was uſed as a Gargariſm, the following: ℞ *Syrup of red Poppies* ℥ſs. *Water of the ſame* ℥iii. *Oil of Vitriol ſo much as made it ſharp.* And thus he was wholly cured in two days.

## Observ. LXXXIV.

ESquire *Rainsford*, aged 35, being miſerably afflicted with a malign Feaver, Thirſt, Wind, Pain of the Spleen, Tumor of the Stones, and Hypochondriac Melancholy, was cured as followeth: ℞ *Manna* ℥ſs. *Rubarb* ʒi. *This he took in Poſſet-drink.* It gave five Stools without any eaſe, with this he purged himſelf. I being called, applied the followiug Plaſter to the Region of the Spleen: ℞ *Labdan.* ʒii. *Ceræ flav.* ℥i. *Empl. Melilot.* ℥ii. *Emplaſt. ex Saturn. rub.* ℥ſs. Being well freed from the Wind, for the flatuous Tumor in the Scrotum was *firſt* applied a Pultis made of *Rue, Chamomel, Parſly,* boiled in Claret-Wine. This removed, was applied a Plaſter framed *ex Empl. Noſtr. Saturnali, & Melilot. ā part. æqual.* By theſe that Tumor was removed. To mollify the Belly was uſed the following Clyſter: ℞ *Ol. Sem. Lin.* ℥viii. *Ol. Rutæ, & Cham.* ā ℥i. *Diaphœn. & Diacath.* ā ℥ſs. *in Vin. Hiſpan. diſſol. f. Clyſt.* It gave two Stools with Wind. He after complained of his Stomach, for which the third day I gave him this: ℞ *Emetick Infuſion* ℥i. *Aqua Cæleſtis three drops.*

*drops.* It gave fix Vomits. This removed his Illneſs, and want of Appetite. The ſame day he took the Vomit, at the hour of Sleep was given the following: ℞ *Diaſcordium* ʒi. *Syrup of Limons* ʒi. It was given in Poſſet-drink. The next day after the Vomit, he received a Clyſter framed of *Diacatholicon*, red Sugar, and Milk, which gave two Stools, and thus was cured.

## Observ. LXXXV.

MR. *Barns*, aged 36, being long lame of a Canker in the Leg, was thus cured: Firſt, I purged his Body with Pills, after I uſed a Decoction of *Guaiacum*. After I applied the following: ℞ *White Copperas* ʒii. *Bole Armoniack* ʒi, ʒii. *Camphire* ʒiii. *Make a Powder, of which take* ʒi. *which was caſt in hot Smiths Forge-water; after a while it was taken from the Fire, and taken from the ſetling.* With this Water (I may ſay) the ſame Ulcer was waſhed, and a Cloth laid upon it wet in the ſaid Water; with which being almoſt cured, to cicatrize it I uſed the following Plaſter: ℞ *White Lead* ℔ſſ. *Cretæ* ʒiv. *Powder them, and with Hogs greaſe make a Plaſter.* It was applied the thickneſs of ones Finger, and lay on nine days. Before it was applied, the Canker was waſhed with the following: Take *white Copperas, and boil it in water.* After the Plaſter was removed, another was applied for ſix days, a third was applied three days, and always it was waſhed before. By theſe he was cured.

OBSERV.

## Observ. LXXXVI.

GOod-wife *Sheffeild*, a Husbandman's Wife of *Old Stratford*, aged 48, was cruelly afflicted with a Dysentery, and much weakned with the Flux of her Courses ; having been retained for five years before, was cured as followeth: ℞ *Laud. Parac.* gr. vi. *Mithrid.* ℈ſſ. *Conſerve of Roſes* ℥iſſ. *Crocus Martis* ℈i. *mix them.* By this she was freed from her Dysentery, and Flux of Courses ; yet being vexed with thirst, this was given: ℞ *red Poppy Water* ℥iv. *Syrup of Violets* ℥ſſ. *mix them.* And thus she was freed from all.

## Observ. LXXXVII.

THe most Illustrious Lord, Lord *William Compton*, President of *Wales*, being troubled with a Distillation from the Head to the Gums ; he had also want of Appetite, which I cured as followeth : ℞ *Sena well picked from the ſtalks* ℥ſſ. *Rubarb* ℥ii. *Agarick* ℥i. *Cinamon* ℥vi. *Infuſe them all for twelve hours in Borage and Succory Water warm,* of each ℥x. *In the morning they were boiled to the waſting of four ounces, after being ſtrained ſix or ſeven times, and ſweetned with four ounces of Sugar :* He took of this ℥ii when he went to bed, with which in the morning he had a great stinking Stool, that being
the

the 21*th* of *April.* The 22*th* in the morning he took ℥v of the said Decoction, by which he had eight Stools. The 23*th*, ℞ *Pil. Aurear. de Rubarb.* ā ℨi. By which he had thirteen Stools. After the third Stool he began to be better, there being taken Broth. The Body well purged, the following Decoction was administred : ℞ *China sliced* ℨii. *Saffafras cut into thin round pieces* ℥ſs. *Boyl them in eight pound of Water till half be wasted.* Of this he took ℥iv at the least for eight days, every fourth day taking ℈ii of *Pil. Ruffi.* And thus he was cured.

## Observ. LXXXVIII.

MY Lady *Beaufou*, troubled with Indigestion of Meat, and Wind after eating, with Obstructions of the Liver, was cured with the following Prescriptions; ℞ *the Roots of Docks pithed* ℥iv. *Leaves of Agrimony* M v. *The Leaves of Succory with the whole* M ii. *Boil them in three gallons of new Beer, till half a gallon be wasted, strain it, and put Barm to it; after put it in a Vessel, and into it the following Bag :* ℞ *Sarfaparilla, Saffafras, Shavings of Ivory, each* ℥i. *Sena, Polypody, each* ℥v. *Hermodactils* ℥ii. *Liquoris* ℥ſs. *Galangal, Rubarb, each* ℥ſs. *Mecoachan* ℥i. *Cinamon, Cloves, each* ℨi. *Cut them all grosly, and mix them, and put them into a Canvas bag, with a stone in the bottom, being put into the Beer, tye it at the top of the Barrel.* After ten or twelve days she took a draught morning, and at four in the afternoon. By this she was well

purged,

purged, and digested her Meat very well.

## Observ. LXXXIX.

ESq; *Packinton*, as he was riding to *London*, in his Inne was suddenly and miserably afflicted with the Gout in hands and feet, so that he could neither stand nor handle any thing. Being called to him, I thus cured him : Rx *Mallowes with the roots cut small, they were boyled in equal parts of Wine and Vinegar, to the wasting of the third part, to which was added Rye bran after a light boyling.* They were laid to the pained Joints, with which he was well eased in one day, and delivered from the Inflammation by fomenting the parts with *Water of the spawn of Frogs.* After was applied *Emplast. Diachalcit.* The same day I gave ℥ii *Pul. Sen. Montag. cum Hermodact.* gr. xv. He was restored the third day, and rid towards *London.*

## Observ. XC.

WIlson of *Stratford*, aged about 48, was miserably afflicted (for a long time) with Pain of the Stomach, and Indigestion, so that he durst scarce eat ; to whom being called, I cured with only the following Powder : Rx *Sena* ℥vi. *Ginger, Fennel seed, Zedoary, Cummin seed, each* ℥ii. *Cloves, Galangal, Nutmegs, each* ℥i. *Rubarb* ℥ii. *Sugar Candy* ℥vi. *make a Powder.* Dose, the quantity
of

of a Bean spread on a Toast, first moistned in Wine, morning; and at night when he went to bed, the quantity of a Filbert with a little Wine, by which he was cured.　Thus the Author.

I remember that both *Riverius* and *Thonerus* cured each one, cruelly tormented with Pain in the Stomach, with letting blood: the latter cured several others, two with *distilled Oil of Carraway seed, five drops in two spoonfuls of hot Broth*; two other with the like quantity of *Oil of Amber*, given in like manner for some days.

---

## O B S E R V. XCI.

Mrs. *Hanberry* of *Worcester*, aged 30, cruelly tormented with the Cholick, and Pain of the Back, that she could not stand upright, was thus cured: ℞ *Emplast. Nost. Caran.* which was applied to the Loins.　To the Belly was applied the following: ℞ *Featherfue, Rhue, Chamomel, each* M i. *Seeds of Carraway, Cummin, Lovage, Anis, Carrots, each* M ß. *Boil them all in sufficient quantity of Claret Wine, after strain them, but not too hard*: Which apply to the Belly till they be cold; after they are cold, heat them again in the same Wine, and so do twice or thrice, or as need is.　There was given inwardly *Seeds and Tops of red Nettles boyled in White-wine*, I mean the Decoction, it was given in a morning hot.　And thus she was delivered from all her Symptoms.

## Observ. XCII.

THe Sister of my Neighbour *Sheffeild*, much debilitated with too great a Flux of her Courses, to whom I gave of *Alum the weight of two pence in Rose water, for three days, fasting.* Two hours after she took Broth made of Mutton, altered with *Milfoil, and the inner Bark of an Oak.* She drunk her Drink steeled. With which she was cured safely and quickly.

## Observ. XCIII.

MY Lady *Rouse*, being in the eight Month of Child-bearing, was infested with Convulsion of the Mouth, very ill-favoured; she was aged 28. ℞ *Rosemary ashes what quantity pleased, with which was made a Lye with Whitewine, with which the affected part was fomented with four double Linnen.* After to anoint was used the Unguent, with the Oils in the beginning of *Observ.* 36. There was held in her Mouth *Rose water sharpned with Oil of Vitriol.* And so she was cured, as in the foresaid Observation.

## Observ. XCIV.

MR. *Barns* of *Clifford*, after the pulling out of a rotten Tooth, was troubled with a Flux of Blood from the same place, two days after, which I cured in a short space: he having bled twenty four hours, having no Remedy for present at hand; I bid him to hold cold water in his Mouth, and often cast it out, and so he continued till other Medicines were provided: After I used this: ℞ *White Vitriol*, part ii. *Bole Armoniack* pa.i. *Camphire* pa.ß. *Rose water hot, sufficient to make a Lotion*, In which dip a Linnen Cloth often, and apply cold to the place. This was used five hours, and then it ceased. But after a time it bled again, which I stayed with a Spunge dipped in the aforesaid Lotion, and *Crocus Martis* put upon it: And so he was altogether cured.

This Observation of the Author's calls to mind a like Accident, which befell to a Maid in *Cornhil*, near *Popes-head Ally*, *London*, which when other means proved succesless, I stayed, by keeping my Fingers only upon the Mouth of the Artery, removing them several times.

## Observ. XCV.

ONe *Hudson*, a poor Man, labouring of a
swimming in his Head, called *Vertigo*. I
caused ℥x of Blood to be taken from the *Cephalica*,
purged him with *Pil. Aurear. & Cochear.* ā ℈ii.
*Troch. Alband.* gr. viij. *f. Pil.* 7. They gave nine
stools. Lastly he took *Peacock dung dried* ℥i. infused in White-wine for a night, and after strained:
And this he continued from New Moon to Full
Moon, and was cured.

## Observ. XCVI.

THE Lady *Rouse*, being with Child, was miserably troubled with the Mother, and Faintings, and extreme Pain in the Head : First, she
had a Fume of *Horse hoofs burnt*, which restored
her as soon as it was drawn into her Nostrils. Then
she had a Suppository put up, framed of Honey,
and *Pul. Sanctus*, which gave two stools, and
brought away much Wind. She had a Fume of
Odorificks below, and smelt to stinking things.
Her Neck was anointed with *Oil of Spike*, after
with *Unguent. Martiatum.* She having the year
before been troubled with *Tortura-Oris*, and now
much fearing it, in a morning fasting she took the
quantity of a Nutmeg of the following Electuary :
℞ *Species Dianthos. Conserve of Borage*, each ℥i.
*Mithridate,*

*Mithridate, Diacymini,* each ʒii. *Harts-horn prepared* ʒiii. In Broths she took Hartshorn prepared.
To her Navil was applied a Plaster of *Caranna,*
in the middest of which was put *Musk* gr. iii.
Thus she was cured, and at due time was brought
to bed, *March* 16. 1620.

## Observ. XCVII.

Mrs. *Mary Murden,* aged 17, labouring of a
few and ill-coloured Courses, Pain of the
Head, and Redness of the Face after Meat, was
cured as followeth: ℞ *the Roots of Fennel and
Parsly,* each ʒii. *of Sparagus, and Butchers broom,*
each ʒiii. *Calamus Aromaticus* ʒss. *Betony, Mugwort,
Avens, Water-cresses, Hyssop, Rosemary, Penyroyal,
Nettles,* each M ss. *Elicampana roots* ʒss. *Liquoris*
ʒii. *Seeds of Anis, Fennel,* each ʒiii. *Raisins stoned,* M i. *Sena, Polipody,* each ʒiv. *Hermodactils*
ʒii. *Rubarb, Agarick,* each ʒii. *Boyl them all in a
gallon of Water till half be wasted;* in the *strained
Liquor was dissolved Syrup of Mugwort, Au-
gustanus, Succory with Rubarb,* each ʒii. Dose ʒiii
to v. By the use of which she was presently
cured.

## Observ. XCVIII.

Dixwel *Brunt* of *Pillerton*, aged 3 years, had a Tumor of the Navil, out of which broke five long Worms out of a little hole like a Fistula; the Nurse pulled out four dead, but the fifth was somewhat alive, the fore-part not moving, the hinder part stirred, as witnessed the Nurse, Father, Mother, and Maid. The Tumor being hard, I appointed a Plaster of Hony to be applied. The same day was given a Suppository of Honey, but no Worms appeared. The next day was applied a *Cataplasm framed of green Wormwood, beat with the Gall of an Ox, and boyled.* There was given a Suppository. After these the Navil was cured, and he lived.

## Observ. XCIX.

THe Countess of *Northampton*, *March* 6. 1620. fell into that Dropsey called *Anasarca*, with swelling of the Face and Feet, and was cured as followeth: ℞ *the Decoction prescribed for Mrs. Murden, Observ.* 97. *adding of Rubarb* ʒii. *Sena* ʒſ. The Dose given was ʒiv for three days. The first day it gave eight Stools, the second day eighteen, and the third fifteen, without any loss of strength. After she took for five mornings the quantity of a Nut of *Electuar. Diacubeb.* After-

she

she used the following Decoction : ℞ *Guaiacum* ℔i. *Soldanellæ ficcæ* M i. *Cinamon* ℥ii. *Currans* ℥ii. *Boyl them in* ℔ix *of Water till half be wasted ; being kept in a hot place, there were poured in three pints of White-wine.* Of this was taken ℥vi in the morning hot, and ℥iv in the evening, covering her well to sweat. Every morning after she had sweat, an hour after she took of the foresaid Electuary, and every third day she was purged with the following : ℞ *Mecoachan* ℥iß. *Syrup of Roses solutive* ℥i. *Wormwood water simple, and Sack, each* ℥ii. It gave first two Stools, after that two Vomits, after that three Stools, after that one Vomit, at last twelve Stools, after which the Tumor was altogether removed. After which she took *Elect. Chalyb. Crat.* By which she was perfectly cured, and brought to a good colour in twenty days space.

## Observ. C,

Mrs. *Goodman,* aged about 54, was troubled with a Pain of her Head and Stomach, and was cured as followeth : ℞ *Maff. Pil. Mastic.* ℈ii. *Aloes rof.* ℈i. *cum Syr. Rof. fol. f. Pill.* They were taken before supper, and so continued for three days. After upon a fasting Stomach take of the following Electuary the quantity of a Filbert : ℞ *Conferve of red Roses* ℥iv. *Spec. Aromat. Gabr.* ℥iß. *Cloves sliced* ℥i. *Amber-greafe* gr. vi. *Mix them with the Syrup of Citron Pills.* By these she was perfectly cured,

The

# The Second Century.

## OBSERV. I.

MAfter *Penil*, Gentleman to Efq; *Grevil* of *Milcot*, was troubled with Spots and Puſtles, that broke forth in his Hands, which being broke, there dropp'd forth a clear venemous Water, which inflamed and excoriated the Hands greatly. Many Remedies being uſed in vain, the Head alſo was enflamed and burned, and full of ſcales; being aged about 38, was thus freed: ℞ *Agrimony, Scurvygraß, Water-creſſes,* each M i. *Sage, Cichory, Fumitory,* each Mſ. *Elicampana* root ℥ſ. *Polipody of the Oak* ℥iii. *Roots of Saſſafras* ℥ſ. *Boyl them all in* ℔xii *of Water till half be waſted. In the ſtraining add Rubarb, Agarick,* each ℥ſ. *Senz, and Liquoris,* each ℥i. *Seeds of Anis, Carraway, Coriander,* each ʒii. *Cinamon* ʒi. *Boyl them again till* ℔ii *be waſted: to the ſtraining, add Syrup of Roſes ſolutive* ℥ii. *Oil of Vitriol* 12 *drops.* The Doſe was ℥iv, continuing it for four days. Every day he had ſix or ſeven ſtools. To anoint, he uſed this: ℞ *White Ointment camphorated, mixed with the Juyce of Houſleek,* as *much as you pleaſe,* with which the Hands were anointed.

anointed. The Liver Vein was opened to ℥vii. Thus he was quickly cured, and delivered from his Scabs.

---

## Observ. II.

ROgers of *Stratford*, aged 17, did labour of Vomiting, Jaundice, stopping of the Courses, and bleeding at the Nose, on *April* 4. 1621, was cured as followeth : ℞ *Emetick Infusion* ʒvii, *Syrup of Violets, half a spoonful.* This given, gave seven Vomits, and five Stools. After this, ℞ *the Decoction of Sarsaparilla* ℥iii. *the laxative Pouder of Sena* ʒiß. This purged very well. The third day there was given ʒß of the *white of Hens dung in White-wine, with Sugar.* And so she was cured.

---

## Observ. III.

MIs. *Randolph,* aged 55, being vexed with a burning Feaver, in which she fell into the yellow Jaundice; her Urine was red, and Saffron-like, having Pain of her Stomach, with Tumor and hardness, Pain of the Loins, Tumor of the Spleen, and the Dropsy, desired my advice, which was given as followeth : ℞ *Emetick Infusion* ʒvi. *Oxymel of Squils* ℥ii. *Syrup of Violets, half a spoonful: mix them.* It gave three Vomits, and four Stools the next day. ℞ *Elect. è Succ. Ros.*

℥ii.

℥ii. *Diacath.* ℥iſſ. *Diaphænic.* ℥iiſſ. *Rub. elect.* ℈ſſ.
*Spic.* gr. v. *Syr. Cichor. cum Rhab.* ℥ſſ.    *Aq. Cichor.*
℥iii. *f. Hauſt.* It gave eighteen ſtools.   For ordinary Drink,  the quiet days ſhe drunk  the Decoction of *Harts-horn.*    And thus her Feaver left
her,  the Jaundice yet remaining:  for the removing
of which was uſed the following,   ℞ *White-wine*
℔i. *Celendine water* ℥vi. *Saffron* ℥i. *Theriac. An-*
*drom.* ℥iii. *Bezoar.* ℈i. *the Juyce of Goose dung, ſix*
*ſpoonfuls* :  *make a ſweating Drink.* She took it four
days, Doſe ℥iv faſting.   At night ſhe took the
following Electuary : ℞ *red and white Sanders, each*
℥iii. *Currans infuſed in White wine, and after pul-*
*ped,* ℥iv. *Rubarb* ℥i. *Saffron* ℈i. *make an Electuary.*
The Doſe was the quantity of a Nutmeg.   For
the Tumor of the Belly,  ℞ *Unguent. Agrip.* ℥i.
*Arthanitæ* ℈ſſ. *Martiat.* ℥iii. *Ol. Nard. Rut. Scorp.*
ā ℥ii. *Aq. Vitæ parum, Aceti. gut. aliquot. f. Ungu.*
*Ar. Sect.*   Thus ſhe was cured beyond the expectation of her Friends.

---

## Observ. IV.

MR. *Broad* of the *Grange,* vexed with a deſpe-
rate Squincy,  with a burning Feaver, heat
and excoriation of the Tongue, aged 42, left of
all, was thus cured : ℞ *the common Decoction for a*
*Clyſter* ℔i. *Diacath. & Diaphen.* ā ℥i. *make a Clyſter,*
which injected gave four Stools.   He was let blood
under the Tongue,  uſed the following Gargariſm,
℞ *Honey of Roses,  Plantain and Rose water,  each a-*
*like*;  *to which was added a little Oil of Vitriol.*   For a
licking

licking this : ℞ *Syrup of Liquoris and Hyssop,* each ʒii. *Oxymel of Squils* ʒß. *best Honey* ʒi. *mix them.* It was used after the Gargarism.   To the Throat was applied the following : ℞ *Green Wormwood, with Hogs grease, make a Cataplasm.*   I commanded he should be let blood, but he would not, although I told him the danger, which fell out, for he fell into continual burning.   For ordinary drink he had the following : ℞ *Liquoris, Anis seeds, Figs, Raisins of the Sun,* each ʒi. *Boyl them in two quarts of Water till a pint be wasted.*   And so I left him. The next day his Feaver increased, and his Strength abated, and he said he could not possibly live, and I was sent for speedily.   When I came, I found his Life in danger, he could scarce speak, I presently had a Vein cut, and took away ʒx, with which his speech returned, and he said he found great ease.   The same day at the hour of Sleep, I gave him our Julep against the Feaver, and he rested pretty well ; for his ordinary drink, the *Decoction of Harts-horn.*   And thus he was delivered from his Feaver, and danger of Suffocation, and became very well ; for which God be praised, that can only work wonderfully.

## OBSERV. V.

Mrs. *Sadler* laboured of a grievous Cough, with difficulty of breathing, and loathing of Meat, she was aged 60.   ℞ *Oxymel of Squils* ʒii. *Syrup of Violets* ʒß. *Emetick Infusion* ʒii. *mix them.*   This gave seven Vomits, and twelve Stools,

by

by which she found her self much eased : ℞ *Pil. de Succin. Cochear.* ā ℈i. *Rhab. Pul.* ℈ß. *f. Pil. cum ſ. q. Oxymel Scill.* These gave seventeen Stools. The Lincture was this : ℞ *Lohoch. San. & expert. de Pulm. Vulp. Syrup. Liquorit. Tuſſilag.* ā ʒi. *Oxymel. Scill.* ʒii. *f. Linct.* It was taken with a Liquoris stick. She also held in her Mouth one of the following : ℞ *Succ. Liquor.* ʒiiß. *Farin. Amyli,* ʒiß. *Croci, Myrrh.* ā ℈iß. *Opii* gr. iii. *Styrac. Calam.* ʒiii. *Syr. Viol. q.ſ. f. Pil.* 24. One of them was taken when she went to bed. And thus in one week she became well.

## OBSERV. VI.

Mrs. *Brown*, young, of a very good habit of Body, was for three years troubled with a watery Flux of the Belly, especially in the night, having every night no less than six or seven stools. It brought her to extream danger, with great dejection of strength ; she was also much griped, and was sleepless ; who desiring my advice, I prescribed as followeth : ℞ *Pil. de Succin.* ʒß. *Rhab. opt. Pul.* ʒi. *cum Syr. de Stœchad. f. Pil.* 7. By which she had eight stools. ℞ *Sarſaparilla, the Bark of Guaiacum,* each ʒii. *Saſſafras* ʒi. *Guaiacum* ℔ß. *Coriander ſeeds prepared* ʒiii. *Cut and bruiſe them, after infuſe them in Spring water* ℔xiv. *for twenty four hours, after boyl them till half be waſted. At the end of boyling, add Cinamon bruiſed* ʒiv. Of this Decoction strained she took three draughts every day, one in the morning hot, at four a clock

in

the afternoon, and at going to Bed, both cold. Of the *Fæces* was made a second Decoction. Her Head being covered, the following Fume was received: ℞ *Roman Nigella, Storax, Calamus, Benjamin,* each ʒiii. *Mace, Cloves,* each ʒi. *Make a gross Powder for a Fume.* ℞ *Leaves of Sage, Marjoram, Stœchados,* each M ß. *Seeds of Anis, Fennel, Cummin,* each ʒii. *Bayberries bruised* ʒß. *Milij.* ℔i. *Common Salt* ℔ß. *torrefy them all in a Frying-pan, and put them into Bags,* which apply very hot to the Head and Neck: when they are cold, after use the Fume. With these she was cured.

## Observ. VII.

Mrs. *Mary Talbot,* Sister to the Countess, a Catholick, fair, was troubled with the Scurvy, with swelling of the Spleen, erosion of the Gums, livid Spots of the Thighs, Pain of the Loins and Head, with Convulsion and Palsy of the Tongue; her Pulse was small and unequal, her Urine was troubled and thick. The Countess asked me whether there were any hopes of Life? I answered, Yes, if she would be patient and obedient, although her Scurvy was confirmed. I first purged her Body with *Pil. Ruffi,* and *Tart. Vitriol.* She used with her Meat Salt of Scurvy-grass, and in her Broths Salt of Wormwood. All other Drinks being forbid, she drunk the following: ℞ *Garden Scurvy-grass* M iv. *Water-cresses, Brooklime,* each M ii. *Juniper-berries bruised* M i. *Wormwood* M ß. *Boyl them in sufficient quantity of new*

Beer

*Beer to four gallons, of which make Beer.* After fourteen
days she begun to drink it in the morning exercising
an hour after. After she swallowed for the space of
six days the quantity of a Nutmeg of an Electuary,
made of the Flowers of Scurvy-grass; afterward
she began to walk, and at last was very well.

---

## OBSER. VIII.

MR. *Handslop*, aged about 61, afflicted with
the Scurvy, with which there was straitness
of the Breast, difficulty of breathing, Thirst, yellow Jaundice, hard Tumors of the Thighs, being
livid and black, Retraction of the Sinews of the
Ham, so that he could not go without a staff, the
Appetite lost, and troubled with vomiting, his
Pulse was little, scarce perceived to move; the
Urine was various, sometimes thin, the next day
yellow without sediment, the Belly was loose; was
thus cured : ℞ *Elect. Diacath. & Venterflœ. Solenand.*
ā ℥ii. *Confect. Hamech.* ℥ß. *Pul. Senæ, cremor. Tart.* ā
℈ß. *cum Sacch. f. Bol.* This gave six stools, but
being weak, he was ready to faint. The next
day, ℞ *prepared Harts-horn, Shavings of Harts-
horn, each* ℥i. *Powder of Earth-worms* ℥iii. *Conserve of Barberries, a sufficient quantity to make an E-
lectuary.* Dose the quantity of a Filbert. After
take six spoonfuls of the following Wine : ℞
*Wormwood Wine* ℥iv. *the Syrup against the Scurvy by
Forest.* ℥ii. *mix them.* The livid Tumors of the Thigh
I bid to foment twice a day with a Decoction of
Brook-lime made in Beer, it is to be with doubled
Clothes

Cloaths hot, ℞ *New Worms prepared, bruise them in a Mortar with two spoonfuls of Wine, after strain them through a Cloth, to which add a quart of White-wine.* Of this was given three spoonfuls morning, four in the afternoon, and night, and an hour after it ℥ii of the following: ℞ *Syrup. Sceletyrs. For. ℥vi. Vin. Absynth.* ℔ß. For the tumor of the Thighs was used this : ℞ *the Powder of the Flowers of Chamomel, the tops of Wormwood,* each ℨiii. *Briony root and Dazies,* each ℥ß. *Meal of Wheat, Orobus, and Beans,* each ℨiii. *Crums of white Bread* ℔ii. *mix them altogether with Cows milk, or rather Goats milk, and by gentle boyling make a Pulteß.* For ordinary drink he took the following: ℞ *Scurvy-graß* M iv. *Brook-lime, Water-cresses,* each M ii. *Wormwood* Mß. *Juniper berries* ℔ß. *Calamus Aromaticus* ℨiii. *Roots of Sassafras* ℥ii. *Boyl them in five gallons of Beer till a gallon be wasted, after tun them up:* he began to drink of it fourteen days after. For the contraction of the Hams, ℞ *Juyce of Scurvy-graß* ℥i. *Oil of St. Johns-wort, Mullen, Elder,* each ℥ß. *Boyl them to the wasting of the Juyces: being strained, there was added Tacamahacca* ℨiß. *Balsam of Peru* Əiv. *Melt them at a gentle Fire, stirring them ; at the end add a little Wax.* He had this Cordial Electuary : ℞ *Conserv. Cochlear.* ℥ii. *de Absynth. Diasorios Horstii, Bugloss, Caryoph. hortens. Ros. Damas. Rad. Helen. condit.* ā ℥ß. *Lign. Rhod. Calam. Aromat. Rad. Aronis. præp. Spec. Diarrhod. Abbat. Diapler. Confect. Alker.* ā ℨß. *cum Syr. Sceliturb. Forest. f. Elect.* Dose, the quantity of a Filbert. To the hard Tumors was applied this Pulteß : ℞ *Wormwood poudered, a sufficient quantity, beat it with new Eggs, shells and all, to the form of a*

*Cata-*

*Cataplasm, and apply it cold to the Tumors.* This was admirable, and highly praised, it removed the Tumor. For the Contraction of the Ham was used the following : ℞ *Vnguent. Dialthæe, Ol. Chamom. de Castor. & Lumbric.* ā ℨß. *Medul. Crur. Vitul. Ol. Lini,* ā ℨiii. *Succ. Raphan. Cochlear. Nasturt. Aquatic.* ā ℨß. *cum s.q. Ceræ & Ammoniac. sol. f. Lin.* He found much ease by this. ℞ *Vuguent. Dialth.* ℨß. *Lilior. albor. Cham. Aneth.* ā ℨii. *Granor. Juniper. contus.* ℈i. *f. Vnguent.* ℞ *Elect. Chalyb.* ℨvii. *Conserv. Absynth. Cochlear.* ā ℨi. *Misc.* There was given ℨiii fasting, after the use of which he was cured, so that he was both able to ride and walk; and he said himself he was perfectly cured.

## Observ. IX.

THe Lady *Puckering*, being often vexed with the beating of the Heart, was thus cured : ℞ *Diambr. Diamosch. dulc. Aromat. Ros.* ā ℨii. *Confect. Alker.* ℨi. *Diacoralli* ℨi. *Theriac. mag. Mithrid. opt.* ā ℈ii. *Conserv. Bugloß Cochlear.* ( because she had the Scurvy ) ā ℨi. *Misc. f. Elect.* Dose the quantity of a Filbert, by which she was eased.

Mrs. *Iremonger's* waiting Maid was cured as followeth, both of the beating and trembling of the Heart : ℞ *Castor.* ℨi. *Rad. Diptam.* ℨß. ( because her Courses did not flow rightly ) *Diambræ, & Diamosch. dulc. Spec. Aromat. Ros.* ā ℨii. *Theriac. mag. Mithrid. opt.* ā ℈ii. *Conserv. Bugloß* ℨi. *cum Syr. Artem. q. s. f. Opiat.* By that time she had taken half of this she was freed, although she had
been

been afflicted for a long time, and ſaid the Electuary was worth Gold. This hath cured many, for which I have had many hearty thanks.

## OBSERV. X.

THe Lady *Brown* of *Radford*, was oppreſſed with theſe Scorbutic Symptoms, as with binding of the Belly, Melancholy, Watchfulneſs, troubleſom ſleep, Obſtruction of the Courſes, continuing for a year, and by thoſe Obſtructions was miſerably tormented with Wind, and ſwelling of the Belly, eſpecially about the Spleen, when ſhe broke wind, ſhe was eaſed; ſhe felt a continual beating at the mouth of her Stomach, ſo that it might be felt with the hand, as if there had been ſome live thing leaping in her Belly. All theſe happened from the death of her Daughter, dying in Child-bed. By the following Preſcriptions ſhe was cured: ℞ *Scurvy-graſs*, *Water-creſſes*, *Brooklime*, *Maiden-hair*, *Ceterach*, ā M ii. *Scabious*, *Hartstongue*, ā M ſs. *Cordial Flowers*, each p. i. *Liquoris* ſhaved ʒvi. *Sena* ʒi. *Polypod.* ʒvi. *Rubarb*, *the Bark of Cappar roots*, *Bark of Myrobalane Ind.* prepared, ā Ɖiv. *Cream of Tartar* ʒii. *Raiſins ſtoned* ʒx. *Barly* p. i. *Squinanth.* Ɖi. *Boyl them in ſufficient quantity of the Waters of Wormwood*, *Agrimony*, *Fumatory*, *to* ℔i ʒiv. *After they are boyled*, *let them ſtand*, *infuſing for all night: to the ſtraining add Syr. Sceletyrs Foreſt.* ʒii. *Diaſireos*, *Syr. Cichor. cum Rhab.* ā ʒi. *mix them with* ʒii *of Cinnamon water.* *Doſe* ſeven ſpoonfuls, which gave ſix ſtools. After to the Region
of

of the Spleen was applied *Cera de Ammoniac. Foreſt.* This diſcuſſed the Tumor, and eaſed the Pain. Yet although well purged, there remained the Scorbutic Pain of the Belly. After purging, the Urine was troubled, and the ſediment was various. To the Beer uſed for Mr. *Handſlop*, was added M ii of *Fumatory.* The Leeches were applied to the Hemorrhoids. After was uſed the Electuary for Mr. *Handſlop, Obſerv.* 8. *Cent.* 2. framed of *Harts-horn, Ivory, Worms,* &c. By the uſe of theſe ſhe was freed from the Scurvy, and came to enjoy perfect health.

## Observ. XI.

Mrs. *Murden,* aged about 53, troubled with *Vertigo,* Pain in the Head and deafneſs, was by me cured preſently: ℞ *Aloes Roſ.* ℥i. *Rhab. Pul. & Aq. Cinam. aſperſ.* ℈ii. *Agarick, Recent. tro.* ℈i. *Maſtic. Myrrh.* ā ℈ß. *cum Syr. Betonic. f. Pil.* N°. 25. *Doſe Pil.* 5. *hor. ante cœnam.* Theſe were adminiſtred *April* 17. 1626. by the uſe of which there was the deſired effect, and they were much praiſed; they were after given for prevention.

## Observ. XII.

MR. *George Underhil,* aged about 64, was much weakned with an immoderate loofneſs of the Belly, and cruelly tortured with the Cholick, by· eating Herrings, was thus cured : ℞ *Elect. Ventriflu.* ʒvi. *Cremor. Tart.* ℈i. *Rhab. pul.* ℈ii. *cum Sacch. f. Bol.* It gave nine ſtools. At the hour of Sleep he took this : ℞ *Diaſcord.* ʒi. *Aq. Scabioſ.* ℥iij. *Syr. Lim.* ℥i. *Syr. Papav.* ℥ß. *Miſc.* He took the Shavings of *Harts-horn* twice a day. For the Stomach, ℞ *Conſerv. Roſ. rub.* ℥ii. *Spec. Aromat. Roſ. Gab.* ʒi. *Caryophil. inciſ.* ʒß. *Amber-greaſe* gr. iii. *Miſc. cum Syr. Cortic. Citr. q. ſ. f. Elect.* Doſe, the quantity of a Filbert. After Meat he took the following Pouder : ℞ *Sem. Coriand. præp. Sem. Fœnic. Aniſi. Carvi,* ã ℈ii. *Cor. Cer. præpar. Coral. rub. præp. Cinam. Nuc. Moſch.* ã ℈i. *Spec. Aromat. Roſ. lætific. Gal.* ã ℈ß. *Sacch. Roſ. tab. ad pond. omnium, f. Pul. groſ.* He alſo had applied *Scutum noſt. Stomach.* and ſo he was cured.

## Observ. XIII.

MR. *P.* afflicted with a Flux of Semen, and Night-pollutions, by which he was much weakned, was cured as followeth : ℞ *Pulp. of Caſſia* ʒvi. *Pulp of Tamarinds* ʒii. *Red Coral,*

H *Maſtich,*

*Maſtich*, each ℈iſs. *make a Bole with Sugar.* This
purged well. After ℞ *Gum. Arabic. Tragacanth.
Carab. Mum. Bol. Arm. Mandibulæ Lucii,* ā ℈ii. *f.
Pil. & cum Syrup. de Roſ. ſicc. vel Myrtin. f. Pill.
pondere* ℈i. *Cap. prima vice Pil.* iii. afterward one
Pill for many days in a morning. He uſed alſo
*chalybiated Milk.* To the Back were applied Plates
of Lead, on the region of the Reins. And thus
he was cured.

---

## Observ. XIV.

Mrs. *Kenton* of *Northampton*, aged 48. weakned and diſcoloured with the Whites, was
cured as followeth : ℞ *Venice Terbentine* ℥ſs. *diſſolve
it with the Yolk of an Egg, adding of the pureſt Honey* ℥i. *Sugar of Roſes* ℥ii. *White-wine* ℥vi. *mix
them : of which take every day* ℥i. She drank her
ordinary Drink warm, which was a Decoction of
Barly, with Liquoris and Mallows. After
the former Potion, ſhe uſed this Bole : ℞ *Olibanum, Bole Armoniack, and ſealed Earth,* of each
℥ſs. *make them into a very fine Pouder, and with two
Whites of new-laid Eggs make a Bole.* This is an
admirable Secret, it is to be uſed for divers days,
ſix hours before Meat. She alſo had this Drink :
℞ *Guaiacum chips* ℔i. *of its Bark bruiſed* ℥iv. *infuſe
them eight days in Spring water* ℔viii. *with a drachm
of Oil of Sulphur, in Horſe dung, being in a Glaſs
Veſſel well ſtopt with Wax and Brimſtone ; after ſtrain
it : in the ſtrained Liquor put a freſh quantity of the
Guaiacum,* &c. *and infuſe it as before ; after three*
days

*days strain it, and after sweeten and aromatize it to
the Patients palat.* The Dose is two, three, or
four ounces, according to the strength and nature
of the sick. Two ounces of this doth more than
℔ß of the ordinary Decoction. It is safe in the
*Spleen, Picrocholis,* and *Jaundice* confirmed; cures
the *Dropsy, Apoplexy, French Pox,* and other grievous Diseases of the Head. Of the *Fæces* may
be made a second Decoction, which may be used
with Meat, instead of Drink. To the Back was
applied, ℞ *Empl. contra Rupt. & pro Matrice,* ā
ℨi. *Ungu. Comit.* ℥ii. *Mastich. Sang. Drac. & Coral.
alb.* ā ℥ii. *Ros. rub.* p. i. *Rad. Bistort. Musc. Querc.*
ā ℨii. *Ter. sigill.* ℨiß. *Malax. omnia simul cum Ol.
Myrtil. f. Emplast.* Of this spread so much upon
Leather as may be for a Plaster for the Back, and
*Os sacrum,* and another to the lower Belly, which
are to be continued on betwixt the time of the
Courses, and then removed. By these she was cured.

## Observ. XV.

Mrs. *Delaberr,* of *Southam* near *Glocester,* having been long sick with loathing of her
Meat, insomuch that no sooner she had eaten, but
it came up, her Urine often changing; and although she was pretty well whilst in Bed, yet
when she rose she was troubled with swooning:
having also the Scurvy, was cured as followeth:
℞ *Pil. Hier. cum Agarick, Ruffi,* ā ℈ii. *de Succin.
aggregat. Crem. Tart.* ā ℈iß. *Oxymel scil.* q. s. f. *Pil.*
15. *deaurent.* She took two at a night, and three

in the morning, every third day, she being well
purged.    To the Spleen was applied this Plaster,
℞ *Cerat. de Ammoniac. Foreſt.* ℥i. *Emplaſt. de Me-*
*lilot.* ℥ſſ. *Miſc.*    Spread it upon Leather,  and a
red Sarcenet upon it.    Thoſe days ſhe purged not,
ſhe took of this Electuary : ℞ *Conſerve of Damask*
*Roſes* ℥i. *Conſerve of Scurvy-graſs* ℨiii.  *Conſerve of*
*Bugloſs,* ℨii. *Spec. plereſarch.* ℨſſ.   *Cream of Tartar,*
*prepared Steel, each* ℈ii.  *Wake-robbin roots prepared*
℈i. *Confect. Alkerm.* ℥i. *with ſufficient quantity of*
*Sugar make a ſoft Electuary.*   Doſe,  in the evening
the quantity of a Bean, and in the morning before
ſhe roſe, the quantity of a Nutmeg, and ſo for
two days,  the third ſhe purged, by which ſhe
came to be ſo much better, as that to walk and
ride, and then would to the *Bath,*  where ſhe uſed
the following Decoction, when ſhe came out of the
Bath, and went to bed and ſwet : ℞ *Chips of*
*Guaiacum* ℥iii. *Bark of the ſame* ℥ii, *Saſſafras* ℥i.
*China cut thin* ℥ſſ. *Shavings of Ivory* ℨiii. *Liquo-*
*ris* ℥i. *Agrimony, Carduus benedictus, Scurvy graſs,*
*Water-creſſes, Brook-lime, each* M ſſ. *the tops of Fu-*
*mitory, Flowers of Bugloſs, Stæchados, Roſemary*
*flowers, each* p. i. *Nutmegs, Cinamon, each* ℨii. *In-*
*fuſe them upon the Fire for twelve hours in ſix quarts*
*of Water, after boyl them to the half, and then ſtrain*
*it, and being ſweetned with Sugar,* Doſe *was* ℥iv.
It was uſed in the morning every fourth day, purging with theſe Pills: ℞ *Pil. Hier. cum Agar. Ruffi.*
ã ℈ii. with which being well purged, ſhe uſed no
other Phyſick, but went home very well.


OBSERV.

## Observ. XVI.

JAcob Ballard, aged 60, being cruelly vexed with a bloody Flux, and spumous, and sometimes chylous, with a *Tenesmus* for three months, was cured as followeth : ℞ *Ordinary Barly* p. i. *the Seeds of Line and Fenugreek beaten, each* ℥i. *Flowers of Chamomel, Melilot, each* p. i. *Rie bran* p. ii. *make a Decoction of all in Water to* ℔ß. *In the straining dissolve the Yolks of two Eggs, Hony of Roses* ℥iii. *and red Sugar* ℥ii. *mix them, and make a Clyster,* which was injected. After which he took this Potion at night : ℞ *Philon Pers.* ℈ii. *Aq. Plantag.* ℥iii. *Syr. Cydonior.* ℥i. *f. Pot.* This profited admirably, for he slept well, his Pain was eased, and his Flux was stayed. After was used an Astringent Clyster to stay the Flux, and heal the Ulcer : ℞ *the tops of Briars, Plantain, Purslain, Coriander seeds prepared, Cummin a little torrefied and beaten, each* ℥i. *Starch torrefied* ℥ß. *Galls, Cypresse-Nuts beaten grosly, each* iv. *Bran* p. ii. *Boyl them in steeled Water to* ℔i. *To the Straining add Goats Sewet* ℥i. *prepared Bole Armoniack* ℨii. *Juyce of Plantain* ℥iv. *Mucilage of Tragacanth* ℥i. *Honey of Roses* ℥ii. *mix them for a Clyster.* To the Belly was applied the following Plaster : ℞ *Mass. Empl. contra Ruptur.* ℥iii. *Empl. Diaphœnic.* ℥ii. *Mastich, Olibanum, Coriand. præp. Bol. Arm. præp. Sang. Drac.* ā ℈iv. *Lap. Hæmatit.* ℨii. *Succ. Plantag.* ℥iv. *Vin. rub. crass.* ℥iii. *Ol. Myrtil. & Cydonior.* ā ℥ii. *Misc. cum Cer. & Terebin.* with your hands moistned with red

Wine,

Wine, and make Rolls, and spread Plasters upon
Leather, which apply to the Belly. For *Tenesmus*,
℞ best *Myrrh*, *Saffron*, *Storax*, *Calamint*, each ℨß.
*Opium* Əi. *Bdellium*, *Aloes*, each gr. xviii. *Wax
liquified*, *sufficient to make a Suppository*; one of
which put into the Fundament. That night the
former Potion of *Philon Pers.* was reiterated, and
after that he took the following astringent Electuary: ℞ *Bole Armoniack præp.* Əiv. *Pearls*, *red Coral*,
each Əii *Pouder of Rose seeds*, *Spec. Diarrhod. Abbat.* ā ℨß. *Conserve of Cumfrey*, *Citron Pills candied*,
each ℨi. *with Sugar dissolved in Rosewater make an
Electuary.* Dose ℨii in the morning, and so much
before supper. He also before meals took some
grains of the best *Olibanum*, his Diet was spare and
drying. And thus he was cured.

Observe well, 1. *If there be a good Digestion,
and not the like separation, then there is a Dysentery.*
2. *If there be Separation and not Digestion, then it is
Lientery.* 3. *If neither Separation, nor Digestion,
there is present a Diarrhea. If the matter in the Stomach be putrified, then there is a Flux of the Belly, with
various colour.*

# OBSERV. XVII.

M rs. *Layton*, born of a noble Stock, long laboured of a Scorbutic Epilepsy, always at
her first falling into it, it was with a Feaver, and
convulsive motions, the rest of the Signs in *Eu-
gal*, *fol.* 86. and *Senertus*, *fol.* 60. In the Fit she
was most miserably vexed with cold horror, and
concussi-

concuſſion of the Members, for half an hour, ſo
that the whole Bed ſhook ; the Fit laſted ten hours,
ſhe not knowing nor feeling any pain. After in the
ſame day ſhe laboured of another Fit for ſix hours,
and yet was delivered from it beyond the expectation of the By-ſtanders. After ſhe fell aſleep, a-
nother Fit ſhe had, wherein ſhe ſaid ſhe had cut-
ting pain. She was alſo afflicted with a Jaundice,
with diminution of the Courſes. I cured her
with the Preſcriptions following : ℞ *Elect. Ventri-*
*flu.* ℥vi. *Crem. Tart.* Ɔi. *Rhab. pul.* Ɔii. *f. Bol.* It
gave ſix ſtools. For the Jaundice, which was
filthy ſhe took this : ℞ *Mithridate* ℥i. *prepared*
*Harts-horn* Ɔii. *Pouder of Worms* ℥ii. *Conſerve of*
*Barberries* ℥i. *mix them,* for two mornings ; by
which ſhe was pretty well delivered from the Jaundice. Afterward I thus purged her : ℞ *Pil. fætid.*
*Alephang. Coch.* ā Ɔi. *Agar. Troch.* Ɔſſ. *Caſtor.*
gr. vi. *cum Syr. de Stæchad. q. ſ. f. Pil.* 7. She took
three of them at night , going to bed, and four
in the morning. After I uſed the following neezing Pouder : ℞ *Nuc. Moſch. Rad. Pæon.* ā ℥ſſ. *El-*
*leb. Nig.* Ɔi. *Pyrethr. Piper. alb.* ā Ɔſſ. *Miſc. f. Pul.*
a Portion of which was blown into the Noſtrils.
Whilſt the time of the Fits was expected, there
was given every morning ℥ii of this Opiat : ℞
*Conſerve of Scurvy-graſs* ℥ii. ( which I always uſed
to mix with other Medicines in Scorbutic Affects
to infringe the Ill of the Diſeaſe ) *Dianthos, Con-*
*ſerve of Betony,* each ℥i. *Old Mithridate, Venice*
*Treacle,* each ℥i. *Miſſeltoe of the Oak, Shavings of*
*Harts-horn, Piony ſeeds, Man's ſcull pulverized,* each
Ɔiv. *mix them.* It is to be taken of it ſelf, or with
Betony water, to which is added Oil of Vitriol.

By thefe fhe was fully delivered from her Fits for many years.

## Observ. XVIII.

*L*Ydia *Trap*, the Daughter of Mr. *Trap*, aged about two years, labouring of a burning Feaver, want of fenfe and motion in fome parts, and the Worms, infomuch that Death was daily expected, by me through God's bleffing was thus reftored: ℞ *prepared Harts-horn* ʒiii. *Spring water* ℔i. *Boyl them to the half; after was added a little Rofe water, an ounce of Syrup of Limons, a fpoonful of Sugar, and fo much Oil of Vitriol as made it fharpifh.* She took this for her drink, forbearing all other. To the region of the Heart was applied this: ℞ *Old Treacle* ʒi. *Pouder of Piony root* ʒſs. *make a Plafter.* About her Neck fhe wore round flices of the fame Root; and the Pouder of the fame Root was ftrewed upon her Head; her Neck was anointed with the Oil of *Amber and Saffafras, each* ʒſs. *Spirit of Rofemary* vi *drops.* To her Navil was applied this Plafter: ℞ *Aloes* ʒſs. *Pil. fine quib.* ℈i. *Worms* ℈i. *Myrrh.* ℈i. *with Oxgall make a Plafter.* To extinguifh thirft, and provoke ftools, was given the following: ℞ *Syrup of Rofes folutive* ʒi. *boyled Water* ʒii. *Oil of Vitriol, fufficient to make it fharpifh.* For the Stomach was ufed *Ung. pectorale.* By thefe in a few days fhe became well.

## Observ. XIX.

THE Lady *Underhil,* aged 53, was troubled
with Pain of the Joynts in the hands, and
when she rubbed one with another, there arose
a flatuous Tumor; she had also on a sudden a
red Face, her Voice was also much lost, so that
when she spake, the By-standers could not un-
derstand her; she felt as it were the sense of
biting of Ants in many parts of the Body, and
these from the Scurvy. ℞ *Sarsaparilla* ℥ iv.
*Saffafras* ℥i. *Agrimony, Scurvy grass, Water-cresses,
Brook-lime, each* M i. *Bark of Capar root, Myrobalans of India, each* ℈iv. *Polypody of the Oak, and
Liquoris, each* ℥ß. *Raisins stoned* ℥x. *Infuse them in
six pints of Water for a night, after boil them to the
half: to the straining, add Sena* ℥i. *Rubarb* ℥i.
*give them two or three walms, adding Syrup against
the Scurvy by* Forestus ℥iv. *mix them.* The Dose
was six or eight spoonfuls, which purged her
well, and she became very well, and so highly
praised the Apozeme, as if it wrought by inchantment.

## Observ. XX.

ESquire *Underhil*, aged 50, was miserably tormented with the running Gout, which pained all the Joynts of his Body, as Ancles, Knees, Arms, Neck, &c. Which was by the ensuing Medicines cured in a few days. ℞ *the Pouder of the Root Sarsaparilla, Sena, each* ℥vi. *Cream of Tartar* ℥iii. *mix them.* The Dose was from ℈ii to iv. which gave him three or four stools a day. The Body being well purged, the following Bath was used : ℞ *Salt* ℔i. *Quick Brimstone* ℥iß. *Alum* ℔ß *Bay berries* ℥iv. *Boyl them in sufficient quantity of Water :* he sat in it daily up to the knees morning and evening. This delivered him not only from the Pain in his Feet, but from that callous hardness under his Toes. For preservation in the month of *October* was used the following : ℞ *Caryocost.* ℥iiß. *Elect. de Tamarind.* ℥ß. *Cryst. Tart.* ℈i. *f. Bol. cum Sacch.* After was used *Pil. Podagr. Plater.* As ℞ *Hermodactils skinned* ℥iß. *Aloes, Turbith, Mecoachan, Rubarb, yellow Mirobalans, also Chebuls, Mastich, each* ℥i. *Roots of round Birthwort* ℈i. *St. Johns-wort, Seed also of Cummin and Ginger, each* ℥ß. *Salt gem.* ℈ß. *with the Juyce of Ground-pine make Pills, adding Diagrid.* ℥ß. *Dose,* sometimes every month was taken ℥i. and so he was delivered from that Pain begun, but yet wholly it was removed by the former Pouder: to which was added *Betony* ℥ß. *Sugar of Roses* ℥i. And thus for

many

many years he was cured, and it never returned again.

## O B S E R V. XXI.

MR. *Izod*, being upon light motion troubled with piffing blood, was thus cured: ℞ *a Mass of Terbentine Pills with Rubarb* ʒii. *clear Terbentine* ʒi. *with Liquoris pouder make fifteen Pills, which was given in a spoon with Syrup of French-Mallowes,* He used the following Tablets: ℞ *Troches of Winter-cherries with Opium* ʒſſ. *Roots of Comfrey, Terbentine hard boiled,* each ʒi. *Sugar* ʒiiſſ. *with the infusion of Gum Tragacanth, make Tablets weighing* Əii. He often drank *Cream of Barly,* as alſo Milk boiled with Eggs, and ſo became well.

## O B S E R V. XXII.

THe Lady *Smith* ( a Roman Catholick) being greatly afflicted with Wind of the Stomach, after it much more tormented her by taking a ſtrong Infuſion of *Stibium* from an Emperick, ſo that for a month together ſhe was forced to take 3 or 4 draughts of Broth in a night, for expelling the Wind, otherwiſe ſhe could not ſleep, nor reſt in Bed for Pain. She was about the age of 27. ℞ *Pil. Hier. cum Agaric. de Succin. Ruſſ.* ã Əi. *f. Pil. ſex, deaur.* She took three of them
when

when she went to bed. In the morning she took
the quantity of a Nutmeg of the following Electuary : ℞ *Elect. Chalyb. Craton.* ℥iß. *Elect. Ventriflu.* ℥ß. *Misc.* After she took it she used exercise : ℞ *Sem. Coriand. præp. Fænicul. de Anisi. Carvi.* ā ℥iß. *C. C. præp. Coral. Rub. præp. Cinamom.
Nuc. Mosch.* ā ℨß. *Spec. Aromat. Rof. Lætific. Gal.
Diamosch. dulc.* ā Ɔß. *Sacch. ad pond. omnium f.
Tragea.* This she took after Meals. The 24*th*
of *October* she sent to me for the same Pouder,
which was for the Countess of *Leicester,* who took
it, and for it returned me many thanks. And by
these was she delivered from those bitter Tor-
ments, and they did not return.

## Observ. XXIII.

Mrs. *Winter,* Widow, (Roman Catholick) aged
28, was troubled with the Flux of the
Belly, Inflammation of the Reins, with great
abundance of Urine, even almost to fainting ; she
was also troubled with the Stone and Scurvy
confirmed, and was much weakned, was thus
cured : ℞ *the best Mithridate* Ɔii. *Diascordium* ℨß.
*Confectio Alkerm.* Ɔi. *Harts-horn prepared* Ɔß. *Bezoar stone* gr. vi. *Manus Christi perlat.* ℨi. *Magistral
of Pearl* gr. iv. *Coral prepared* Ɔß. *El. Lætific.
Gal.* ℨi. *Mix them with Syrup of Corn-Poppy, to
make an Electuary.* She took half of it upon a
knifes point, with which the Flux was bridled,
with great ease and chearfulness of mind : at bed-
time she took the other half, and rested that
night.

night. For drink she had the Decoction of *Harts-horn.* To the mouth of the Stomach was applied this: ℞ *Spec. Aromat. Rof. Cab.* ℥ß. *Labdan.* ℥ß. *Mithridat. opt. Theriac. Andromac.* ā ℥i. *Cer. flav.* ℥ii. *diſſol. Ol. Stomach. Craton. f. L. A. Empl.* By theſe the Belly being bound, she took the following Pills: ℞ *Pil. Ruffi. de Succin.* ā ℥i. *f. Pil.* N°. 10. She took three at bed-time. After the former Cordial was repeated. After I gave the following Potion: ℞ *Aq. Antiſcorbut. Doncrel.* ℥iv. *Splenetica ejuſdem* ℥ii. *Syr. Sceletyrb. Foreſt.* ℥iii. *Miſc.* Sh took eight ſpoonfuls of it in mornings. Afterward she uſed the following Electuary: ℞ *Conſerve of Bugloſs, of Clove Gilly flowers, Dianthos,* each ℥i. *Conſerve of Scurvy-graſs* ℥ii. *Elicampana root candied* ℥iii. *Spec. Diarrhod. Abbat.* ℥i. *Diapleresarchont* ℥ß. *Confectio Alkermes* ℈ii. *with the Syrup againſt the Scurvy by* Foreſt. *make an Electuary.* The Doſe was the quantity of a Filbert, faſting. The *Decoction of Harts-horn* was repeated. And ſo she was cured, and freed from all her Symptoms.

---

## Observ. XXIV.

THe Lady *Jenkinſon* (fair, pious, chaſt,) was vexed with Pain of the Head, and a light Vertigo, Pain of the Mouth, of the Stomach and Sides, fainting, watching, heats in hands and feet, languiſhing without cauſe, the Fleſh of the Gums looſe, and often bleeding, all being a diſco-

difcovery of the Scurvy. Ŗ *Pil. Hier. cum Aga-*
*ric. Ruffi.* ã Ʒi. *Alephang.* Ͽii. *cum Aq. Betonic. f.*
*Pil.* There was added *Diatartari.* Ͽii. and it
made fifteen Pills. She took three of them when
fhe went to bed. In the morning fhe took a
fmall draught of the following: Ŗ *Roots of Oris,*
*Elder bark, of Danewort, and of Capers, Ta-*
*maris, Succory, Squich grafs, Fennel, Sparagus,*
*Madder, each* Ʒ ß. *Gentian.* Ʒ ii. *Wormwood* M i.
*Soldanella, Mugwort, Agrimony. white Horehound,*
each M ß. *Tops of Centaury* Ʒ iiß. *the Cordial Flow-*
*ers, each* Ʒ iß. *Calamus Aromaticus* Ʒ ii. *Liquoris*
Ʒ i. *Sena* Ʒ ii. *Agaric.* Ʒ ß. *Mechoac.* Ʒ iii. *prepared*
*Steel* Ʒ ß. *Cream of Tartar* Ʒ i. *Rubarb* Ʒ iii. *Ginger*
Ʒ i. *Cinamon* Ʒ ß. *Anis feeds* Ʒ ii. *Infufe them for*
*three days in four pints of White-wine in* Bal. Mar.
*well ftopped up in a double Veffel, after boyl them at a*
*gentle Fire for an hour, the Veffel being ftill fhut.*
Of this when cold take Ʒ iv. *Syrup againft the*
*Scurvy by* Foreftus Ʒ i. For three mornings after
fhe took the Beer againft the Scurvy, prefcribed
*Obferv. 7.* of this Century; adding to the Ingredients, of *Saffafras* Ʒ ß. *Sarfaparilla* Ʒ ii. *Betony,*
*Agrimony, Fumatory, each* M i. Whilft it was ready, fhe took the following: Ŗ *Conferve of Scurvy-*
*grafs* Ʒ ii. *of Wormwood, Diaferios, of Buglofs,*
*Clove Gilly flowers, Damask Rofes, Elicampana root*
*candied, each* Ʒ ß. *Wood of Rhodium, Calamus Aro-*
*maticus, Wake robbin root prepared, Spec. Diarrhod.*
*Abbat. Diaplerefar. Confectio Alkermes, each* Ʒ iß.
*with* Foreftus's *Syrup againft the Scurvy, fo much as*
*will make an Electuary, cover it with a leaf of Gold.*
After the taking of the quantity of a Nutmeg of
this, fhe drank of the following; Ŗ *the Water*
*againft*

*against* the *Scurvy* ℥iii. *that against the Spleen* ℥ii. *the foresaid Syrup of* Forestus ℥iii. Dose eight spoonfuls. For her Catarrh there was used the following Pouder for the Coronal Suture: ℞ *Ma-stich, Myrrh, Amber, Cloves, Sandarac, Wood of Aloes, red Roses, each* ℥i. *mix them, and make a Pouder.* As there was need she was thus purged, ℞ *Pil. Ruffi. Alephang. Diatartari* ā ℈i. *Pil. Hier. cum Agaric.* ℈ii. *Aq. Antiscorb. q. s. f. Pil. N. 6.* There was three given at Bed time. The fifth of *December* she was cruelly tormented with the Tooth-ach, ℞ *Scurvy grass water* ℥vi. *Red Rose water, and of Plantain, each* ℥iii. *Honey of Roses, Honey of Mulberry simple, each* ℥i. *Spirit of Vitriol sufficient to make all tart.* Of this she took in her Mouth, which delivered her from the Tooth-ach, and other Symptoms. And by these she was cured.

---

## OBSERV. XXV.

BUtler of *Stratford,* from gentle motion of his Body, was much troubled with pissing blood, which came in abundance, with Pain in the Kidneys; his Urine was so hot, that it very much tormented him, especially about the Prepuce, which I thus cured: First he drank of the De-coction of *Sarsaparilla* for eight days. After he drunk *Tormentil in Wine.* To his Back were applied Plates of Lead, full of holes, moistned with Vinegar; it was often changed, and so in the

the space of eight days he was much amended,
and after cured.

---

## O B S E R V. XXVI.

Mrs. *Richardson* ( a Roman Catholick ) was
troubled with Wind in the Womb, so
that when she went to make water, the Womb
sent forth the Wind, as if one had broke wind
backward ; she also had the Scurvy, swooning, Pain
of the Head, over-flowing of her Courses, also
abundance of Whites. She was also troubled
with much heat in her Loins, weakness of her
whole Body, she could eat well, but could not
endure Physick or the Light. She was thus
cured, First she had a Restorative made of a
Leg of Veal, a Cock, Harts horn shaved, and
*China*, she took of it every morning, first drinking our Milk water with *Manus Christi perlatæ*.
To stay the Flux was used the following, ℞ *Wa-*
*ter of Milk* ℥iii. *Spawn-Frog water two spoonfuls,*
*Manus Christi perlat. Confect. Alkerm.* each ℈ij.
To her Back were applied Plates of Lead perforated and moistned in Vinegar. To the region
of the Womb was applied *Emplast. pro Matrice.*
℞ *Harts horn burnt* ℈i. *Confectio Alkermes* ℈ß.
*Bezoar stone* gr. iii. *Scabious water* ℥ii. *Syrup of*
*Limons* ℥ß. *mix them.* It was given whilst she
was cold, for she had an Erratic Feaver. ℞ *Snail*
*water of my preparation, of Spawn Frog water,* each
℥iv. *Confectio Alkermes* ℈ii. *Manus Christi perlatæ*
℥ß.

℥ß. *Water againſt the Scurvy* ℥vi. *againſt the Spleen* ℥ii. *mix them.* This was reiterated, and to it added ℥iß of *Syrup. Lætiſic. Rod. à Fonſe.* By the uſe of this ſhe gained ſtrength very much, and ſaid it was as good as *Aurum potabile,* and would never be without it. And thus ſhe was cured wholly.

## OBSER. XXVII.

Mrs. *Peerſe* of *Aufon,* (Roman Catholick) aged about 28, was vexed with a fruitleſs endeavour to vomit, Melancholy, Tumor of the Feet at night, Weakneſs of the whole Body, a Scorbutic daily Feaver, with light horror, Pain of the Spleen and of various Joints of the Body, her Urine was like clear Water. She was cured as followeth : ℞ *Elect. de Tamarind.* ℥ß. *Syr. Dyaſerios* ℥i. *Oxymel. Noſt.* ℥ß. *Aq. Bugloſs* ℥ii. *Ol. Vitriol.* gut. vi. *Miſc.* This gave ſix ſtools. The following day the Urine was filthy, and ſhe took the ſaid Potion, only there was added *Spec. Arom. Roſ.* ℈i. and ℥ii taken off from the Electuary. At the hour of ſleep was exhibited the following : ℞ *Bezoar.* gr. iii. *Laudanum Paracelſi* gr. ii. *Confectio Alkermes* ℈ß. She reſted quietly. The next day there was given this : ℞ *Syrup of Poppies* ℥i. *Scabious water* ℥iß. *Bezoar.* gr. iv. *Roſewater a little,* and *Spirit of Vitriol ſufficient.* After ſhe uſed the Chalybiated Wine, preſcribed *Obſerv.* 24 of this Century. To which was added, *Syrup. Schelet: Foreſt.* ℞ of the *Wine* ℥vi. of the

I                                                             *Syrup*

Syrup ℥iv. *Water against the Scurvy* ℥ii. *against the Spleen* ℥ii. *Syr. Latif.* ℥iii. *mix them.* ℞ *burnt Hartshorn* ℈i. *Confect. Alker.* ℈ii. *Magist. of Pearl, Tinct. of Coral,* each gr. vi. *Man. Christi perlat.* ℨß. *Bezoar,* gr. vi. *Conserve of Scurvy-grass, sufficient. Make a soft Electuary, adding Spec. Pleresarchon.* By these she was freed from her Symptoms. From her Melancholy she fell into the Mother : ℞ *Castor* ℨi. *Facul. Brion.* ℈ß. *cum Aq. Historic. f. Pil.* N° 5. They were given at night. To the Navil was applied *Emplast. e Caranna, cum Mosc.* She drew into her Nose the Fume of *Assa fœtida.* By these she was well eased. After she was purged thus : ℞ *Pil. Ruffi. Spec. Hier. simpl.* ā ℈iß. *Castor* ℈i. *Facul. Brion.* ℈ß. *cum Aq. Hist. q. s. f. Pil.* 5. She took them at night. And thus she was recovered.

## Observ. XXVIII.

Alice Collins, Servant to my Lady *Puckering,* aged about 24, was tormented with the Mother, Obstruction of her Courses, and at the end of her Fit she shed tears. Her Urine was like Spring water. For the removing of the Disease and Symptoms, I prescribed the following : ℞ *Briony roots* ℥ß. *Sena* ℥ß. *Ginger* ℨß. *Cinamon* ℨi. *Sugar* ℨvi. *They were infused for a night in a pint and half of Whey, and in the morning boyled a little, and then strained ;* to which was added the compound Syrup of *Mugwort* ℥ii. Of this she drank for some days in a morning ℥v. hot ; by which she was well purged and cured.

Observ.

## Observ. XXIX.

HEster *Sylvester*, Daughter to Mrs. *Smith* (now
*Marit*) of *Burford*, being grievously troubled
with the Worms, was cured twice with the following Pouder: ℞ *Coraline, Worm seed, each* ℥i.
*white Dictamny, Bistort, Tormentil, each* ℥ſs. *make
them all into a fine Pouder, which besprinkle with the
sharpest Wine Vinegar, and after dry it in the shade.*
Dose from ℈ſs to ℈iii. (but she took a drachm)
according to the age of the Patient, and strength
of the Disease. It is to be given either in Wine,
Purslain water, or the Pulp of a rosted Apple.

## Observ. XXX.

LInes of *Stratford*, aged 53, in 1630, was
troubled with a Timpany, her Belly being
much swelled, so that she could scarce go, with
hoarsness of her Voice, and loathing of Meat,
insomuch that she was left by her Friends as hope-
less, yet by God's blessing she was cured as followeth: ℞ *Roots of Oris, and Assarabacca, each*
℥ii. *Pellitory of Spain, Elicampana, and of Brier,
also the Bark of the Roots of Spurge, each* ℥iii. *Origanum, Calamints, each* p. i. *Soldanella* ℥ſs. *Me-
choachan* ℥iii. *Anis seeds, Bay berries, each* ℥ſs. *boyl
them altogether in B. M. in a quart of White-wine
(the Vessel being well stopp'd) for four hours; after*
I 2 *being*

*being strained, it was sweetned with Sugar.* Of this was drunk ℥vi morning and evening. After evacuation was made with *Pil. Soldanellæ,* thus made: ℞ *the tops of Soldanella* ℈ii. *Cinamon* ℈i. *Pil. aggregativa* ℨi. *Troch. Alhand.* ℈ß. *Elaterii* gr. iv. *with the Juyce of Oris roots make Pills,* 5 *of* ℨi. There were three taken about midnight; as there was need they were reiterated. To strengthen the Stomach, and the rest of the Bowels, was used the following Electuary: ℞ *the Juyce of Oris roots* ℨiij. *Galangal, Cinamon, each* ℨii. *Cloves, Mace, each* ℨi. *Zedoary* ℈ii. *Soldanella* ℥ß. *Pouder them to be poudered, and with Honey purified make an Electuary.* Dose, the quantity of a Nutmeg. After meals I appointed the following Pouder, to free the Stomach from crudities, to gently heat it, to help Concoction, and discuss Wind: ℞ *Coriander seeds prepared* ℥ß. *of Fennel and Anis, each* ℨii. *Carawaies* ℨi. *Cinamon* ℨii. *Roots of true Acorus, Galangal, Citron Pills dried, each* ℥i. *red Roses* ℨß. *Sugar, the weight of all; make a Pouder.* Dose, half a spoonful. Thus she was cured, *Jan.* 4. 1630.

---

## OBSERV. XXXI.

Mrs. *Baker* of *Stratford,* aged 38, had much pain in her Loins, and was cruelly tormented with a desire to piss, yet little Urine came, and that while she was troubled with the Mother, Melancholy, and the Scurvy was feared. To whom the following was used with desired success:
℞

℞ *Syr. Lætific. Rodor. à Fonseca* ʒii. *Diatartar. ejusdem* ʒi. *Aq. Buglos.* ʒ iii. *Misc.* It gave six stools. After ℞ *Pil. Ruffi.* Ɔi. *Hier. cum Agaric.* Ɔi. *Pil. fætid.* Ɔi. *Caster* Ɔß. *cum Aq. Artemis. f. Pil.* N° 7. *deaurent.* These gave seven stools. ℞ *Lign. Saffafr. incis.* ʒiß. *Cinam. opt.* ʒi. *infund. in Aq fontan.* ʒxiv. *per hor.* xij. *deinde bull. ad dimid. adde Sacch. alb.* xii. *bul. ad confist. Syr. cui adde Dianth. Confer. Bugloss,* ā ʒvi. *Flor. Caryoph.* ʒß. *Rad. Enul. Cam. condit. Zinzib. condit.* ā ʒii. *Spec. Aromat. Ros.* gr. vii. *Confect. Alkerm.* ʒß. *Ambræ gris. Mosc.* ā gr. vi. *Misc. f. Elect.* After she had taken of it fourteen days, she was much better ; and continuing it thirty days, she became well.

---

## OBSERV. XXXII.

SMith of *Stratford,* aged 38, being long troubled with an immoderate Cough, and Pain of the Head, was thus cured : ℞ *Flower of Brimstone* ʒii. *Roots of Elicampana, Oris,* and *Liquoris,* all poudered, each ʒi. *Honey fufficient to make an Electuary* ; to which was added twelve drops of *Oil of Sulphur,* and so licked. After ℞ *Orpiment* ʒi. *Yolk of an Egg,* as much made a Mass, which after it was dried, it was poudered ; to which was added of *Tobacco* ʒß. *Coltsfoot* ʒi. *Anis feeds* Ɔiii. *Oil of Anis feed* three drops. Of this he took in a Pipe, and so was cured.

### Observ. XXXIII.

Wife (whether of the Author, which is most probable, or of the Man that went before, or of some other, I know not, because not mentioned) was troubled with the Scurvy, accompanied with Pain of the Loins, Corruption of the Gums, stinking Breath, Melancholy, Wind, Cardiac Passion, Laziness, difficulty of breathing, fear of the Mother, binding of the Belly, and torment there, and all of a long continuance, with restlesness and weakness. There was given this Bole : ℞ *Electuary of Tamarinds* ℥ß. *Cream of Tartar* ℨi. *mix them.* To the Back was applied *Emplast. Oxycroceum,* which freed her from pain of the Loins and Belly, *Febr. 9. 1630.* The tenth day taking cold, she had again miserable pain in her Joints, so that she could not lye in her Bed, insomuch as when any helped her, she cried out miserably ; for which I used this Ointment : ℞ *Capons greafe, Oil of fweet Almonds, of Dil. and Rofes, Mucilage of the Roots of Althæa, drawn with Mallow water, each* ℨi. *mix them.* After anointing, the forefaid Plafter was applied with good succefs, for she was quieter all night ; but yet in the morning she was troubled with Wind. Then I gave of *Sennertus*'s Electuary, which is thus framed : ℞ *the Conferve of the tops and leaves of Scurvy-grafs* ℥iii. *the Flowers of Buglofs, Clove Gilly-flowers, and Damask-Rofes, each* ℥ß. *the flefh of Candied Nutmegs, Citron Pills candied and cut, each* ℥i. *Honey*
of

*Juniper-berries* Ʒiii. *Confectio Alkermes* Ʒſſ. *Syrup of Cinamon* Ʒvi. *Syrup of Scurvy-graſs,* or that of Foreſtus, *ſufficient to make an Electuary, to which was added Oil of Sulphur, ſufficient to ſharpen it.* For the conſtipation of the Belly, was uſed this Suppoſitory, ℞ *Honey* Ʒi. *Spec. Hier. Pic.* Эii. *Troch, Alhand.* Эſſ. *Cummin ſeed* Ʒſſ. *make a long Suppoſitory.* For the Cardiac Paſſion was uſed *Elect. Plereſarchon.* Doſe Ʒ ſſ. faſting; yea, at any hour it was uſed, drinking the following ſteeled Wine after it: ℞ *Fumatory, Brook-lime, Water-creſſes, Scurvy-graſs, Betony, Agrimony, Harts-tongue,* each Mſſ. *Bark of Capparis, Aſh, Tamaris,* each Ʒſſ. *Roots of Elicampana, Polipody,* each Ʒiii. *Madder, Liquoris, Calamus Aromaticus, Eringoes,* each Ʒſſ. *yellow Sanders, red Coral, ſhavings of Ivory,* each Ʒvi. *Cloves, Mace, Cinamon, Ginger,* each Ʒiii. *Ceterach, Flowers of Broom, Roſemary, Marygolds, Epithymum,* each p. i. *Juniper berries* Ʒi. *Steel prepared according to* Crato Ʒiv. *White-wine* ℔viij. *infuſe them together at the Fire in* Bal. Mar. *for eight days at leaſt ſtirring them twice a day; after ſtrain it three or four times, and to the ſtraining add Saffron* Ʒſſ. *firſt drawn out of Scurvy-graſs water, Confect. Alkermes* Эii. *Sugar ſufficient to ſweeten it.* Doſe is two or three ſpoonfuls in the beginning, which may be increaſed, if there be need. And by theſe ſhe was cured.

## O b s e r v. XXXIV.

Mrs. *Combs*, aged about 36, being troubled with a long confirmed Scurvy, accompanied with the like and more dreadful Symptoms, than are in the former Observation described, was cured as followeth : To prepare the humors, ℞ *our Oxymel* ℥iii. *Syr.Diaserios* ℥ii. *Syr.Schelet.Forest.* ℥ii. *Water of Water-cresses* ℥iii. *Dose* ℥iiij), with White-wine for three mornings together, which gave two or three stools a day. After I purged her thus : ℞ *Pil. Hier. cum Agarick , Alephang. Ruffi.* ā ℈ii. *Ol. Salv. Chym.* gut. vii. *cum Aq. Bet. f. Pill.* 7. *Deaurat.* She took three at the hour of sleep. Being well purged, she used that *Chalybiated Wine*, prescribed in the former *Observation*, as also the *Electuary* in the same. After was taken the *Antiscorbutic Water*, prescribed *Observ.* 26 of this Century. For the Loins was used the Ointment in *Observ.* 33. After which was applied *Emplast. de Ammoniac. Forest.* For the corruption of the Gums we used this : ℞ *Scurvy-grass water, Water wherein Iron was quenched,* ā ℥vi. *Honey of Roses and Mulberries simp.* ā ℥ii. *Oil of Vitriol, sufficient to make it sharp.* With this she washed her Mouth. She drunk the *Antiscorbutic Beer*, prescribed, *Observ.* 7. and 24. of this Cent. For the Stomach was prescribed this : ℞ *Spec. Diamb. Aromat. Ros.* ā ℈iiſ. *Ol. Mastic.* ℨi. *Cer. fl iv.* ℨvi. *Labdan.* ℨiii. *f. Emplast.* To the Back was applied *Oxycroceum.* There were often used at the hour of sleep five Pills framed of *Cyprus Turpentine,*

pentine, and Cream of *Tartar*. By these she was freed, and brought forth a goodly Daughter, beyond all expectation.

## Observ. XXXV.

THe Lady *Clark*, aged about 44, afflicted with a Bastard Tertian, was cured as followeth : I gave the following Vomit upon the coming of the third Fit ; ℞ *Emetick Infusion* ʒ vi. It gave eight Vomits and one Stool, and she had a gentle Fit. After the heat coming on, she drank of the Decoction of Harts-horn. The intermitting day she had the following Clyster : ℞ *Mallowes, Beets, Mercury, Origanum, Calamints,* each M ß. *Seeds of Anis* and *Fennel,* each ʒii. *Whole Barly* p. i. *Flowers of Chamomel* and *Melilot,* each p. i. *make a Decoction in water to* ʒx. *in the straining dissolve Diacatholicon and Diaphænicon,* each ʒi. *Spec. Hier. Picr. Holland Pouder,* each ʒi. *make a Clyster.* Which purged well. Before the fit she took the following : ℞ *Confect. Alkermes* Эß. *Laudanum Paracelsi* gr. ii. *Magistery of Pearl* gr. iii. *mix it.* After which she became well.

## Observ. XXXVI.

MR. *Thomas Underhil* of *Lamcot,* aged about 39, was exceedingly weakned with pissing blood, with pain from very light motion of the Body,

Body, as also heat of the Urine, who was cured as followeth: ℞ *Maff. Pil. de Tereb. cum Rhab. Craton.* ℥ii. *form. Pil.* vi. *of a drachm.* Three were given in the morning rolled in the Pouder of Liquoris, in a spoonful of some Syrup of *Althæa.* These taken, ℞ *Troch. Alkekengi cum Opio* ℥ß. *Rad. confolid. Terebint. coction. indurat.* ã ℥i. *Sacch.* ℥iß. *cum infuf. Gum. Tragac. Aq. Malv. f. Tab. pond.* ℈ii. Take one morning and night. ℞ *Tereb. Limpid.* ℥ß. *diffol. cum Vitel. Ovi, ut artis eft ; adde Mel.* ℥i. *Sacch. Rof.* ℥ii. *Vin. generof.* ℥vi. *Mifc.* Of this was drank ℥i every morning, which gave three or four stools, at night he took the *Troches.* He wore at his back a Plate of Lead perforated, and moistned in Vinegar, both night and day, and by these he was cured.

## OBSERV. XXXVII.

KAtherine *Sturley* of *Stratford,* aged 44, being fat and corpulent, cast out altogether bloody Urine without any pain of the Loins, or Neck of the Bladder, yea, there was little sense in its coming away, was thus cured: ℞ *Liquoris fhaved* ℥vi. French Barley p. i. *Jujubes, five leaves of Water-Lillies, Violets, Rofes,* each p. i. *Seeds of Purflain,* and *Sorrel,* also *four greater cold Seeds,* each ℥i. *Roots of Succory* ℥i. *Endive, Sorrel, Plantain, Fumitory,* each M i. Boyl them in *Cicer-broth,* with water to ℔i. after strain them ; to which add *Sugarcandy* ℥ii. and make an *Apozeme.* Of which give the third part at a time fasting, it was taken for eight

eight days. To strengthen the Kidneys I appointed this Electuary, ℞ *Harts-horn prepared,* *red Coral prepared, each* ℥i. *Old Sugar of Roses,* *Marmalad of Quinces, each* ℥ iß. *Syrup of dried* *Roses, sufficient to make an Electuary.* Of which was taken ℥ß two hours before meat daily, twice a day. By these she was cured. First I applied the following: ℞ *Sanicle, Ladies mantle, Golden* *rod, Sen-green, Betony, Agrimony, each* M i. *Althæa,* M ii. *Fearn, Flowers of Chamomel, St. Johns-wort,* *Mugwort, Bryers, Origanum, Tormentil leaves and* *roots, each* M i. *They are all to be in three Bags of* *half a yard long a-piece, being equally laid and basted,* *after they are to be boiled in the Fæces of red Wine,* *and applied to the Loins, the Patient lying upon her* *Belly.* These were used one after another, till the Flux of blood was stayed.

---

## Observ. XXXVIII.

THe Lady *Hunks,* aged 69, cruelly vexed with a continual burning Feaver, with torment of the Side, and pain of the Stomach, as also with binding of the belly for eight days; the Urine was confused, and there was great danger of death, yet she was recovered as followeth: ℞ *Mallowes,* *Althæa, Mercury, each* M i. *make a Decoction in* *Water, of which* ℞ ℥ xii. *Diaphænic. Diacathol.* ā ℥i. *Pul. Sanct.* ℥i. *make a Clyster.* This gave her two stools. After we gave our Antiscorbutic Julep. To the pained Side, the following: ℞ *Unguent. Dialth.* ℥ii. *Ol. Amygd. dulc.* ā ℥ß. *dissol.*

*&*

*& misc. ad ignem.* With this was the pained Side
anointed; after which was applied a double Linnen Cloth, anointed with Butter, by which the
Pain remitted. The next day was taken of the
former Decoction ℔ß. the *Emetick Infusion* ʒii.
*make a Clyster.* Which injected, gave three stools.
For expectoration, ℞ *the Magistral Syrup of Scabious* ʒi. *Lohoch of Currants by* Quercetan ʒii. *f.
Linct.* Which was taken with a Liquoris stick.
The Diet was moistning. The Drink was this:
℞ *French Barly* ʒiii. *Roses, Violets,* each p. i. *shaved Liquoris* ʒiii. *Raisins* ʒii. *Figs three, Sugar-
candy* ʒii. *boyl them in two gallons of Water to the
consumption of a third part;* and drink the strained
Liquor. Thus the Fever ended, Thirst remitted,
Appetite was restored, she was freed from difficulty of breathing, and she slept well, and all
this beyond all expectation within fourteen days:
praise to God alone.

## Observ. XXXIX.

BAronet *Puckering,* aged about 38, very learned,
much given to study, of a rare and lean Constitution, yet withal phlegmatick, was troubled
with a *Vertigo,* and after Meat with sudden dejection of strength; sometimes there was present
pain of the Head, and darkness of Sight; his Appetite was mean, his Urine well-coloured, but spumous. There were other Accidents from consent,
by reason of the fault of Concoction, therefore
first Concoction was helped; secondly the Head
and

and Nerves were strengthned, and their offending cause removed. But first of all, the first ways were gently emptied with ℥ i ß of *Manna dissolved in Broth, altered with Agrimony and Succory, roots and all.* After he was purged thus : ℞ *Pil. de Pæoni. ℨi. de Succin. Ruffi.* ā ℈i. *Cephalic. Fern.* ℈ii. *cum Aq. Betonic. f. Pil.* 15. He took three at the hour of sleep, and had three stools in the morning. These ended, he took the Carminative Pouder prescribed *Observ.* 12. of this Century. After meals, adding to it *Diamosch. dulc.* ℈i. I appointed the following Capital Roll : *Spec. Diamosc. dulc. ℨi. Ol. Nuc. Mosch. per expr.* ℈i. *Ol. Succin. alb.* gut. iii. *Ambr. gris.* gr. iv. *Sacch. in Aq. Lavend. dissol. ℥iv. f. Confect. in Rotul.* Of which he took two or three fasting, by which he found much ease. After he had the Leeches, and so became well. For preservation, in the Fall, he used the following : ℞ *Roots of Fennel and Parsly, each ℥i. of Butcher-broom and Sparagus, each ℥iß. Calamus Aromaticus ℨii. Agrimony, Betony, Maidenhair, each* M ß. *Roots of Elicampana ℨii. Raisins of the Sun stoned, each* M i. *Liquoris ℨi. Flowers of Broom and Rosemary, each* p. i. *Seeds of Anis and sweet Fennel, each ℨii: make a Decoction, in which was infused Sena ℥iß. Rubarb ℨii. Cinamon* ℈ii. *in Embers for a night; in the morning being strained, there was added Syrup of Succory, with Rubarb ℥iiß. Syrup August. ℥i. Oil of Vitriol sufficient to make it sharp.* It was divided into two equal parts; the first Dose gave four Stools, the other seven. The Humor thus prepared, he took the foresaid prescribed Pills, three at night, and two in the morning, which gave five Stools. When these were

ended

ended, he took the Carminative Pouder, adding *Puk. Diamosc. dulc.* ℈i. *Confect. Alkerm.* ℈ii. In the morning he used the aforesaid *Rotula's*, to which was added *Confectio Alkerm.* By which means he was perfectly cured.

## OBSERV. XL.

BAronet *Clark* of *Broom-court*, aged about 57, being troubled with a burning Tertian, with pain of the Stomach and Head, his Urine was red. Being called, I cured him in three days, as followeth : ℞ *Emetick Infusion* ʒ ß. *Oxymel nostr.* ʒ iv. This gave five Vomits and eight Stools, by which all was well remitted, and he enclined to health. The following day I gave the Decoction of Harts-horn, which he took often in a day, which he much extolled. This administred for three days, with a convenient Diet, he became very well.

## OBSERV. XLI.

THe Lord of *Northampton*, aged about 29. was vexed with a desperate Squinsy, insomuch that he could scarce draw his breath, could not swallow, from his Mouth flowed abundance of viscid humidities. He would not admit of bleeding, although pressed unto it. Therefore I thus purged him : ℞ *Sena* ʒi. *Rubarb* ʒiii. *Agarick*

rick ʒii. *Cinamon* ʒß. *Seeds of Anis and Fennel*
each ʒi. *Calamus Aromaticus* ʒ ß. *Liquoris* ʒiii.
they were infused for twelve hours in ℔iij *of Water,*
*after boiled at a gentle Fire, till a third part was wast-*
*ed ; to the straining was added Syrup of Succory, Ru-*
*barb, Diaserios, each* ʒi. Of this, being at hand,
I took ʒiv. *Syr. Diaserios, and Succory with Rubarb,*
each ʒvi. *mix them.* Much ado he had to swallow
it, it gave him six stinking stools. This being
reiterated, gave eight stools. For the first day I
prescribed this Gargarism : ℞ *Honey of Mul-*
*berries simple, Honey of Roses, each* ʒii. *Waters of*
*Plantain, Barly, and Honey-suckles, each* ʒiv. *Spi-*
*rit of Vitriol and Sulphur, sufficient to make it sharp.*
Some of this was kept hot in the Mouth as long
as he could, wasting all the parts by moving of
it gently in the Mouth. Outwardly was applied
a Cataplasm of *green Wormwood and Hogs grease,*
morning and night, with happy success. That
night being restless, he sent for Dr. *Clayton* from
*Oxford,* yet would not be let blood, who prescribed the following Cataplasm, which delivered
him from pain and danger ; ℞ *Swallows nests,*
*straw, dirt, dung and all,* N. ii. *they were boiled*
*in Oil of Chamomel and Lillies, afterward they were*
*beaten, and passed through a Sive ; to which was added*
*white Dogs turd* ʒi. *the Meal of Linseed and Fenu-*
*greek, each* ʒi. *Unguent. Dialthæa, and Hens grease,*
*each* ʒß. *and so make a Pultess.* It was applied hot.
There was used a Fume of Amber, and at bed-
time was held in his Mouth one of the following
Trochis : ℞ *the Juyce of Liquoris, white Sugar,*
*each* ʒi. *seeds of Purslain, Cucumbers, Melons, Gourds*
*cleansed,* ā Ɔi. *Starch, Trag.* ā ʒß. *Penid.* Ɔiv. *f. Troch.*

For

For his Wife and others troubled with the Squin-
ſy, I prepared theſe following : ℞ *Seeds of white
Poppies* Ɔii. *Gum Tragacanth and Arabick*, each ʒſſ.
*Seeds of Purſlain*, *Melons*, *Cucumbers and Gourds*,
*each* ʒſſ, *Juyce of Liquoris.* ʒi. *Sugar of Roſes and
Penidies*, *each* ʒii. *with Syrup of Poppies make
Troches.* But he contented himſelf with the former. After the application of the Cataplaſm he
had this Gargariſm ; ℞ *Plantain water* ℔iſſ. *Scabious water* ʒiv. *red Roſes* ʒi. *Pomegranate Pills*
ʒſſ. *after they were gently boiled and ſtrained there
was added Syrup of Mulberries*, *and Honey of Roſes
each* ʒii. This he waſhed his Mouth withal often in a day, and taking after half a ſpoonful of
the following ; ℞ *Syrups of Liquoris and Maiden-
hair*, *each* ʒſſ. *Diatrag.frig.* ʒiſſ. *Syrup of Mulberries
and Poppies* ā ʒſſ. *mix them*, *and make a Licking.*
For ordinary drink he took this ; ℞ *Seeds of Anis*,
*Figs*, *Raiſins of the Sun*, *and Liquoris boyled in* ℔iv
*of water*, *till a pint be waſted.* By theſe all the Tumors were removed, and he cured.

## Observ. XLII.

Mrs. *Stockſn*, Servant to Mrs. *Sheldon* of *Weſt-
on*, aged about 44, was grievouſly afflicted with the Jaundice, accompanied with Pain and
Torment on the right Side, being in danger of
Death, was thus cured : ℞ *Electuary of the Juyce
of Roſes* ʒii. *Diacatholicon* ʒiſſ. *Diaphænicon* ʒiiſſ.
*Rubarb* Ɔi. *Spike* gr. v. *Syrup of Succory with Rubarb* ʒſſ. *Succory water* ʒiiii. *make a Potion.* This
gave

gave two ftools. She was ( all the time of her
Jaundice ) miferably afflicted with binding of
the Belly. I caufed a Vein to be opened, and
there were removed ℥iv of Blood. By this fhe
was freed from the pain of her Side. After fhe
was purged thus : ℞ *Ammoniacum* ʒi. *Oxymel* ℥ii
*Agrimony water* ℥i. *mix them; and fo for four days.*
Being well purged, I prefcribed a Gelly framed
of *fhaved Harts-horn* ℥i. *with ten Worms wafhed in*
*White-wine, after boiled all in* ℔iß *of Water, till*
*half were wafted; at the end of the boyling I added*
*Saffron finely poudered* ℈i. Of this was given two
fpoonfuls in Broth, altered with *Celendine, Bar-*
*berry bark,* and *Mary-gold flowers.* Her Drink was
a Decoction of Harts-horn. She alfo took the
following : ℞ *White-wine* ℥ iv. *Celendine water*
℥iii. *Saffron* ʒß. *Venice Treacle* ʒiß. *Bezoar* ℈ß.
*the Juyce of Goofe-dung three fpoonfuls; make a Su-*
*dorifick Potion.* Dofe ℥iv, at four a clock in the
morning. At night fhe took the following E-
lectuary: ℞ *yellow and white Sanders* ʒiii. *Currants*
*infufed in White-wine, and after paffed through a*
*Sive,* ℥iv. *Rubarb* ʒi. *Saffron* ℈i. *f. Elect.* Dofe, the
quantity of a Filbert. By thefe fhe was cured. After
I advifed to ufe the following : ℞ *Elect. Chalyb.*
℥ii. *Rhab. Pul.* ʒi. *Ammoniac. Pul.* ℈iv. *Elect. de*
*Tamarind.* ʒ ß. *Diatrionfant.* ʒiii. *Mifc. f. Elect.*
Dofe ℥ß. ufing exercife. And thus in twenty
days fhe was delivered from Death.

K

## Observ. XLIII.

ONe of *Northampton*, aged about 65, was much troubled with the heat of Urine, and Strangury, with an Ulcer in the neck of the Bladder, was cured as followeth: First I gave him the Terbentine Potion, prescribed *Observ.* 14. of this Century. For eight days for ordinary Drink, he took the same appointed there. All this while he wore Plates of Lead much perforated, and often changed, to his Back. I appointed the following Injection: ℞ *Troch. alb. Rha. sine Opio* ʒiß. *Lap. Calamin. & Tutiæ præp.* ā ʒi. *Plumb. ust. lot. in Aq. Plantag. Bol. Arm. puris.* ā ʒii. *f. Pul. subtilis. cujus* ʒi *Misc. cum Decoct. seq.* and inject it, adding ʒi of the *Mucilage of Gum Tragacanth, made in Plantain water.* ℞ *Horse-tail, Plantain,* each M i. *Comfrey roots* ʒii. *red Roses* p. i. *Pomegranate Pills* ʒii. *first beat them, and after boyl them in steeled Water.* At the end of these was used the following Tablets: ℞ *Troch. Alkekeng. cum Opio* ʒ ß. *Rad. consolid. Terbent. coct. indurat.* ā ʒ i. *Sacch.* ʒiß. *cum infus. Gum Tragac. f. Troch.* Ͻii *pond.* One was taken with Milk, or the Water distilled off Whites of Eggs, &c. For many days a Leaden Pipe was put into the Yard, and there kept (which was anointed with *Ung. Rubrum*) as long as he could. His Cods being tumified, were anointed with *Unguent. de Minio,* for which also he drank the Decoction of *Sarsaparilla.* Thus was he freed from the heat of his Urine.

But

But now being vexed with a virulent Gonorrhea, he took the following Pouder for ten days : ℞ *Sarsaparilla* ʒ i ß. *Bark of Guaiacum* ʒ ß. *Cinamon* ℈ii, gr. v. *Sena* ʒii. *Dodder, Hellebore root, each* ʒi. *fine Sugar* ʒii. *mix them, and make a Pouder.* Dose ʒ iß. Sometimes the *Dodder* and *Hellebore* was omitted. And by this he became well. But after riding to *London,* ( by what occasion I know not ) it broke forth again, where he had the advice of Doctor *Harvy,* who prescribed what follows: ℞ *Troch. Rhasis alb.* ʒ ß. *Troch. Gord.* ℈i. *Aloes opt.* ʒiiß. *Penidior.* ʒiß. *Aq. Plantag.* ℔ß. *f. Inject.* The following Electuary he used at night, the quantity of a Bean, when he went to bed : ℞ *Troch. Alkekeng. cum Opio* ʒ ß. *Syr. Limon. q. s. Gum Tragacanth, Mastich, Crystal. præp. Coral præp.* ā ℈i. *f. Elect.* By these he was again restored. After he went to St. *Vincent's* Well, and was much better by their use. After this, being hurt with the forcing in a Pipe ʳto remove a Caruncle by a Chirurgeon, he again relapsed, and never was cured.

---

## Observ. XLIV.

Mrs. *Mary Comb* of *Stratford,* aged about 13, *Febr.* 15. 1631. Two years before this she had her Lunar Evacuations sufficient, they beginning to flow abundantly in the eleventh year of her Age ; but now they being stopped, upon which she felt a light Convulsion in the

K 2 right

right eye ( to use her owm word, a twitching )
as though her Eye was pulled inward, and presently it would be gone : after both eyes did suffer
with great pain of the Head, for which I administred at bed-time, *Pil. Cephal. Fern.* ʒ ſs. by
which she had three stools, the next day they
were repeated.   Then she became cruelly vexed
with the Mother, continuing in the Fit for nine
hours, with some light intervals of ease, from
which she was delivered by the following Medicines: She had a Fume of *Horse-hoofs.*   There was
also given *Aq. Hysteric.* now called *Aq. Brioniæ
compos.* Doſe three ſpoonfuls, by intervals as ſhe
could take it.   I applied *Emplaſt. Hyſter.* below
the Navil.   Laſtly, I appointed the following
Ointment to anoint the inner part of the Matrix:
℞ *Muſk* gr. iv. *Nutmeg* Ɡi. *Oil of Lillies* ʒſs. *mix
them.*   By this it returned to its place.   For a
Fume ſhe had the following, uſed to the Noſe : ℞
*Caſtory, Galbanum diſſolved in Vinegar, each* ʒſs.
*Sulphur* ʒi. *Aſſa fœtida* Ɂi. *make Troches with Oil
of Caſtory.*   ℞ *Pil: de Pæon. de Chamæp.* ā Ɡii. *Ol.
Salu. Chy.* gut. v. *f. Pil.* N° 10.   Three of theſe
were given at bed time, to which was added *Extract. Hyſt.* Ɡi .   By theſe ſhe had five or ſix ſtools.
The following day ſhe had another Fit, but leſs ;
but by the foreſaid Fume and Ointment ſhe was
well amended.   Inwardly were given two ſpoonfuls of *Aq. Brion. comp.*   At night ſhe took two
of the foreſaid Pills ; coming to her in the morning, I found her eaſed of her pain of Head and
Stomach.   The 11*th* of *Febr.* ſhe was gently afflicted with the Mother, and a light Fever ; to
prevent which I gave *Extract. Hyſteric.* ʒii. *cum*
                                                            *Aq.*

*Aq. Hiſt. q. ſ. f. Pil.* 10. She took one of them in the morning faſting, and ſo ſhe became well. *March* 28. ſhe fell again into the Mother, with Convulſion of the Eyes, the ſaid Convulſion having grieved her two days before ſhe was afflicted with the Mother : ℞ *Pil. de Pæon. Chamæpit. Hier. cum Agarick,* ā ℈ii. *Pil. de Succin. Ruffi.* ā ℥i. *Extract. Hyſter.* ℥ii. *cum Aq. Hyſter. f. Maſ.* Of this there were made five of a drachm covered with Gold , of theſe ſhe took three at bed-time. By theſe ſhe was delivered.

---

## Observ. XLV.

THe Firſt-born Son of my Lady *Harrington,* after the Pox, laboured of a Tumor of the Noſe and Lips, and ſometimes the Cheeks, with a Rheum diſtilling from the Head ; he was about the age of 10, which I cured as followeth: ℞ *Scurvy-graſs, Water-creſſes, Brook lime,* each M iv. *Juniper berries* ℔ß. *Agrimony* M i. *Wormwood, Carduus benedictus,* each M ß. boyled them in five gallons of Beer, till a fourth part were waſted. Of the ſtrained Liquor was taken ℔ii. *Sena* ℥ii. *Agarick* ℥ß. *Rubarb* ℥ii. *Sarſaparilla* ℥ ii. *Saſſaphras* ℥ i. *Hermodactils* ℥iß. *Liquoris* ℥i. *Polypody* ℥ii. *Seeds of Anis, Carraway, Coriander,* each ℥ß. *Cinamon* ℥ii. To the ſtraining, add Sugar ſufficient to make a Syrup. Of this was taken ℥x. *Syrup of Succory with Rubarb* ℥ii. Doſe was three or four ſpoonfuls. For the Lips was uſed *Aq. Mercur. Ruland.* and at night a Plate of Lead. He drank of the foreſaid

Beer.

Beer. Which Courfe having been continued for few days, he was cured of his Lip.

## Observ. XLVI.

MArgaret Baker, aged 9, having after the Pox a grievous ugly Tumor upon her Nofe and Lip, was perfectly cured as followeth : ℞ *Pil. de Succin.* ℨß. *f. Pil.* iij. They were given her at a night when fhe went to bed, and fo for four days. Being well purged, the Lip was wafhed *cum Aq. Merc. Ruland.*

## Observ. XLVII.

MY Lady *Rainsford,* (beautiful, and of a gallant ftructure of Body,) near 27, was three days after her being laid of a Child miferably tormented with pain in her Belly, from which I delivered her with the following: ℞ *the white of Hens-dung* ℨi. being put in Beer and Sugar, fhe took it. To the Belly the following was applied hot : ℞ *new Milk and Honey, each* ℔i. *Horehound* M i. *Wheat flower* ℥iij. *Saffron* ℨi. *boyl them to a Pulteß.* By thefe fhe was delivered. The Tranflator hath freed feveral from this Diftemper with Chamomel Poffet-drink.

## Observ. XLVIII.

M rs. *Grace Court,* Wife to my Apothecary, aged
27, being grievously afflicted with a burning Fever, and that continual, Pain in the Loins,
small bleeding at the Nose, Pain of the Head,
with small Delirium, was cured as followeth :
First, I appointed her to bleed four or five ounces,
although she had passed fourteen weeks of her
time, being with Child. The same day I gave
the following Cordial : ℞ *burnt Harts-horn, Spec.
liberant. pul. Pannon. rub. Confect. Alkerm.* ā ℈ii.
*Conserve of Barberries* ℥i. Of this she took the quantity of a Bean every three hours. She drank no
drink but the following : ℞ *Spring water boyled*
℔iii. *Syrup of Pomegranats* ℥iss. *Julep of Roses* ℥ii.
*Spirit of Vitriol, as much as made it sharp.* To the
Soals of her Feet were applied Radishes beaten with
Salt, and besprinkled with Rose-vinegar, which
was renewed every fourth hour. For the inflammation of the Tongue, was used the following
Gargarism : ℞ *Spring water* ℔ii. *Julep of Roses*
℥iss. *Honey of Mulberries* ℥vi. *Rose vinegar* ℥i. *Spirit of Vitriol sufficient to sharpen it.* With this she
washed her Mouth, which brought away much
Phlegm. Now and then the dry places were an-
ointed with *Honey of Roses,* and sometimes Butter. To the Wrists I caused to be applied *Ung.
Antifebri.* ℞ *Ung. Popul.* ℥i. *Tel. Aranear. multus,
Nuc. Arbor. parum, Misc.* For the Back, ℞ *Ung.
Popul. Ros.* ā ℥ ß. *Alabast.* ℥ii. *Ol. Nymph.* ℥vi.

*Camphor.*

*Camphor.* ℈ß. *Misc.* But becauſe there was no Oil at hand, the following was uſed: ℞ *Ol. Scorp.* ℥ii. *Amygd. dulc.* ℥ß. *Ung. Roſ.* ℥i. *Misc.* For the pain of the Head was uſed the following: ℞ *Aq. Roſ. Plantag. Flor. Sambuc.* ā ℥iii. *Ol. Roſ. Aq. Lactuc. ablut. aliquot.* ℥ıß. *Pul. Santal. rub.* ℥iß. *Misc.* In this were dipped Linnen Clothes, and applied to the Head. And left ſhe ſhould fall into *Carus,* we uſed the following Decoction: ℞ *pure Spring water* ℔ii. *Seeds and Pills of Citrons,* each ℥i. *burnt Harts-horn* ℥ß. *Spec. Liberan.* ℥ii. *boyl them till a quart be waſted; to the ſtraining was added the Juyce of Citrons, and Sugar, and after boyled, being not only ſcummed, but purified with Whites of Eggs.* Of this ſhe took three draughts in a day, one in the morning, the other an hour before dinner-time, and the third at four a clock in the afternoon. For the ſtrengthning of the Heart, and repelling malign Vapours, ſhe took twice a day ( before ſhe drank the foreſaid De-coction) the quantity of a Nutmeg of the follow-ing Cordial: ℞ *Rob of Barberries, Conſerve of the Pulp of Citrons,* each ℥i. *Spec. Liberant. prepared Pearls and Smaragdines,* each ℈i. *with the Syrup of Citrons make an Electuary.* Of this ſhe alſo took at night. After her third draught the next day ſhe took of the Electuary, wherein was *Pul. Pan. rub.* And afterwards a Clyſter: ℞ *Althea roots* ℥i. *the four emollient Herbs,* each M i. *Barly* p.i ß. *Gourd ſeeds* ℥ß. *make a Decoction to* ℥xii. *in which diſſolve Caſſia* ℥i. *Honey of Violets* ℥i. *Oil of Violets* ℥iii. *with Salt make a Clyſter.* The 20th day of *June* ſhe vomited a Worm with Melancholy matter. Then I gave of the following Electuary the quan-tity

tity of a Bean every fourth hour: ℞ *Conserv. Roſ. vitriolat.* ʒi. *Spec. Diarrhod. Abbat.* ʒi. *Pul. Pan. rub.* ℈i. *Conſer. Barb. q. ſ. f. Elect.* Theſe remitted her Fits, and ſhe came to a compoſed mind, and in a ſhort time became well.

---

## OBSERV. XLIX.

THE Counteſs of *Northampton*, (born of a noble Off-ſpring, notably educated, and of a very good diſpoſition, very fair and beautiful,) in the ſeventh month of her Child-bearing, fell into a Baſtard Tertian, as alſo a filthy yellow Jaundice, Torment of the Belly and Head, and Pain of the Back, being aged about 26, deſiring my advice, being not willing to purge, I preſcribed as followeth : ℞ *the Flowers of Marygolds and Roſemary, each p.* i. *Carduus benedictus p.* ſſ. *Flowers and leaves of Melilot p.* ii. *boyl them in ſufficient Poſſet drink to* ℔ſſ. *with a little Sugar.* She took half of it an hour before her Fit, hot, by which the Fit was retarded two hours ; it beginning, ſhe took the other half, which freed her from her ſhaking, then her Jaundice appeared in her Water manifeſtly, after ſweat broke forth, the next Fit was leſs. In the heat of the Fever and ſweat, ſhe took the Decoction of *Harts-horn*, with Juyce of Limons, of which ſhe drank liberally, in which Decoction ſhe would not admit Roſe-water. On her quiet day ſhe took every third hour the quantity of a Bean of the following : ℞ *Conſerve of Barberries* ʒſſ. *Pul. Pan. rub.* ℈ii. but after ſhe had taken

of

of it once, she abhorred it. She had a Gelly of *Harts-horn* with *Marygold flowers*, and *Saffron*. The 22*th* of *July*, before her Fit, she had five grains of *Bezoar*; and an hour before her Fit the foresaid Posset-drink. This Fit she was troubled with shaking, but the hot Fit and sweating was less by six hours. The 23*th* day, by five in the morning it left her. She took this: ℞ *Tincture of Coral, Magistral of Pearl, each* gr. iv. *Pul. Pannon. rub.* gr. xii. *mix them.* She took it an hour before dinner, and an hour before supper. The 24*th* day by three a clock in the morning she took as before, and the Posset-drink, which mitigated the Fit; the 25*th*, as the 23*th*. The 26*th* there was applied hot to the Feet the following: ℞ *Wormwood, Rue, Fetherfew, Nettles, each equal parts.* She also had the Posset-drink, as before. The foresaid being hot, was anointed with *Ung. Popul. with Opium.* To the Back was applied *Emplastrum Oxycroceum,* which removed the Pain of her Back wholly; that day her Fever was very little. The 28*th* she took the following: ℞ *prepared Hartshorn, Pul. Pann. rub.* each ʒß. *Carduus water* ʒii. *Syrup of red Poppies* ʒß. *Bezoar* gr. iv. *mix them.* It was given five hours before the Fit, and the Herbs were applied to the Feet. The heat coming, ℞ *Syr. Papav.* ʒi. *Lim.* ʒß. *Aq. Scab.* ʒii. *Ol. Vitriol.* gut. v. *Aq. Cælest.* gut. vii. *Misc.* With these Remedies in twelve days she was wholly cured. *August* the 5*th* taking cold, she relapsed. Then before the Fit two hours, were applied the Herbs to her Feet; to her Pulses this: ℞ *Ung. Popul.* ʒß. *Tel. aran. multas, Nuc. arbor. parum.* Her Temples were anointed with *Populeon.* For
her

her Coldnefs, ℞ *Aq. Bezoar. Coch. f. Lap. Bezoar.*
gr. v. *Succ. Lim. Coch.* ii. It was given two hours
before the Fit. When her heat came, her Temples were anointed with *Vnguent. Popul.* ℥ ſſ.
*Opii in Aq. Rof. diffol.* Ɔ ſſ. By thefe fhe was
again cured, and after fhe was brought to bed
with a Daughter, which I faw in her Arms.

## O B S E R V. L.

MR. *Foffet*, ( a Minifter ) aged about 55,
was cruelly tormented with the Hemorrhoids, for which many Medicines had been
ufed, yet fruitlefs. After he came to me, to
whom I ufed the following : Firft, I caufed
them to be fomented with warm Milk, after
applied this : ℞ *Oil of Linfeed, and Elder*, of
*the firft* ℥ii. *the other* ℥i. They were applied with
double Linnen Clothes night and day. After
was ufed *Tapfi valentia*. And after this, ℞ *Vng.*
*Popul.* ℥i. *Opii torrefact. & pul.* Ɔi. *Mifc.* It was
applied to the part. By thefe he was cured.

## O B S E R V. LI.

ANne *Ward* of *Stratford*, had black evacuations
both from Mouth and Belly, after fell into
the rifing of the Lungs, fo that all looked on her
as dead ; fhe could not fpeak, her Breath was
fent out with a noife ; for an hour fhe lay thus.
Being

Being called, I prefently caufed a great Cupping-
glafs to be fet to the Mouth of the Stomach, and
prefently fhe fpake.   And fo twice before I delivered Mrs. *Goodyear*, and Mrs. *Savage*, from danger of Death.   All the night after fhe held in her
Mouth of our pectoral Rolls, and after had this
Clyfter : R *Ol. Carmin. Quer. Diacathol.* ā ℥ ii.
*Decoct.Carmin. pro Clyft.* ℔ß. It gave two ftools the
following day.   R *Elect. de Tamarind.* ℥ß. *de Succ.*
*Rof.* ℥iii. *Crem. Tart.* Ɔi. *cum Sacch.f. Bol.* It gave
eight ftools, and fo fhe was cured.

---

## Observ. LII.

Mrs. *Fines*, aged 22, 1632. (Wife to the Lord
*Say*'s eldeft Son, a very religious excellent
Woman,) was miferably afflicted with the following Symptoms, *viz.* Obftruction of the Courfes
for the fpace of two months; and when fhe had
them at a fit time in a laudable quantity, they
were of an ill watery colour, with great pain in
the Womb; there was alfo difficulty of breathing,
with trembling and beating of the Heart, as if it
would have burft through; after fleep fhe was
fick, with torment of the Belly, and gnawing
about the Navil, but thefe Pains were moft mife-
rable about the time of her Courfes; upon breaking wind fhe was fomewhat eafed; her Belly was
alfo very hard,and moved,as if with child; but hot
Clothes being applied removed the Pain and
Wind.   She was alfo vexed with pain of the
Spleen, Whites, Leannefs, Pain of the Loins,
a

a light *Vertigo*, as alſo of the Scurvy, and truly I judged all theſe Symptoms to ariſe from it. Which I cured as followeth: ℞ *Pil. de Succin.* ℥ii. *Ruffi.* ℥i. *f. Pil.* N. 15. She took three at bed-time, and two in the morning, which wrought excellently. For the Wind, ℞ *Spec. Plereſarc.* ℥ß. *Sacch. Roſ.* ℥iv. *Miſc.* Doſe, half a ſpoonful after meat. By the uſe of theſe her Courſes flow-ed well, with many lumps like Fleſh, not diſſolu-ble in water, they were expelled with torment, as in Child-birth. To cleanſe the Womb, ℞ *Hier. cum Agaric. de Succin.* ā ℥iß. *Terb. Cypr. Pil. Ruffi.* ā ℥ß. *f. Pil.* N. 20. She took theſe as the former, *cum cuſtodia.* Theſe ended, ſhe took *Spec. Plere-ſarc.* ℥ii. and uſed exerciſe. The fifth of *March,* at four a clock in the morning, ſhe took *Crem. Tart* in Broth. An hour after that, of our *Chaly-biat Water,* thus framed: ℞ *Oil of Sulphur* pint i. *Spirit of Wine* pint ii. *boyl them in a great new made Iron Spoon at a gentle Fire, till half be evacuated; the Pouder remaining, keep very cloſe, leſt it diſſolve.* Of this ℞ ℥ii. *to which put Agrimony water* ℥iv. *and infuſe them upon hot aſhes.* Of this ſhe took ℥ß in Broth, and uſed exerciſe; the firſt day ſhe vomited, and the ſecond and third days ſhe did not; ſhe uſed it for fifteen days. It is excellent in all Diſeaſes ariſing from the Liver, as *Dropſy, Cachexia, Green-ſickneſs.* To her Spleen was ap-plied *Empl. ex Ammoniac. Fer. & Oxycroc.* She uſed every day *Pleriſar. and Sugar.* Scorbutic Beer was not omitted, as *Cent.* 1. *Obſerv.* 1. By theſe ſhe was cured, taking in the morning *Dia-cubeb* ℥ii.

OBSERV.

## OBSERV. LIII.

FRances *Finch* of *Stratford*, aged 47, being troubled with the Worms, Pain of the Back and
Sides, was thus cured: ℞ *Pul. Dudlian. Scamon.
præp.* ā gr. xiv. *Crem. Tartar.* gr. x. *Aq. Boragin.*
℥iß. *Syr. Roſ. Coch. half.* This being exhibited,
gave four ſtools, with abundance of little Worms.
The next day being given again, ſhe was cured.
It is obſervable, that *Riverius* hath ſeveral Obſer-
vations about Worms, and his ſpecial Remedy is
*Mercur. dul. cum Scam. aut Reſin. Jalap.* the which
the Tranſlator hath proved very often, given in a
due Doſe.

## OBSERV. LIV.

Mrs. *Jackson*, (Wife to Mr. *Jackson* Jun.) aged
about 24, being not well purged after birth,
fell ſuddenly into a grievous Delirium, no other
Diſeaſe preceding; ſhe was moſt angry with thoſe
that formerly ſhe moſt loved, yet her talk was very
religious. By intervals there was a Fever acute,
which made me fear a Frenzy. By reaſon of much
buſineſs I could not have time to viſit her, yet
there was a happy ſucceſs by the following Preſcriptions: ℞ *Syr. Artem.* ℥i. *El. Lenit. Diacath.*
ā ℥iii. *Rhab. Caſtor.* ā Əß. *Aq. Betonic.* ℥iii. *Miſc.*
Her Stomach being full of wind, ſhe vomited
after

after without Pain, she had five stools. She took it again. The 22th of *May* there were taken away ℥vi of blood, very black and aqueous; yet the Delirium was not wholly removed. The 23 day, ℞ *Leaves of Mallows, Violets, Beets, Lettice, Borage, each* M ii. *Barly* ℥i. *Seeds of Gourds and Cucumbers, each* ℥ß. *make a Decoction with a sufficient quantity of Water, to* ℥xii. *To the strained Liquor add Oil of Violets* ℥iii. *Cassia new drawn, Diacath. each* ℥i. *Salt* ℥i. *make a Clyster.* After for watching and restlesness I gave the following Syrup: ℞ *Syrup of red Poppies* ℥iß. *Syrup of Violets* ℥ß. *Scabious water* ℥iii. *Rose-water a little, Oil of Vitriol to sharpen it.* To the Forehead was applied this: *Oil of Roses omphac.* ℥iii. *Vinegar of Roses* ℥i. *Pouder of red Sanders* ℥iß. *Waters of Lettice, Plantain, and Roses, each* ℥i. *mix them.* To the Head was applied a Hen new cut thorow. To the soals of the Feet, Radishes bruised with Salt and Vinegar, every third hour, for revulsion. The 25th, ℞ *Cassia newly drawn with Betony water* ℥i. *Syrup of Roses solutive* ℥ß. *Waters of Buglos, Borage, Violets, each* ℥ij. *make a Potion.* It was given in the morning. There were also Scarifications, with Cups to the Scapula's and Shoulders. And thus in seven days she was happily cured.

## Observ. LV.

MAy the 2d, Mrs. *Woodward* of *Aven-daſſet*, (a Maid very witty and well-bred, yet gibbous,) aged 28, ſix days before this fell into a continual burning Fever; then by the Phyſician being purged, and let blood, from it ſhe fell into a Baſtard Tertian, pernicious, with a yellow Jaundice, and ſpots like flea-bitings, which after left marks, which diſcovered the Fever to be joined with the Scurvy. For often it happens both in Continual, Tertian, and Quartan Fevers, as appears in *Eugaleus*. She wanted her Courſes, and had conſtipation of the Belly. I coming on the intermitting day, gave this: ℞ *Tincture of Coral* gr. vi. *Spec. Liberant.* ℈ß. *Manus Chriſti perlat.* ℈ii. *Lap. Bezoar.* gr. v. *with Conſerve of Barberries.* In the ſame day ſhe took often the Decoction of *Harts-horn, with Manus Chriſti perlat.* For her Broth I appointed theſe Herbs, *Brook-lime, Water-creſſes, Borage, Cichory.* May the 26th, ℞ *Diaturb. cum Rhab.* (becauſe there was no other ready at hand) ℈iv. *It was infuſed all night in Poſſet-drink, in the morning it was ſtrained, and taken with Sugar.* I being abſent, it gave four ſtools without pain. Towards evening ſhe expected her unwelcom Enemy, with grief of mind. To the Wriſt I applied *Ung. Antifebrif.* to the Feet, *Wormwood, Rue. Chamomel, boyled in Water,* and applied hot in bladders before the Fit came. ℞ *Spec. Liberant.* ʒii. *Conſerv. Barbar.* ʒii. Of this ſhe
took

took the quantity of a Bean often in a day, with
our *Antifcobutic Water, Obferv.* 26. of this Cent.
For the Jaundice and Scurvy, ℞ *Ammoniac. Pul.*
Ɔii. *Oxym. fimpl.* ℥ii. *Aq. Agrim.* ℥i.  It was repeated on the quiet day, as need required. To the
Spleen was applied *Empl. de Ammon.*  There was
ufed *Elect. Diacurcum.* the quantity of a Nutmeg,
after meals. Being altogether freed from the Fever,
yet not the Scurvy, I prefcribed the *Chalybiat
Wine* ( Obferv. 42. *Cent.* 1.) ℥vi. *Syrup of Scurvy-
grafs* ℥iij. *of Brook-lime and Water-creffes, each* ℥ii.
Dofe was fix fpoonfuls, with exercife.  And every other day, ℞ *Pil. Stomac. Ruffi. cap. Pill.* iiij
*ex* ℥ß. at going to bed.  And fo fhe was cured.

---

## Observ. LVI.

Mts. *Hopper,* aged 24, after birth, the After-
birth was retained and corrupted, fo that
it was caft forth in little ftinking bits, whence a
direful ftink afcended to the Stomach, Heart, Liver, Diaphragma, and from thence to the Brain ;
fo that there was Pain of the Head, often fainting, and cold fweats ; fo that there was great
danger of death, yet was recovered as followeth :
℞ *Colocynthis boyled in equal parts of Water and Juyce
of Rhue, with which was mixed Myrrh, the Meal of
the Seeds of Line, Fenugreek, and Barly, of each a
fpoonful ; boyl them all together, and make a Plafter.*
Which apply to the whole Belly from the Navil
to the Privity.  The Matrix was anointed with
*Ung. Bafilicon.* ℞ *Caftory* gr. vi. *Myrrh, Saffron,*
**L** *each*

e*ich* gr. iij. *Mithrid.* ℈ß. *make three Pills.* Which
was given at bed time. And thus in twenty
four hours she was delivered.

---

## O B S E R V. LVII.

GOod-wife *Archer* of *Stratford*, was suddenly
taken with Convulsion of Face and Eyes,
loss of speech, her Matrix carried from its proper
place, and so cast, as if she had been the very
Image of Death, sometimes vehemently opening
and casting her Eyes hither and thither ; was cured as followeth; ℞ *Castory* ʒi. *Juyce of Rhue a
spoonful, Sage water* ℥ii. *Syrup of Mugwort* ℥i.
She was constrained to take it. To her Nose
were applied stinking things. Within the space
of few minutes she both spake and stood up.
The next day, ℞ *Spec. Hier. cum Agaric.* ʒß. *Pil.
fætid. de Pæon.* ā ℈i. *Fæcul. Brion. Diagrid.* ā gr. vi.
f. *Pil.* 5. They were taken in the morning with
custody. After ℞ *Briony root* ʒiii. *Sena* ℥ß. *Ginger* ℈ß. *Cinamon* ʒi. *Sugar* ℥i. *infuse them for a
night in hot Whey* ℔iß. Of this Infusion was taken ℥v for several days together. With which
the Cure was perfected.

---

## Observ. LVIII.

Mrs. *Lewes*, Sister to Mr. *Fortescue*, three days after Child-birth, getting cold, fell into an Ague, with torment of the Belly, was cured as followeth: She drank the *Decoction of Harts-horn*, our *Julep against the Fever*, two spoonfuls every fourth hour. She also had a Clyster of *Milk and Sugar*. There was *Origanum* and *Marjoram* lapped up between a Linnen Cloth, and applied hot to the Belly. And so she was suddenly helped.

## Observ. LXI.

Mrs. *Vernon* of *Hanberry*, Wife to the Minister, aged about 30, *August* 13. 1632. was afflicted with the Scurvy, joined with various Symptoms, as coldness in the soals of the Feet, which like a cold vapor ascending to the Stomach, made her grievous sick; after that she was afflicted with heat, after with a cold sweat, and all in the space of two hours, and then she was well. Further she was afflicted with Melancholy, trembling of the Heart, and pain of the Spleen, so that she was forced to press it hard with her hands; she had cruel pains of her Teeth and Gums, Loins, Laziness of the whole Body, Tumor of the Feet towards evening. In the time of her Courses she

was

was miferably tormented, her Flux being much
and inordinate, by which fhe was weakned. The
Fits of the Mother often afflicted her, of which
fhe was not delivered till fhe fhed tears. Sometimes fhe had filthy black fpots on her Thighs,
fometimes fhe was alfo without ftools for four
days. Her Urine was of various colours. ℞ *Mallowes, Mercury, Althæa*, each M i. *boyl them in
fufficient quantity of Milk to* ℔i. *in the ftraining was
diffolved Diaphœnic. Diacathol.* each ʒvi. *Holland
pouder* ʒi. *make a Clyfter*. It gave three ftools with
wind. At her going to bed fhe took ʒii of *London Treacle*. The fourteenth day, ℞ *Brook-lime,
Water-creffes*, each M i. *Marygold flowers, and of
Rofemary*, each p. i. *boyl them in fufficient quantity of
Whey to* ℔ifs. *To the ftraining was added* ℔fs *of Sugar*; *it was again boyled and fcummed*; *after was
added* ʒfs *of Saffron tyed up in a fine rag*; *after a
walm or two it was taken from the Fire*. Of this Decoction were taken eight fpoonfuls, *Holland pouder*,
and *Cream of Tartar*, of each as much as lay upon
a Six-pence, in the morning, fafting two hours
after, and then taking Veal broth, altered with
*Borage, Buglofs, Brook-lime, Water-creffes*, and *Succory*; dining at the ufual time, fupping at five.
At bed time fhe took *London Treacle*, as before.
For the Mother was prefcribed *Aq. Brion. compof.*
now fo called. For the coldnefs of the Feet was
applied this Plafter : ℞ *Pitch* ℔ii. *beft Rofin poudered and fifted, Frankinfence*, each ℔ii. *Sheep-fewet*
ʒi. *Saffron and Mace*, each ʒii. *Labdanum* ʒiv.
*Cloves* ʒi. *mix them, and boyl them for half an hour,
or more*. It is to be fpread on Leather, like to a
Shoo foal. This was continued for fourteen days,

or

or six weeks, and then removed. And for certain this Plaster is profitable in all pain. By this Plaster I cured Mr. *Feriman* of an old pain in the Feet. For tumor of the Spleen I used *Ung. Magist. pro Splen.* In pain of the Back was used our *Emplast. Nephritic.* As ℞ red *Lead* and *Wax* ℥ii. *Opium* gr. xv. *Oil of Roses, of Water-lillies, each* ℥ii. *Juyce of Night-shade* ℥i. *boyl them to a Plaster.* Spread it upon Leather. For wind of the Stomach, ℞ *Conserve of Buglofs* ℥ii. *Spec. Plerisarch.* ℥ii. Dose, the quantity of a Nutmeg. There was also used our Scorbutic Water, with Syrup of Clove Gilly-flowers. She had also an Antiscorbutic Beer, and Chalybiat Wine. By the use of which she became well.

## Observ. LX.

THou, O Lord, which hast the power of Life and Death, and drawest from the Gates of Death, I confess, without any Art or Counsel of Man, but only from thy Goodness and Clemency, thou hast saved me from the bitter and deadly Symptoms of a deadly Fever, beyond the expectation of all about me, restoring me as it were from the very jaws of Death to former health; for which I praise thy Name, O most merciful God, and Father of our Lord Jesus Christ, praying thee to give me a most thankful Heart for this great favour, for which I have cause to admire thee. About the 57*th* year of my age, *August* 27. 1632. to *Septemb.* 29. I was much debilitated with an

L 3 *immoderate*

*immoderate Flux of the Hemorrhoids* ; yet daily was
I conftrained to go to feveral places to Patients.
By riding, a hardnefs being contracted, the Flux
was ftayed for fourteen days.    After I fell into
a moft cruel torture of my Teeth,  and then into
a deadly burning Fever, which then raged very
much,  killing almoft all that it did infect, for
which I ufed the following method,  which by the
help of God fucceeded.    Firft,  I purged thus :
℞ *Rubarb infufed* ℥i. (furely it was infufed in fome
proper water, fuppofe ℥iii.)   *Syrup. Diaferios* ℥i.
*Elect. è Succ. Rof.* ℥iii.  This gave four ftools.
After I ufed the *Decoction of Harts-horn*, and fo
the Difeafe was almoft caft out by Urine, it flowed
very much for four days fpace ; fo that I was not
only much maciated , but alfo  weakned ,  fo
that I could not move my felf in my Bed without
help.    I alfo had *Convulfion of the Mouth and Eyes*.
Then was a Pigeon cut open alive, and applied
to my feet, to draw down the Vapours ; for I
was often afflicted with a light Delirium.    Then
my Wife fent for two Phyficians.    I had ufed a
Clyfter with *Emollient Herbs*, and *Electu. Diacath.
& Leniti*.    By the Phyficians my Friends, was
prefcribed the following Electuary, of which I
fwallowed the quantity of a Nutmeg twice a day.
℞ *Elect., de Gem. cal.* ℥ii. *Spec. Plerifarch.* ℥i.
(from fear of the Scurvy ) *Manus Chrifti perlat.*
℥i. *Conferv. Buglof. & Violar.* ā ℥ii. *Syr. Luju.* ℥i.
*Syr. Viol.* ℥ſs. *Limon* ℥i. *Ol. Vitriol.* gut. vi. *f. Elect.*
The 27*th* of *Septemb.* I was thus purged :  ℞ *Elect.
Lenit.* ℥ſs. *Aq. Abfynth.* ℥iv. *Mifc.*   It gave three
ftools.    At the hour of fleep I took *Diacodium*,
*Syrup of red Poppies, with Diafcordium*.    For the
heat

heat of the Back, ℞ *Refrig. Gal.* ℥iſs. *Cerat. Santal.*
℥ſs. *Succ. Sed. Acet. Vini alb.* ā coch. i. *f. Unguent.*
*mol.* An Emplaſter for the region of the Heart,
℞ *Labd.* ʒvj. *Styrac. Calam.* ℥ſs. *Spec. Aromat.*
*Roſ.* ℈iv. *Moſc.* gr. iv. *Miſc.* I again was purged
thus: ℞ *Syr. Diaſerios* ℥iſs. *Elect. e Succ. Roſ.* ʒiii.
*Aq. Cichor.* q. ſ. It is to be obſerved, before the
Phyſicians came, there were drawn ℥vii of Blood
from the Liver vein, and three days after that
were the Leeches applied to the Hemorrhoids,
and thence removed ℥x. After the Decoction of
Harts-horn. Thus I was pretty well able to take
Meat. After I uſed *Chalybiat Wine*, with Juyce
of Scurvy-graſs, and *Syr. Sceletyrb. Foreſti*, and
purged once a week with *Pul. ſanct. Syr. Dia-*
*ſerios, & infuſ. Rhab.* For the pain of the Teeth
I uſed *Ol. Lig. Heraclei.* After I was troubled
with Itch in the *Scrotum*, which was cured with
our Decoction of *Sarſa.* with *Antiſcorbutic Herbs.*
And ſo I became perfectly well, praiſed be God.

---

## Observ. LXI.

**B**Aronet *Puckering* of *Warwick*, aged about 44,
was cruelly vexed with pain of the Head, eſpecially in the morning, and about evening; yet
when he caſt himſelf upon his back, with his Head
a little declining, he felt eaſe. I by the help of
God cured him as followeth: ℞ *Pil. de Pæon.* ʒi.
*de Succin. Ruffi.* ā ℈i. *Cephal. Fernel.* ℈ii. *cum Aq.*
*Betonic. f. Pil.* N. 15. He took two at going to
bed, and three in the morning. Theſe ended,
the

the Leeches were applied to the Hemorrhoids with happy and defired event, for he was altogether freed from the Pain of his Head. After he ufed the following Opiat: ℞ *Lign. Saffafr. incif.* ℥vi. *Cinam. pul. Cal. Aromat.* ā ℥ß. *infund. in Aq. Bugloſ.* ℥xii. *per hor.* 24. *deind. coq. ad dimid. colat. adde Conferv. Flor. Cichor. Bugloſ.* ā ℥ ß. *Theriac. Venet.* ℨ i. *Confect. Alkerm. de Hyacinth.* ā ℨ i ß. *Chalyb. præp.* ℥i. *Diatri. Santal. Diamb. Diamoſc. dulc.* ā ℈iß. *Lap. Bezoar.* ℈ß. *C. C. præp. Margarit. præp.* ā ℈ii. *cum Syr. Confer. Citri. f. Opiat.* Dofe, the quantity of a Filbert, morning, and going to bed. Having taken cold, he fell into a Quotidian Fever in the night. I purged him thus : ℞ *Syr. Diaferios* ℥ii. *Rhabar. expreſ.* ℨi. *Cremor. Tartar.* ℈i. *Aq. Betonic.* ℥ii. *f. Hauſt.* Which he retained for half an hour, and then vomited it, yet had four ſtools. The next day for his Cough and Phlegm, ℞ *Syrup of Maiden-hair and Hyſſop,* each ℥i. *Syrup of Scabious, Magi.* ℥ß. *make a Lincture.* He liking it well, it was repeated, with which he caſt up abundance of Phlegm. I framed him a Julep with *capillary Herbs, Snails, yellow Sanders, China, ſhavings of Ivory and Harts-horn, with Syrup of Limons and Violets.* With three ſpoonfuls of this Julep were taken two ſpoonfuls of *Aq. Saxon. frigid.* ℞ *Magiſt. perlar.* ℨi. *Aq. Scabioſ.* ℥iv. *Syr. Caryophil.* ℥i. *Confect. Alker.* ℈i. *Miſc.* Thus he was delivered from his Fever. Afterwards for the preſervation of his Health was prefcribed the following Opiat, by Doctor *Lapworth*; ℞ *Confer. Flor. Betonic. Caryophil. hortenſ.* ā ℥i. *Cortic. Citri. condit.* ℨvi. *Extract. Calam. Aromat.* ℨ . *Cortic. Winteran. pul.* ℈iiß. *Sem. Pæon.*

℥i.

ʒi. *Ol. Cinam.* gut. iv. *cum Syr. Betonic.* q. ſ. ſ.
*condit.* Of this he took the quantity of a Nutmeg, which was uſed with great ſucceſs. For
his Spleen I preſcribed this : ℞ *Emp. Magiſt. pro
Lien.* ʒiſſ. *Diachyl. comp.* ʒvi. *Caran. in Acet.
Scillitic. diſſol.* ʒiv. *Rad. Helleb. alb.* ℈ii. *Ol. Lig.
Rhod.* ℈i. *Miſc. f. Empl.* It was ſpread upon
Leather, and covered with ſome Sarcenet, and
applied to the Spleen. By theſe he was delivered
from all his Symptoms, and to prevent, had a
Fontinel opened in his left Arm.

## Observ. LXII.

ALderman *Tyler*, being exceedingly troubled
with heat and roughneſs of his Tongue,
was cured with the following : ℞ *Syr. Scabioſ.
mag. Becabung. Naſturt. aquat. Succ. Cochlear. præp.*
ā ʒiſſ. *Syr. Tuſſilag. Liquirit. Papav. Erratic.* ā ʒi.
*Miſc.* It was taken often with a Liquoris ſtick.

## Observ. LXIII.

THe Daughter of Alderman *Smith*, aged about
22, from diminution of her Courſes, and
fear, fell into the Mother, with Convulſion of the
Eyes, and darkneſs of ſight, it continuing all the
Fit, together with diſtortion of the Neck, and
palpitation of the Heart, as alſo a Fever, ſo that
ſhe toſſed up and down her Bed. In the time of
her

her Fit I commanded to diftil into her Mouth three fpoonfuls of *Aq. Hyfteric.* After I fumed her with *Ungula Gaballina,* which delivered her from her Fit. To prevent, was given as followeth : ℞ *Caftor. pul.* ℨſſ. *Pil. Fætid.* ℨj. *f. Pil.* 7. *deaur.* This purged her well, and delivered her from the Symptoms. Laftly, ℞ *Pul. Caftor.* ℨſſ. *Extract. Hyfter.* ℨi. *f. Pil.* N. 9. Of thefe fhe took three at bed-time, and two in the morning. By thefe few Remedies fhe was perfectly cured, and never had it after.

## Obser. LXIV.

THe only Son of Mr. *Holy-oak* (which framed the Dictionary) fell into a burning Fever, pain in the Loins, and Cough, the fore-runners of the Small-Pox, which appeared after the taking of the following Potion : ℞ *Diafcord.* ℨi. *Tinctur.Coral. Lap.Bezoar.* ã gr. iii. It was given in Fennel water. By this he was freed from pain in his Back and Stomach, and they began to appear. To preferve the Eyes, ℞ *Plantain water, Eye-bright water, and Rofe-water, each* ℨi℧ *Camphire* ℈i. *Saffron* gr. ii. *make a Collyrium.* With which the Eyes were gently anointed often with a Feather. To preferve the Throat and Mouth, I prefcribed that he fhould continually gargle Milk and Plantain water mixed, which is a moft excellent Remedy. *Syrup of Pomegranats* is alfo a Secret both to defend the Lungs, Throat, Mouth, and Breaft. Therefore I prefcribed this : ℞ *Syr. Gran. dul.* ℨii.

Peni

*Penideor.* Ʒiii. *Syr. de Rof. ficc. Diamor.* ā ℥ß. *Diatrag. frigid. in Tab.* Ʒiii. *Amyl. purif.* Əii. *f. Eclegm.* But becaufe this was not to be had, there was ufed, *Syrup of Scabious, Magiftral.* ā ℥ ß. *Syrup of Maiden-bair, and Liquoris, each* ℥i. *mix them.* This was very fuccefsful. To refrefh the Senfes, ℞ *a little Bread dipped in the Vinegar of Rofes, held to the Nofe in a fine Rag.* For Diet he ufed this Hordeat : ℞ *Hord. mund.* p. i. *Amygd. dulc.* ℥ii. *f. Hordeatum* ℔i. Which was fweetned with Sugar of Violets, that the Pox might be expelled more. To the Skin was ufed a Decoction of *Liquoris, Figgs, and common Barly*; which was given hot. He was kept conftantly in bed, with a Fire in the Chamber. His Drink was *Ptyfan.* And thus he was cured.

---

## OBSERV. LXV.

THE Lord of *Northampton*'s Gentleman had the ambulative Gout, wherein he had extreme pain, fometimes in one knee, fometimes in the other, fo that he could fcarce walk. There was alfo fometime a Retention of Urine, he was aged 34. He was prefently eafed by the following Medicines : ℞ *Pil. fine quib. fætid.* ā Ʒi. *ex Opopan.* Əii. *Troch Alhand.* Əi. *Sal. prunel.* gr. xv. *f. Pil. deaurat.* He took one at ten a clock at night, and four about feven a clock the next morning, and fo for three days; by which he was well purged. ℞ *Emplaft. Oxycroç. Diachyl. cum Gum.* ā ℥i. *Ol. è Laterib.* Ʒi. *f. Emplaft.* Which

Which being applied to the pained part, eafed it. The 27*th* of *Decemb.* to prevent, was given this: ℞ *Elect. Caryocoft.* ʒſſ. *Crem. Tart.* Ɗi. *Syr. Diaſ.* ʒi. *Aq. Betonic.* ʒiv. *M.* After, ℞ *Pil. fine quib.* ʒi. *Fætid.* ʒiſſ. *Troch. Alhand.* Ɗi. *f. Pil.* 10. There were given five for a Dofe, by which he was wholly delivered.

---

## Observ. LXVI.

Mrs. *Boves,* of *Kings-cotton,* aged 46, was miferably afflicted with Itch in the Fundament, and *Afcarides,* which were prefently cured as followeth: ℞ *Pil. Hier. cum Agarick,* ʒii. *Ruffi.* ʒi. *Fætid.* Ɗi. *f. Pil.* N' 15. Two of which fhe took at going to bed, and three in the morning. Thefe done, I gave a drachm of the following Rotula's: ℞ *Sem. Macedonic. Sem. Santon.* ā Ɗiv. *Cortic. Granat. C. C. ufti.* ā ʒſſ. *Dictam. alb. Rhab. elect. Caryophil.* ā Ɗi. *Cinam.* ʒii. *Croc.* Ɗi. *Mifc. f. Pul.* with fufficient quantity of Sugar make Rotula's, weighing a drachm. There were Suppofitories ufed fometimes of Lard, fometime Clyfters of Milk and Sugar. She ufed the *Rotula's* for fifteen days, by which fhe was delivered from the Itch and Worms. *Thonerus* cured a Girl of fix years old, only with thefe following: *Elect. de Tamarind. cum Fol. Sen.* ʒiii. *Magift. Jalap.* gr. vi. *Mifc.* To preferve, he prefcribed *Rotul. contra Verm. Auguft. ex Fol. Sen. &c.*

## Observ. LXVII.

THe Lady *Brown* of *Radford*, aged 49, *Jan.*
1. *1633.* having laboured of the Scurvy
long confirmed, and now of a Scorbutic, continual, burning Fever, accompanied with the following Symptoms, with which she was vexed, as
beating of the Heart, Wind of the Stomach and
the Belly, of which she found very little ease, although she vented wind both ways. Her Mouth
was continually dry, although she could content
her self with a little Drink. Her Pulse was varia-
ble, weak, unequal, and often vermicular: The
Heat in this Scorbutic Fever was more gentle than
in an exquisit, and joined with less thirst and
restlessness; or if it were much, yet it was by
intervals. Her Urine was thick and red, with
the like sediment, unequal, yet thirst less. She
was very subject to fainting when she rose out of
her Bed, with many other deadly Symptoms, yet
was she helped in a few days with the few following Medicines. Having great torment in the
Belly, there was injected this Clyster: ℞ *the
common Decoction for a Clyster* ℥xii. *course Sugar*
℥iv. *fresh Butter* ℥ ii. *mix them.* It gave two
stools. But before the Clyster was administred,
she took the following Electuary: ℞ *Spec. Liberant.* ℨi. *in Conserv. Barber.* It was given an hour
before the Clyster. At the hour of sleep she took
five grains of *Bezoar,* and the next morning the
foresaid Electuary. The Clyster was again injected,

jected, and procured three stools, which gave great ease. She often took the Gelly of Hartshorn in Broth, altered with Antiscorbutic Herbs. At the hour of sleep she took this : ℞ *Aq. Cord. frig. Sax.* ℥i. *Syr. Sceletyrb. Forest.* coch. ii. The third day I thus purged her : ℞ *Man.* ℥i. *Rhabarb* ʒi. *Crem. Tartar.* ℈i. *Syr. Sceletyrb. Forest.* ℥i. *Aq. Cichor.* ℥iii. *Misc.* This gave four stools. For her thirst she used the Decoction of Hartshorn. And thus she was cured.

## Observ. LXVIII.

THe Lady *Rainsford*, aged about 62, cruelly tormented with the Stone, Fever, Thirst, Pain of the Back, was cured as followeth: ℞ *Pul. Holland.* ʒi. *Tereb. Cypr.* ʒii. *Misc. f. Pil.* Of which was given ʒi made in five Pills. ℞ *Ol. Scorpion.* ʒi. *Amygd. dulc.* ʒii. With this her Back was anointed. ℞ *Decoct. comm. pro Clyst.* ℥xii. *Elect. Lenit. & Diaphænic.* ā ℥i. *Syr. Ros. sol.* ℥iii. *Misc.* This gave two stools. Six hours after it came away, was given another prepared only of the said Decoction, red Sugar ℥iv. and Butter ℥iv. But note, every third hour she took the following : ℞ *Spec. Liberant.* ʒi. *Syr. Papav. erratic.* ℥ß. *Hypos. q. s.* She rested quietly this night. ℞ *Rhab. pul.* ʒii. *Aq. Fumitor.* ℥viii. *bul. ad quartam Col. adde Tart. Cryst.* ℈i. *Syr. Diaserios* ʒn. *f. Haust.* This gave five stools. The following day she had a Clyster framed only of Oil of Linseed. At bed time she took this :
℞

℞ *Spec. Liberant.* Əii. *C.C.præp.* Əi. *Tinctur. Coral,* Əß. And fo in the morning fhe was well.

---

## Observ. LXIX.

DOctor *Thornberry,* Bifhop of *Worcefter,* aged about 86, *Febr.* 1. 1663. was long tormented with a Scorbutic wandering Gout, falfly imagined by his Phyfician to be a true Gout, as appeared not only by the frequent Change of his Urine, both in colour and fubftance, but alfo livid fpots in his Thighs. He had very unquiet Nights from falt and fharp humors, and Vapors afcending to his Head; and if he did fleep, it was with terror, which happened from the fudden flaughter of one in his Family, which did much terrify and perplex his Spirits, and afflicted him grievoufly with Melancholy. His Pain lay fometimes in his Knee, otherwhiles in his Foot, without any tumor in the Foot, but about the Knee and Inftep there was great fwelling, and after in the Feet. I faid he might be eafed, but never perfectly cured, which I effected as follows. I omitted purging, he being very weak, and having been before purged. He had a Gelly framed of Harts-horn, with Knuckles of Veal, Partridg, Raifins, Dates, and Antifcorbutic Herbs. It being ftrained, there was added a little Tincture of Saffron and Alkermes, with Sugar-candy to fweeten it. He took the Juyce of Scurvy-grafs prepared in Wine twice or thrice a day. For the Pain and

Tumor

Tumor was applied live-Worms, which I have often applied to others in like pains with good succeſs. Afterwards I uſed the following, which removed the Tumefaction in three or four days. The Feet were bathed with this : ℞ *Brook-lime* M x. *boyl it in ſufficient quantity of Beer, for a Bath* ; which was uſed morning and night. After bathing, was applied a Pulteſs framed of the *Pouder of Wormwood, and Yolks of Eggs.* The firſt night he ſlept more quietly. There were uſed alſo inwardly our *Antiſcorbutic Water,* with the Juyce of Scurvy-graſs, as before, as alſo the Gelly. He alſo had an Antiſcorbutic Beer. By all which he was wholly delivered from the pain and tumor in his Feet, ſo that he could walk abroad.

## Observ. LXX.

MR. *Simon Underhil,* aged about 40, troubled with extream Vomiting, wind of the Stomach, difficulty of breathing, conſtipation of the Belly and Scurvy, was cured as followeth : ℞ *Jalap.* ℈i. *Crem. Tartar.* ℈ſſ. *Tereb. Cypr. q. ſ. f. Pil.* N. 3. which wrought well. For difficulty of breathing : ℞ *Spec. Pleriſarchon.* ℥ii. *Conſerv. Cochlear.* ℥ii. *Confect. Alkermes* ℈i. *Miſc,* Dole the quantity of a Nutmeg an hour before Meat. It was often repeated. There was alſo uſed *Diacurcuma* before ſupper ℥ii. By theſe he became much better, ſo that he ſent me away, and after came home to me, and ſaid I ſhould either
cure

cure him perfectly, or kill him. The 7th of *March*, after his firft fleep at night, he was much troubled with Wind in his Stomach, for which was ufed this : Ɍ *Pul. Pan. rub.* ℈ii. *Conferv. Flor. Viol. & Cochlear. Misc.* He flept after that better in the morning. He had a Clyfter of a Decoction framed of *Brook-lime, Water-crefses, Scurvy-grafs, and Nettles,* ã ℥xii. *Holland pouder* ℥i. *Diaphœnic.* ℥i. *Spec. Diaturb. cum Rhab.* ℥iſs. mix them, and make *a Clyfter.* This brought away abundance of Wind. But before the Clyfter he fwallowed this : Ɍ *Conferve cf Scurvy-grafs* ℥iij. *Pul. Pan. rub.* ℈i. The 9th day, Ɍ *the Juyce of Scurvy-grafs prepared* ℥viii. *Syrup of Brook-lime and Water-crefses,* each ℥ii. He ufed *Chalybiat Wine,* and *Elect. Plerifarch.* after meat, and continuing the Antifcorbutic Beer for fourteen days, he became perfectly well.

---

## Observ. LXXI.

Mrs. *Swift,* ( dwelling with Baronet *Brook* at *Warwick* Caftle, a Maid, ) aged about 20, was miferably afflicted with the Mother, Convulfion of the Mouth, as alfo of the Arms and Hands. She had been well purged by expert Phyficians, and many other Medicines fruitlefly ufed ; yet by the affiftance of God I thus cured : Ɍ *the Decoction of Briony with Uterin Herbs* ℔ſs. *Spec. Hier. Picr.* ℥ii. *Holland pouder* ℥i. *make a Clyfter.* This injected, gave two ftools with fuccefs. I gave her *Aq. Hyfteric.* ( now called *Aq. Brion.* ) ℥i. which fhe vomiting up, I prefently exhibited the following

M ing.

ing : ℞ *Extract. Hysteric.* ℈i. *Fæcul. Brion.* ℈ß. *f.*
*Pil.* N. iii. *deaur.* Half an hour after she had taken them, she vomited them up with some Phlegm
and acid Melancholy, complaining of great heat
of her Stomach, as if it were excoriated. I presently commanded she should drink half a pint of
clear cold Water, which she presently cast up; it
was reiterated, and as soon as it was hot in her
Stomach, she cast it up again; it was again repeated, and then she contained it with ease. For her
Convulsion, ℞ *Ung. Martiat.* ℥ ß. *Ol. Saßaf. &*
*Succin.* ā gut. 5. *Misc.* With this was her Neck
anointed. To the Navil I applied an *Emplaster of*
*Caranna*, in the midst of which was put of Musk
and Civet gr. v. in Cotton-wooll. For many
days she used a Gelly of Harts-horn, with a little
*Fæcul. Brion. & Aron.* There was used *Sternut.*
*Ruland.* Being troubled with faintings, twice
in an hour there was given her the following, by
which she was wholly delivered : ℞ *Mosc.* opt.
gr. 5. *Cinam. Caryoph. Nuc. Mosch.* ā ℈i. *cum Con-*
*fect. Alkerm.* *f. Pil. deaur.*

## Observ. LXXII.

Mrs. *Finnes*, being delivered of her third Child,
the third day fell into a burning Fever, with
thirst and great weakness, her Midwife being
with her, gave her Posset-drink made of the Juice
of Limons and of Wood-sorrel; and with her
Chickens gave her the Juice of Sorrel as Sauce. By
which her Stomach being too much cooled, she
fell

fell into an Hydropick Tumor, with swelling of the right Thigh and Leg, so that for the pain the Midwife could not move it. To which she applied a Plaster of red Lead, rolling it hard on; the Pain and Tumor yet increasing, I was sent for, when being come, perceiving it hard, I conceived it to be a Scorbutic Dropsy. She implored earnestly my help, being in a very desperate condition. She being almost suffocated with Phlegm, I prescribed this Lincture, ℞ *Syr. Hyssop. Becabung. Nasturt. aquat. & Scabios. Magistr. ā ℥ i. Misc.* She took of this often with a Liquoris stick, with good event. For a Clyster, ℞ *Mallowes, Brooklime, Water-cresses, Scurvy grass, each* M i. *Roots of Fennel and Parsly, each* ℥ii. *Tops of Elder* M ß. *boyl them in a quart of Water till it come to* ℥xii. *in the straining dissolve course Sugar* ℥iv. *Misc.* This cast in, purged her well of Wind and Phlegm. It was reiterated the next day with good success. At bed-time she took this: ℞ *Pul. Pan. rub.* ℨß. *C. C. præp.* Ɉß. *Confect. Alkerm. cum Syr. Limon. f. Bol.* That night she was in a fine moist sweat. It was repeated the next morning. She was subject to fainting upon rising, or when moved, for which I appointed this: ℞ *Conserv. Cochl.* ℥iii. *Spec. Plerisarch.* ℨß. *Misc.* She took the quantity of a Nutmeg three hours before she rose. Multitude of business calling me away, and hindering my return to her, she sent again to me, telling me she had like to have been suffocated with Phlegm the night before; for which I repeated the foresaid Syrup, and our Antiscorbutic Water, of which she took every morning six spoonfuls, as also at bed-time. By these she was recovered beyond all

M 2                                   expecta-

expectation of all who gave her over for dead. She took a Clyster every other day, which was this: ℞ *the buds of Elder* M i. *Scurvy-grass, Water creſſes, and Brook-lime, each* Mſſ. *Nettles the whole* M i. *Roots of Parſly and Fennel, each* ℥i. *boyl them in ſufficient quantity of Water to* ℥xii. *to the ſtrained Liquor add Diæcatholicon* ℥ii. *Diaturb. cum Rheo.* ℥ii. *mix them.* It gave three ſtools. To reſtore, ſhe had a Reſtora ive framed of Snails, Earth-worms, with Antiſcorbutic Herbs, as alſo with Chicken and Partridg, with Cinamon. She alſo had the following Scorbutic Beer, ℞ *the buds of Elder, Betony, Agrimony, Scabious, Wormwood, each* M i. *Carduus benedictus, Fumitory, Germander, each* Mſſ. *Water-creſſes, Brook-lime, each* M ii. *Scurvy-graſſ* M iv. *Juniper berries* ℔ſſ. *Shred and contuſe them, and ſteep them in unboyled Beer, five gallons ; after boyl them to four, the following Species being in a bag are alſo to be boiled therein, and with the Beer hung in the Barrel, as the Seeds of Coriander and Anis, each* ℥ſſ. *Liquoris* ℥i. *Sarſaparilla* ℥ii. *Saſſaphras* ℥j. *Cortic. Winteran.* ℥ſſ. It ſtood fourteen days before it was drunk of, and then there was taken a draught in the morning faſting, as alſo before dinner and ſupper, and at going to bed. For the Contraction of the Leg, from the beginning, was uſed the following: ℞ *Ol.Cham. Lumbric. de Caſtor.* ā ℥i. *Ping. Anſer, Gallin.* ā ℥ſſ. *Ung. Dialth.* ℥ii. *Succ. è Fol. Cochlear. Becabung. Naſtur. aquat.* ā ℥i. *Cer. q. ſ. f. Unguent.* This proved excellent, for in three days ſpace ſhe was able to go with a Staff. Every day ſhe alſo took four ounces of the following: ℞ *Scurvy-graſs, Water-creſſes, equal parts, Brook-lime half ſo much ; beat them in a ſtone Mortar,*

*a n d*

*and boyl them in* Milk, *pouring not much Liquor upon them;* and drank it as before, till the Beer was ready. She took the following Clyster twice a week : ℞ *of a Childs Urine* ℥ xii. *in which boil Leaven* ℥iß. *Seeds of Fennel, Anis, and Dill, each* ℥iß. *purified Honey* ℥i. *make a Clyster.* And so she was restored to her former health.

## Observ. LXXIII.

MR. *Fortescue,* ( Catholick ) of *Cook-hil,* aged 38, ( a great Drinker, of a very good habit of Body, sanguine, very fat,) fell into a Scorbutic Dropsy by a Surfeit, with difficulty of breathing, hard tumor of the Belly, Cods, and Feet, Wind in the Sides, the yellow Jaundice spread over the whole Body, and tumor of the Sides and Belly, and by all these was much troubled. To whom coming, I appointed what followeth, *March* 12. 1633. ℞ *Pul. Sen. Lax. Spec. Diaturb. cum Rhab.* ā ℈ii. *Syr. Cichor. cum Rheo.* ℥i. *Ser. Gerevis. q.s. f. Haust.* It gave eight stools. The 13*th,* ℞ *Pil. Stomach. Ruffi, sine quib.* ā ℈i. *f. Pil.* 5. which gave six stools. The 14*th,* a Vein was opened, and ℥vii taken. The 15*th,* ℞ *Polipody, Liquoris, each* ℥i. *Roots of Succory* ℥ß. *Brook-lime, Scurvy-grass, Water-cresses, Fumatory, Centaury, each* M ß. *Sena* ℥iii. *Agarick sliced* ℨvi. *Rubarb* ℨii. *Cream of Tartar* ℨi. *Flowers of Chamomel, Elder buds, each* p. ii. *Seeds of Fennel, Carrots, each* ℥iß. *Cinamon, Cloves, Corticis Winterani, each* ℨi. *Zedoary* ℨß. *Saffron* ℈ß. *Raisins of the Sun stoned* ℥iii.

*make*

*make an Infusion in eight pints of Water for twelve
hours ; in the morning boil it till a third part be wasted.* Dose, eight spoonfuls every day, which gave
daily five Stools. The 18*th*, ℞ *Pil. Aggregativ.
Stomach. Ruffi,* ā ʒ ß. *Gum. Got. præp.* gr. xiv. *f.
Pil.* N. x. for two Doses, which gave five Stools,
each. After meat he took this : ℞ *Diambr.* ʒii.
*Sacch. Rof.* ʒii. *Misc.* Dose was half a spoonful.
The Restorative was made as in the former Observation, as also that in *Observ.* 59 of this Century ;
every third day purging. For quenching thirst,
instead of Beer we used the following: ℞ *the shavings of Saffafras, shaved Liquoris,* ā ʒ ii. *Fennel
seeds* ʒii. *Currants* ʒiß. *put them all into a Pewter
pot, and pour upon them three quarts of scalding Water, after stop it very well, and set it in a cold place,
till it be cold.* He used *Diacrocum* to ʒii, every
morning for five mornings, and after Meat. ℞
*Spec. Plerifarchon.* ʒ ii. *Sacch.* ʒi. Dose, half a
spoonful. The 24*th* day he was purged with
these Pills prescribed for the 18*th* day, which gave
eight stools. After to sweat was this prepared :
℞ *Guaiacum shaved* ℔i. *Water nine pints, boil it to
the half , towards the end cast in Soldanella dried* M i.
*the inner Bark of Cinamon* ʒii. *Raisins unstoned* ʒii.
*after they are boyled enough, pour them into a Glass
Vessel, in which there are three pints of White-wine.*
Of which take ʒix in the morning, and vi in the
evening, covering him well that he may sweat.
His Diet was drying. Every third day he had the
Clyster prescribed ( of Urine ) in the former Observation. And once a week the following Bole,
℞ *Jalap.* Əiß. *Cream of Tartar* Əi. *Elect. of Tamarinds* ʒß. *make a Bole.* It gave six Stools. By
the

thefe the Tumor was altogether removed. But
the third of *April,* by what Fate I know not, he
fell into a Fever. He had two Fits, with fhaking
fix hours long, three in heat. I purged him a-
gain with the forefaid Bole, which gave him five
great watery Stools; by which he was delivered
from his Fever. Afterward he ufed the forefaid
Antifcorbutic Beer for a month, and the following
Pouder after Meat: ℞ *Pul. Pannonic. rub. Spec.
Diambr. Spec. Diamofch. dulc.* ā ℥ i. *Ol. Anifi.*
gut. iij. *Sacch. alb.* ℥iv. *Mifc. f. Pul.* Dofe, as
much as would lie on a Six-pence. By thefe
means in fix weeks time he was perfectly cured.

## Observ. LXXIV.

MR. *Kimberley,* aged about 26, had laboured
long of a general Laffitude, had a greater
Appetite than Digeftion, a filthy yellow Jaundice,
Pain in the Loins, weaknefs of the Legs, a pricking Pain of the Head, efpecially near the Ears,
a frequent change of the Urine, fometimes thick,
and fometimes clear like Spring water; fometimes great pain of the Legs, Tumor of the Gums,
fwelling of the Fingers, with pain, Hypochondriac Winds, with many other Signs of the
Scurvy confirmed, with which was joined fweat-
ing and wandring Pains. He had ufed the natural Bath without fuccefs, and had had often purging and Sudorific Decoctions, and all fruitlefs,
yet he was reftored as followeth: *May* 1. ℞ *Diatartar.* ℥ii. *of which he took every day a fmall fpoonful.*

Which

Which gave four Stools. About three or four a clock in the morning, when his sweating usually began, and at four a clock in the afternoon, he took ℥iv of the Juyces expressed out of the following Herbs, being mixed with Sugar, and ℨi of Cinamon. ℞ *Scurvy-grass, Water-cresses, each* ℔ß. *Brook-lime* ℥ iv. *bruise them, and strain them, adding* ℨi *of Cinamon, and sufficient Sugar.* He also used this Antiscorbutic Beer : ℞ *Bark of Ash, Tamaris, and Capers, each* ℥ii. *Horse Radish sliced* ℥vi. *Wormwood, Fumatory, Germander, Carduus benedictus, Celendine, each* Mß. *Betony, Scabious, Ceterach, Valerian, Nettles, each* M i. *Water-cresses, Brook-lime, each* Mii. *Scurvy-grass* M iv. *let the following be put also in a bag, and boiled in the Beer, as Juniper berries bruised* ℥vi. *Cortic. Winteran.* ℥ß. *Sarsaparilla* ℥ii. *Sassafras* ℥ß. *Liquoris* ℥i. *Seeds of Anis, Carraway, and Coriander, each* ℥ß. *Nutmegs two. After the Beer is boiled, hang the Bag in the Vessel.* It is for four gallons of Beer. After it is barm'd, pour in of the Juyce of Pippins ℔i. *the Juyce of Scurvy-grass* ℔ii. *White wine* ℔i. After a fit time use it for ordinary Drink. For his Tumors in the Fingers were used live-Worms, as *Observ. 69.* He was purged with these Pills : ℞ *Pil. Hier. cum Agarick, Mastic. Stomac. Imperial. Ruffi,* ā ℨß. *Misc. fiat* 5 *Pil. ex* ℨi. Which was the Dose taken, and gave five Stools. *May* the 13*th,* ℞ *nine fresh Worms, and bruise them in a Mortar with two spoonfuls of White-wine ; after strain them, and put it into the rest of the pint of Wine.* Of which he took three spoonfuls in the morning, noon, and evening. And every third day purged with the following : ℞ *Pil. aggregat,*

Ʒi. *Stomac.* Ʒſſ. *Gamboi. præp.* gr. xiv. *f. Pil.* 10.
Doſe five, which gave ſo many Stools. When
he began to be well, he drank the foreſaid Beer,
an hour after which he took ſome of the follow-
ing : Ḻ *Elect. Chalyb.* ℥ iv. *Conſerv. Cochlear.* ℥ii.
*Miſc.* Doſe, the quantity of a Nutmeg. The
Beer and Electuary were uſed for fifteen days.
After meat the quantity of a Nutmeg of the fol-
lowing : Ḻ *Conſerve of Scurvy-graſs* ℥i. *Bugloſs* Ʒſſ.
*Spec. Pleriſarchont.* Ʒii. *Miſc.* Every fourth or ſixt
days he took the following to purge : Ḻ *Conſerv.*
*Violar.* ℥i. *Spec. Diatrag. frigid.* Ʒ iſſ. *Turbith.*
*Gum. Mechoac. a.biſ.* ā Ʒſſ. *Diagrid. cum Ol. Fæ-*
*nic. præp.* Ʒii. *Sacch. in Aq. Fænicul. diſſol.* ℥ xiv.
*Ol. Cinam.* gut. vi. *Ol. Aniſ.* gut. iv. *f. Confect.*
*in Morſul.* Of which he took Ʒvi, which gave
eight Stools ; it is called *Morſul. purgant. de*
*Mechoac.* He uſed his Beer for three months, in
which time he was delivered from thoſe cruel in-
tenſe Pains, and they did not return again. For
which he returned me many thanks, and called
me his Father, becauſe he ſaid I had delivered him
from the jaws of Death, and made him perfectly
well.

## Observ. LXXV.

Mrs. *Editha Staughton*, aged 16, was miſerably tormented with *Aſcarides* night and day,
whom I cured perfectly and ſpeedily, as I cured
Mrs. *Bove* ; for which ſee *Obſerv.* 66. of this
Century.

Observ.

## Observ. LXXVI.

Mrs. *Wilson*, who for the recovery of her health, took a Journey to *Bristol*, for as she thought she was tormented with the Stone, for which she drank of St. *Vincent's* Well too greedily, to the quantity of eighteen pints a day, for the expelling of the Stone; so that thereby cooling her Body too much, she fell into a Palsy. She presently got her self conveyed to the Bath, where being purged by Dr. *Lapworth*, and using the Bath, she was restored. Returning home in rainy and tempestuous weather, that night she was assaulted with the Mother, with fainting, and a light Palsy on the left side. To whom being called, by Divine assistance I helped as followeth : ℞ *Aloes lucid.* ʒii. *Agaric. Troch. rec. Rhab. elect.* ā ʒi. *Cortic. Rad. Cappar. Winteran. Tamarisc.* ā ℈i. *Faculæ Brion. & Aron.* ā ℈ß. *Castor* ʒiß. *Crem. Tartar.* ʒß. *Spir. Succini* gr. iv. *cum Syr. de Fumar. compos. q. s. f. Pil.* N. 6. *ex* ʒi. Of which she took three at a night when she went to bed, which gave her four Stools the next day. For the wind of her Stomach, ℞ *Spec. Diamh.* ʒi. *Ol. Salv. Chy. Nuc. Mosch. Caryoph.* ā gut. iv. *Sacch. in Aq. Ros. dissol.* ʒii. *f. Rotul.* To be taken after meat. For the Palsy, ℞ *Spir. Rorismar. Ol. Succin.* ā *part. æq.* With which her Neck was gently anointed. For fainting, ℞ *Spec. Plerisarch.* ʒß. *Sacch. opt.* ʒii. *Misc.* Dose half a spoonful. When she fainted, this delivered her both from her
fainting,

fainting, and trembling of her Heart, with which
she had usually been troubled. It is a Pouder
worth Gold, which I always carry about with
me. She used also this Decoction : Rx *Gaaiacum*
℥viii. *Bark of the same, Rosemary, Sassaphras, Sar-*
*saparilla, each* ℥ i. *Betony, Sage, Lavender, Ger-*
*mander, each p. i. Roots of Elicampana, Piony, Oris,*
*Citron Pills dried, each* ℥i. *Spring water* ℔vi. *infuse*
*them for twenty four hours in a hot place, after boyl*
*them in a close Vessel ; after straining, sweeten it*
*with Sugar, and aromatize it with Spec. Diambr.* ℥ß.
She took ℥vi of it in the morning, and sweat, and
as much at four a clock in the afternoon, without
sweating. She had *Clysters framed of the common*
*Decoction, and Carminative seeds, to which was added*
*Holland pouder.* She used also *Cyprus Terbentine*
framed into Pills very often. And thus she was
delivered from all these, and danger of Death.

## Observ. LXXVII.

Mrs. *Wagstaff* of *Warwick,* ( Widow ) aged
about 48, was troubled with a continual
vomiting, pain of the Stomach and Head, as if
pricked or stabbed with Needles and Daggers ;
also she had pain of her Loins, and numness of
her Feet, whom I cured as followeth : Rx *our E-*
*metic Infusion* ʒvi. It gave her three vomits, and
three Stools. For the pain of the Stomach, Rx
*new Conserve of Roses* ℥i. *Spec. Aromat. Rosar.* ℈i.
*Theriac. Lond.* ʒi. *Misc.* For two Doses. For the
Back, Rx *Oil of Scorpions* ʒii. *Oil of sweet Almonds*
℥ii.

℥ii. *mix them.* She had a quiet night, and well eaſed of her pains. The next morning was caſt in the following Clyſter: ℞ *Althæa roots* ℥i. *Pellitory of the Wall* M ii. *Melilot, Mallows, Chamomel flowers,* each M i. *Seeds of Line, Fænugreek,* each ℥ß. of *Fennel ſeed* ℥ii. *boyl them in Water* ℔ii. in ℥x of the *ſtraining was diſſolved Caſſia drawn for Clyſters* ℥i. *Oil of ſweet Almonds* ℥ii. *Capons or Gooſe greaſe* ℥i. *make a Clyſter.* For her Side, ℞ *Ung: de Althæa* ℥ii. *Ol. Amygd. dulc.* ℥ß. *Miſc.* With which her Side was anointed, and upon it put a Linnen Cloth anointed with Butter warm'd. It was done twice a day. For the wind, ℞ *Conſerv. de Anthos, Bugloſs,* ā ℥iß. *Conſerv. Caryoph. hort.* ℥i. *Rad. Enul. Camp. condit. Zinzib. condit.* ā ℥ß. *Spec. Armat. Roſ.* ℥ i ß. *Confect. Alkerm.* ℥ß. *cum Syr. Regis, vel Pomis, f. Elect.* Doſe the quantity of a Nutmeg. After meat ſhe took of the following Rotula's: ℞ *Spec. Diamb.* ℥ß. *Diamoſc. dulc.* ℈i. *Ol. Aniſi.* gut. iii. *Sacch. in Aq. Bugloſs. diſſol.* q.ſ. *f. Rot.* She purged twice a week with *Diatartar:* For watching, ℞ *Ung. Alabaſtr. vel Popul.* ℥ß. *Laud. Paracel. diſſol. in Aq. Roſ.* gr. x. with which her Temples was anointed: And ſo ſhe was healed.

## Observ. LXXVIII.

Mrs. *Cooks,* near 48, of a thin body, was much troubled with pain of the Stomach, darkneſs of the Eyes, deafneſs and noiſe in the Ears, beating of the Heart, with ſeveral other Symptoms

toms, conftant Companions of *Flatus Hypochon-driacus*, arifing from the ill Difpofition and Ob-ftructions of the Liver and Spleen, whom I cu-red as followeth: Firft I purged the firft ways with the following: ℞ *Sarfapar.* ʒ ii. *Hermo-dact.* ʒiſs. *Guaiac. Liquor.* ā ʒi. *Sen.* ʒii. *Polipod. Querc.* ʒii. *Epithem.* ʒſs. *Enul. Camp.* ʒvi. *Agaric. Rhab.* ā ʒ ii. *Sem. Anif. Carui. Coriand.* ā ʒ ſs. *Infufe them in a clofe fhut Veffel in four pints of Wa-ter for twenty four hours; after boyl them, keeping the Veffel clofe, leſt the Vapor exhale. Take of this Decoction being ſtrained* ℔ſs. *Syr. Magiſt. ad Melan-chol.* ʒiv Dofe was from ʒii to iv. Being well purged, fhe took this: ℞ *Elect. Chalyb.* ʒiſs. *de Tamarind.* ʒi. *Mifc.* The quantity to be taken was ʒſs. to be ufed with exercife. Twice a week was given of the following: ℞ *Pil. Stomach. fine quib.* ā ʒſs. *de Pæon. Chamæpit.* ā Ɔi. *f. Pil.* N. 12. Of which three was given at the hour of fleep. After was taken the Electuary prefcribed *Obferv.* 72. *Of Conferve of Scurvy grafs,* ʒii. &c. For deafnefs was ufed *Carduus benedictus* Water, twice diftilled, and dropped into the Ear. By thefe fhe was perfectly cured.

# Observ. LXXIX.

Nurfe *Degle* of *Bengwort,* aged 29, troubled with fpitting of Blood from the Lungs, as alfo with the yellow Jaundice, was cured as fol-loweth: ℞ *Oxymel fimpl.* ʒiv. *Syr. Capil. Vener.* ʒii. *Mifc.* for two mornings. After fhe was thus purged;

purged: Ꝑ *Rhab. Pul.* ℥iſs. *Syr. Roſ. Sol.* ℥i. *Aq⋅ Plantag.* ℥iv. *Syr. Capil. ven.* ℥i. *Miſc.* Being thus well purged, ſhe had a Vein opened. After Aſtringents were uſed, as, Ꝑ *Lapid. Hæmatit. ſubtiliſ. pul. & cum Aq. Plantag. lot.* ℥i. ( which hath an admirable quality in ſtopping of Blood ) *Coral. rub. Bol. Arm. ita præp.* ā ℥iii. *Ter. ſigil.* ℥iſs. *Pul. Diareos ſimp.* ℥i. *ſ. Pul. tenuiſ.* Doſe ℥iſs in Barly water, in which was boiled Plantain and Knot-graſs. It it is to be given in the morn-ing faſting, and at the hour of ſleep, to the quan-tity of ℥ii of *Aq. Spernol. Crol.* and ſo for many days. Every ſecond or third day ſhe had a Clyſter, as, Ꝑ *Mallows, Althea, Beets, Mercury,* each M i. *Prunes* 5. *Figs* 12. *Melon ſeed bruiſed* ℥i. *the ſeeds of Anis and Fennel,* each ℥i. *French Barly, Rye bran,* each p. i. *boyl them in Whey* to ℥xii. *in the ſtrain-ing diſſolve Catholic.* ℥i. *Caſſia extracted for Clyſters* ℥v. *courſe Sugar* ℥ ii. *make a Clyſter.* And thus by God's help ſhe became well.

## Observ. LXXX.

Mrs. *Editha Staughton*, aged 17, was miſerably afflicted with Melancholy, her Courſes as yet not having broken forth, as alſo with the Mother ; ſhe was very eaſily angry with her near-eſt Friends, ſo that ſhe continually cried out that her Parents would kill her, as alſo of all others that came unto her. She had been purged well by expert Phyſicians, yet her Father deſired my counſel, whether ſhe was curable ; to which

I answered, Very hardly, being her Constitution was Melancholy. I advised there should be few to trouble her, and so began with emollient and dif- cuffive Clyfters, as also such as refpected the Hu- mor : As ℞ *of Chicken-broth ( wherein was boiled Sorrel, Pimpernel, Borage, Hyffop )* ℔ i. *common Oil* ℥iiß. *Salt of Tartar* ℥i. *make a Clyster.* This was ufed two days. After she was thus purged : ℞ *of the forefaid Broth* ℥v. *Cream of Tartar* ℈iv. *Oil of Vitriol* 5 *drops, make a Potion.* By this the Humor was rendred more obfequious. After was opened a Vein on the left Arm. She was the next day after purged again. After was appli- ed the Leeches to the Hemorrhoids. Again she was purged with an Helleborated Apple, in which Apple was rofted ℥i of *Hellebore*; after- ward the Hellebore was caft away, and the Apple given. Being well purged, we laboured to di- vert the Humor from the Brain by Ligatures and ftrong Clyfters, ftrengthning the principal parts with the following : ℞ *Conferve of Rofes vitriola- ted, Borage, Buglofs, each* ℥i. *candied Citron Pills, Conferve of Clove Gilly-flowers, each* ℥ ß. *Spec. de Gem. Lætific.* ā ℈ii. *Hyacinth. præp.* ℈i. *Confect. Alkerm.* ℥i. *Spec. Diamarg. frigid.* ā ℥iß. *with the fyrup of Apples make an Electuary.* The Dose was ℥i before meat. To difcufs wind, that Pouder was ufed, prefcribed *Obferv.* 34. *Cent.* 1. As, ℞ *Coriand. præp.* ℥ii. *Sem. Fænic.* &c. It was given after meat. There was alfo ufed the following Wines : ℞ *the opening Roots, each* ℥i. *Bark of Cappar roots* ℥i. *Saffafras* ℥iß. *Wormwood, Ground- pine, each* M iß. *Ceterach, Balm, Germander, each* M i. *Flowers of Borage, Buglofs, Scabious, each*

p.

p. ii. *Broom leaves* p. i. *seeds of Fennel* ʒi. *of Car-raway, and sem. Siler. Montan. of each* ʒi. *All these were beaten, and put into a Vessel, in which was put the shavings of Juniper, and there was poured up-on them of White-wine* ℔ xxx. *And so being well stopped, they were set in a Cellar. After they were infused eight days, I took* 9 ℔ *of it, wherein I in-fused Rhubarb* ʒvi. *Sena* ʒii. *Mechoacan* ʒß. *Dod-der and Cinamon, each* ʒß. *Cloves* ʒi. And so it was used instead of Purges. It was given every morning two hours before dinner, with taking some spoonfuls of Broth. After three days ta-king, she had that prescribed for comforting the Brain and Heart. In all Medicines we added Humectors. For her watching, I gave at bed-time a spoonful of *Diacodium.* This caused rest, and in it she sweat. There was *Tartar* often used by reason of its great force in contemporating Melancholy, and *Atra bilis.* And thus by the blessing of God she was delivered from her Dis-temper.

## Observ. LXXXI.

MR. *John Trap,* ( Minister, for his piety and learning second to none ) about the 33 year of his age, of a melancholy temper, and by much Study fell into Hypochondriac Melancholy, and pain of the Spleen, with some Scorbutic Symptoms, *viz.* difficulty of breathing after gentle motion of the Body, beating of the Heart, with fainting at the rising of the Vapours, and became

became a little better when they were dispersed.
He had a gentle Erratic Fever, so that he was
much amaciated; after he had done preaching on
the Sabbath, he could scarce speak; his Urine
changed often, his Pulse was mutable and unequal,
and he languished much. Some ordinary Medicines were used, but not succeeding, he desired
my help and counsel, which was readily performed by me in prescribing the following, by which
he was restored from the very jaws of Death, both
safely, quickly, and pleasantly. *March* 11. 1635.
℞ *Tartar. Vitriolat.* ℈iv. *in pomo sub cineribus coct.*
With this he had two Stools, and his Urine came
in greater quantity, but like clear Spring water.
The 12*th* day, ℞ *Merc. dulc.* gr. xx. *Tart. Vitr.*
℈i. *Gut. Gamb. præp.* gr. iii. *Misc.* This was
given in the Pap of an Apple; it gave him four
Stools. The 14*th* day he took ℥i of *Cream of*
*Tartar,* it gave one Stool. For his Cough and
Catarrh, in the night he held in his Mouth one of
our pectoral Rolls. The 15*th* he took of our
Chalybiat Wine; as ℞ *Vin. Chalyb.* ℥iv. *Syr. Sce-*
*letyrb. Forest.* ℥iii. *Misc.* The first day he took
two spoonfuls, the second day four, exercising
two hours after. For the strengthning of the
Spleen, ℞ *Raisins of the Sun* ℔i. *boyl them in Sack*
*to the consistence of a Pultess, pass it through a strainer,*
*and mix therewith Conserve of Rosemary flowers, of*
*Bugloss, each* ℥ß. *Spec. Lætificant. Aromat. Rosar.*
*Diamarg. calid. Diacinam. each* ℈ij. *Lig. Aloes ade-*
*rati.* ℥ß. *candied Citron Pills, Cinamon, each* ℥i.
*Chalyb. præp. cum Sulphur.* ℥ß. *Saffron* ℈i. *mix*
*them.* The Dose was the quantity of a Filbert in
the morning. The 19*th,* ℞ *Syr. Magist. ad Me-*
lanchol.

N

*lanchol.* ℥ii. *Aq. Buglof.* ℥ii. *Tartar. fubtilif. pul.*
*Mifc.* It gave four ftools. The next day he
took the Chalybiat Wine. *April* the 2. he was
purged as before, with which he was cheared
for three days after he took the Wine. The fe-
venth day he purged with *Cream of Tartar* ℥i.
Now he had our Antifcorbutic Beer ; and his E-
lectuary being ended, he took fix fpoonfuls of
the following Water : ℞ *Aq. Limacum noftr. Aq.*
*Ranar. fimpl.* ā ℥iv. *Confect. Alkermes* Ɔii. *Manus*
*Chrift. perl.* ℥ß. *Syr. Sceletyrb. Foreft.* ℥ ii. *Aq. noft.*
*Antifcorbutic.* ℥vi. *Splenetic.* ℥ii. (both *Doncrelius*)
*Mifc.* This being ended, he defired his Electuary again, in which he faid the greateft hope of his
Cure lay, and was worth Gold. He having it,
ufed it for eight days, purging every fourth day.
But being much troubled with bitternefs of his
Mouth, I gave him ℥v of our *Emetic Infufion,*
which removed it, and he returned to the ufe of
his Electuary. And thus by God's blefling he was
freed from all his Symptoms, and was well cured,
for which he returned me hearty thanks.

## O B S E R V. LXXXII.

THe Earl of *Northampton*, aged about 32, being following his Hounds in a cold and rainy
day, got cold, and fuddenly was miferably tormented with a flatuous Pleurify, and pain of the
Belly, like to a true Pleurify. He had a fmall Cough,
was reftlefs, feverifh, thirfty, and the Pain was
ftretching. I being prefent when he came home,
prefcribed

preſcribed this Clyſter : ℞ *Decoct. com. pro Clyſt.* ℔i,
*Diaphænic. Diacatholic.* ā ʒi. *Pul. Hol.* ʒii. *f. Clyſt.*
This gave three ſtools with much wind, and deſired event, for the Pain was mitigated ; yet in
his Breaſt he felt a pricking, to remove which was
this preſcribed : ℞ *Vng. de Alth.* ʒii. *Ol. Amygd.
dulc.* ʒſſ. *diſſol. & miſce ad ign. pro Vng.* With
which his Breaſt and Side was anointed, and upon
it a double linnen Cloth ſpread with Butter
warm'd. By this the Pain remitted, and he had
a quiet night, and fell to ſleep. The day following he uſed this expectorating Syrup : ℞ *Syr.
Scabioſ. Magiſtral. Capil. Vener. Liquor. Hyſſop.*
ā ʒi. *Miſc.* He took it often upon a Liquoris
ſtick. In the night he held in his Mouth one of
our Pectoral Rolls. In the morning he was anointed again, and ſo was freed from all his pain,
and he became whole.

# INDEX

For purposes of clarification, page numbers in roman type in this Index refer to the present author's material, while the page numbers in italics refer to the pagination in the facsimile reprint. In the latter, references to individual patients give only the first page on which the Observation appears. Diseases, except scurvy, are not indexed herein as Hall himself has done so in *his* Table of Contents. Places are indexed as given in Hall's text, but localities, in general, appear only if they bear relevancy to Hall and his patients.

BIRMINGHAM

ð HANBURY

ð KING'S COUGHTON
ALCESTER

WORCESTER

ð ROUS LENCH
ð WHITELADY-ASTON

BROOM'S GT.
OGRAFTON
OM

R. AVON

ð PEBWORTH